TWAYNE'S UNITED STATES CLASSICS SERIES

SYLVIA E. BOWMAN, *Editor*
INDIANA UNIVERSITY

A HISTORY OF NEW YORK

A HISTORY
OF NEW YORK

by WASHINGTON IRVING

Edited for the Modern Reader by
Edwin T. Bowden
UNIVERSITY OF TEXAS

College & University Press · *Publishers*
NEW HAVEN, CONN.

INTRODUCTION

When *A History of New York* by Diedrich Knickerbocker first appeared in two small volumes in December, 1809, the world may not have known at first what a delightful Christmas present it had been given. But thousands of readers soon knew, and even the American literary periodicals of the time, few as they were and suspicious and critical in nature as they generally remained, quickly joined in the praise. The *Monthly Anthology and Boston Review* for February, 1810, for instance, called the amusing book "the wittiest our press has ever produced." In a short time Irving was even receiving praise in the new West, so that his friend Henry Brevoort could write in 1811 from Mackinac, "Your History is going the rounds through the Village from the Commandant to the smallest Indian Trader, so that you contribute more to their merriment and pleasure than you probably would if you were here yourself."

As *Knickerbocker's History* went through edition after edition on both sides of the Atlantic—and in French and German and Swedish too—the praise continued to swell. If a few later writers such as Emerson and Whitman found it merely "shallow burlesque," the majority enjoyed it. Sir Walter Scott wrote Irving that his sides ached from laughing at its fantasy; Fanny Kemble reported that she had nearly killed herself laughing at it; Charles Dickens is said to have worn out a copy reading it. The London *Athenæum* of October 14, 1829, gave the coveted English approval: " 'Knickerbocker's History of New York' was an honest and manly attempt to found an American literature. Those who read it must have exclaimed involuntarily, 'Yes, this is the work which was wanted. The umbilical cord is now severed. America is indeed independent.' " Condescending as that particular review may have been, it did state an accurate point: America's first internationally popular classic had been born, and it is one that has remained—despite its potentially blighting label of a "classic"—still young, still friendly and likable and amusing.

5

I

In 1809, its author, only twenty-six years old, had some of these same qualities himself. Born in 1783, the eleventh child of a prosperous New York merchant and a stalwart of the Presbyterian Church and named after the great American hero of the day, Washington Irving somehow managed to avoid the solemn and weighty childhood and education that such an inheritance would seem to demand. There is an undoubtedly apocryphal story that, when as a boy he discovered his delight in the theater, he would sneak out of his house at night, return for evening prayers at nine, and then out the window and back to the theater again. Even if not true, the story does tell something about his boyhood. He had a conventional education which he seems to have resisted mildly—his first teacher thought him not very bright—and at fourteen he not only planned to run away to sea but even put himself in training for the life that never came.

When a little older, he spent six years reading law and was finally admitted to the bar: a choice of profession that seems to have grown not from any great interest in the law but because of his desire for a life of genteel associations, no great demands on his time or effort, and, as he later wrote, because the law was free from "the risks and harrassing cares of commerce." In 1804 his brothers sent him on the grand tour of Europe for two years; and, judging fom his notebooks and letters, he had an amusing and enlightening time in Napoleonic Europe. When he returned to New York in 1806, he was one of the gayest young men in the small city.

Between his casual explorations of the civilized little city and the old Dutch areas surrounding it, his wanderings in Europe, his relaxed study of the law (he did serve as one of the lesser members of the counsel for Aaron Burr at his trial), he had already begun to write and to take part in the literary life of the city. In 1802-03 he had published in The New York *Morning Chronicle* a series of essays on the theater and New York society as "The Letters of Jonathan Oldystyle, Gent." On his return from Europe he also tried his hand at translating and at light verse. By this time too, he had joined the literary group of the city, the sort of literary circle that was a few years later to be the "Knickerbocker Group" that published so much of our literature in the second and third decade of the century. In 1807-08 he collaborated with his brother William Irving and their friend James K. Paulding in the twenty numbers of the *Salmagundi* papers. With that collaboration, his true literary career began.

II

The *Salmagundi* papers, with their announced intention "to instruct the young, reform the old, correct the town, and castigate the age," are important to any student of *Knickerbocker's History*, not only because they are partly Irving's and show his growing fondness for print, but because in their cheeky satire they look forward to the more sustained performance of Knickerbocker two years later. Although popular in the New York of the day, these slim volumes—something less than four by seven inches in size, they were small pocket pamphlets—do not hold attention well today. Their satire on politics and local issues is merely antiquarian now; their drama criticism is without real interest; their sentimental essays lack the charm of Irving's later essays; perhaps only the sketches of New York life have some of the effect that we associate with Irving at his best.

Yet the burlesques, the mock advertisements, the joking travel notes, the comic documentation, and the postscripts all prefigure the *Knickerbocker's History* to come. The tone is there at least —carefree, daring, mocking, satiric, sometimes reminiscent or sentimental, and bubbling with gay spirits—the tone that Irving was to make more and more his own. And New York is there, to be laughed at and laughed with and scrutinized with satiric affection, as it was to be again two years later. "Salmagundi" was a dish of meat chopped up with pickled herring, onion, oil, vinegar, pepper, and apparently whatever the cook liked to toss in. The title (even though it had been used before) was a good one for the Washington Irving of the first decade of the century.

III

The Letters of Jonathan Oldstyle, Esq. and the *Salmagundi* papers are interesting as examples of Irving's youthful work, and they have some small importance in the history of American literature as examples of the growing literary concerns of the youthful Republic; but it is *A History of New York* by Diedrich Knickerbocker that shows that both the young author and the young country could publish a book that could grow immediately out of the times and yet stand the test of later eras as well. Scholars have been busy trying to track down the immediate sources of the book and have made many suggestions, some based on Irving's reading and some on internal evidence. But these sources gave him only information and parallels to use or to make fun of as he saw fit. The book itself came out of his own high spirits, his observation of the city around him, and the convergence of literary and historical circumstances that eventually made Washington Irving one of the great representatives of the period of American literature between the Revolution and the Civil War (1783-1859).

The first identifiable impetus for writing *Knickerbocker's History*, as Irving explains in his introduction to the 1848 edition, was to parody a recently published guidebook to the city, S. L. Mitchill's *The Picture of New-York; or The Traveller's Guide, through the Commercial Metropolis of the United States* (1807). Washington Irving and his brother Peter saw the opportunity for a successful long joke and, beginning to play with the idea, gathered for the purpose a mass of mock erudition. But Peter soon dropped out of the plan, and Washington, increasingly caught imaginatively by the material, went on to write his own book, forgetting entirely the original idea of a parody. For here was the chance to write the book that his life and his earlier writing had prepared him for: a gay, mocking, satiric, affectionate look at the city that he knew so well. Mitchill may have given him the idea, and historians may have provided information, but Irving seems simply to have taken his city, set it back to Dutch times, and talked of it—as he had in *Salmagundi*—as he willed. It is history all right, of a comic sort; but it is primarily a comment on the times and the people that he knew for himself. It is almost fair to say that Irving was in fact writing about the early nineteenth century as much as he was about the mid-seventeenth century.

In 1809, New York society was taking itself too seriously for the taste of young Washington Irving, whose own family was solid enough but hardly at the peak of society. The old families were beginning to hold a stiff, public pride in their age and aristocratic past, particularly in view of the growing democratic temper of the Republic—and so the good-humored fun at the expense of some of the finest old names. In Book VII he even falls back on open derision. And so too, Irving began to hear, mixed with the laudatory reviews from literary men, bitter comments from those who felt themselves insulted or who professed to find the humor coarse and the whole book in bad taste. There is probably nothing to the story that one old lady of Dutch descent went looking for Irving with a horsewhip, but it is quite true that Gulian C. Verplanck in a speech of 1818 before the New York Historical Society (to whom the book was mockingly dedicated) said, "It is painful to see a mind, as admirable for its exquisite perception of the beautiful, as for its quick sense of the ridiculous, wasting the riches of its fancy on an ungrateful theme, and its exuberant humour in a coarse caricature." The bright young author could be too young and too harshly bright for the sensitivities of some of his prouder and more staid contemporaries.

Even on first reading today, it does not take long to discover that *Knickerbocker's History* is a good-humored, satiric glance at the contemporary world—and that can be the world of 1809 or sometimes even the world of the twentieth century. The first two books, in which Irving is making fun of high-flown historical theories, of wildly imaginary history and of scholarly pedanticism, are perhaps dated—although the faults are still known, if in slightly different forms. But through all the books runs a steady stream of laughter at politicians and lawyers of all sorts, at the bustling of men of business and at the blustering of men of war, at shrewd Yankee schemers and at placid Dutch dreamers, at grasping colonists and at explorers, at men of overweening ambition and at men of no ambition at all. Here is laughter at political parties (under the Swiftian guise of the Long Pipes and the Short Pipes), at "democratic" mob rule and aristocratic pretensions, at treaty-making and diplomatic negotiations, mixed with such far more serious subjects as pipe smoking, over-eating, and the pleasures of bundling.

The laughter is not restricted to New York or to the Dutch. Yankees, always at the border, are described by William the Testy as "a squatting, bundling, guessing, questioning, swapping, pumpkin-eating, molasses-daubing, shingle-splitting, cider-watering, horse-jockeying, notion-peddling crew." To the west are the new backwoodsmen, "styled half man, half horse and half alligator by the settlers on the Mississippi, and held accordingly in great respect and abhorrence." And to the south (thinly disguised as Swedes) there are the southerners, "a pack of lazy, louting, dram-drinking, cock-fighting, horse-racing, slave-driving, tavern-haunting, sabbath-breaking, mulatto-breeding upstarts." The history of New York would seem to involve the whole United States of its day.

Some of the satire is aimed at targets no longer recognized by the casual reader. Some are of no importance: if General von Poffenburgh, who is sent by Governor Kieft to defend the southern frontier, is meant to represent General James Wilkinson, the betrayer of Aaron Burr, it does not make much difference today. Other identifications are of greater interest, particularly the attack on Jefferson through the half-imaginary character of William the Testy. Stanley T. Williams has demonstrated in detail how Irving stretched and even distorted the governorship of William Kieft in order to make his reign a satiric parallel to Jefferson's tenure as president from 1801 to 1809. Certainly Jefferson's progressive, experimental policies are laughed at, as well as his advocacy of economy in government and his belief in negotiation and economic pressures instead of war. President Jefferson's troubles with New England fitted Irving's scheme without the need for rewriting history, although Irving had to make up a new character for Kieft in order to laugh at Jefferson's love of gadgetry, of learning and philosophy, and at his "fog of contradictions and perplexities." Here is satire of a figure important enough and familiar enough to make the specific attack still effective. The reader who recognizes the contemporary and local targets will find *Knickerbocker's History* richer and more complex for the knowledge, but he does not *need* to recognize them. Like other satires that have lasted, those of Dryden or Swift for example, this one can be read for its general and universal interest. Perhaps it is enough to know that Irving's contemporaries recognized their own world in it, and prized the humor that much more.

IV

Irving was hardly the first American to examine his times and his world with chastizing laughter. The previous century had been the age of the satirist, in America as in England; Washington Irving, with his roots firmly in the eighteenth century, came nearer to the end of that line than to the beginning. Benjamin Franklin, for example, with such satiric comments on America's affairs as "Exporting of Felons to the Colonies" (1751), "Rules by which a Great Empire May Be Reduced to a Small One" (1773), or "The Sale of the Hessians" (1777), showed occasionally something of the geniality of laughter that Irving was later to make his own. John Trumbull in his two long verse satires —*The Progress of Dulness* (1773) on education, and *M'Fingal* (1782) on the Tories and British during the Revolutionary War —had the high spirits and the feeling for comic exaggeration that Irving was to have. In contrast, Philip Freneau, who was still writing during Irving's young manhood, might illustrate a kind of satire that Irving found uncongenial. In such verse as "George the Third's Soliloquy" (1779) or "To Lord Cornwallis" (1786), or in the especially bitter account of his own experiences, "The British Prison Ship" (1781), Freneau was the wartime writer of angry, forceful invective. Even though he shows little evidence of being aware of it, Washington Irving was the inheritor of a strong tradition of American satire.

His conscious inheritance from European writers, on the other hand, is clear. It should be remembered, in fact, that Irving was considered in the America of his day to be a native spokesman for European culture. Jonathan Swift (whose works are alluded to directly once or twice) was undoubtedly a greater influence than Franklin, even though Irving lacks Swift's organized ruthlessness of indictment. John Dryden, Samuel Butler, Ariosto, and Rabelais had more to do with forming the book than Trumbull or Freneau or Irving's contemporary, H. H. Brackenridge, the author of the comic satiric novel *Modern Chivalry* (1792-1815) with which *Knickerbocker's History* has much in common.

Many other European writers too had their direct influence, even though they were not primarily satirists. Laurence Sterne in particular deserves mention. Irving's joshing comments to the reader and his self-conscious "art of the historian" probably were suggested by his early reading of *Tristram Shandy* (1759-67), that oddest and funniest novel of the English eighteenth century. Certainly the slightly bawdy presentation of Antony Van Corlear and his trumpet comes directly from Sterne. Cervantes' *Don Quixote* was even more formative and is alluded to a number of times. In fact, it seems fair to say that Cervantes was the major influence on Irving's tone and presentation. Close examination will reveal many similarities, but it is enough to mention here the kindly manner, the affection for his characters, the good humor, the indulgence toward antiquarianism, the concern—particularly in the Peter Stuyvesant section—with the idealist in a hostile and materialistic world. Perhaps the mock epic form, generally attributed to the example of Fielding's *Tom Jones* (1749), owes something to Cervantes also. *Knickerbocker's History* is a work by a literate man of the world as well as by an American of the turn of the century.

V

Despite his wide reading, it would be a mistake to overlook the American character of Irving's writing. Just as he was later to take German folk tales and turn them into such thoroughly American stories as "Rip Van Winkle" and "The Legend of Sleepy Hollow," he made *Knickerbocker's History*, whatever its sources, distinctively American too. The subject and setting, of course, raise no question; but in the character of the humor Irving is equally American.

In the two months before the book was published, newspaper readers in the city noticed advertisements of the disappearance of "a small elderly gentleman, dressed in an old black coat and cocked hat, by the name of KNICKERBOCKER"; reports that he had been seen; and finally announcements that a *curious kind of a written book* has been found in his room, in his own handwriting." (How many were fooled is hard to tell; certainly some were.) Here was a form of hoaxing derived from the English, but already being added to the humor sweeping in from the new West. It was just the first joke. When the book did appear, Irving's mock seriousness, his straight-faced exaggeration, his irreverent laughter at local and national bigwigs, all belonged to the tradition of American humor that, looking back, we now see running from Benjamin Franklin and before, up to Mark Twain, and on to Will Rogers or to William Faulkner of the twentieth century.

Much of Irving's humor is close to frontier variety, whether it is William the Testy's magnificent curses, or the description of the killing of a mighty sturgeon by a sunbeam reflected hissing-hot off the nose of Antony the Trumpeter, or disquisitions on the art of fighting by proclamation and philosophical specula-tions showing that a treaty of peace is a great national evil. Benjamin Franklin had earlier caught something of this frontier humor in "To the Editor of a Newspaper" (1765), in answer to a silly report in the English papers that a cod and whale fishery was to be instituted in the upper Great Lakes: "Ignorant people may object that the upper Lakes are fresh, and that Cod and Whales are Salt Water Fish: But let them know, Sir, that Cod, like other Fish when attack'd by their Enemies, fly into any Water where they can be safest; that Whales, when they have a mind to eat Cod, pursue them wherever they fly; and that the grand Leap of the Whale in that Chase up the Fall of Niagara is esteemed, by all who have seen it, as one of the finest Spec-tacles in Nature." The early period of American history and literature was shaping a humor that was an integral element of the new civilization, and Washington Irving more than did his part.

VI

Americans, like the people of any country presumably, have always been fascinated by their own history and have been anxious to preserve and record it, seeing the account of their past as significant in the history of mankind. The writing of the national story began early. The chronicle-histories of the great Puritan experiment in New England, notably Governor Bradford's *Of Plymouth Plantation* (to 1647) and Governor Winthrop's *Journal* (1630-49), or such formal histories as Cotton Mather's *Magnalia Christi Americana* (1702), or the descriptive-histories of the South, such as Robert Beverly's *History and Present State of Virginia* (1705), all illustrate the impressive beginning that was to lead through the nineteenth-century his-torians—Bancroft, Parkman, Henry Adams—to the present. In his later career, Irving was to write serious history—*The Life and Voyages of Christopher Columbus* (1828), *Voyages and Discover-ies of the Companions of Columbus* (1831), *Life of George Wash-ington* (1859)—but even as early as *Knickerbocker's History* he was beginning to take an interest in the national historical pastime.

Irving discovered a love for genuine history while writing in the name of the comic little historian Diedrich Knickerbocker, and Stanley Williams believes that it was this new enthusiasm that carried Irving on to the end of the book. It is comic history here, of course, and Irving felt free to vary the material as he needed for his comic purposes. Yet, despite all its comedy and mock history, it is reasonably close to the historical facts. Irving made Wouter Van Twiller his first governor, ignoring those who came before, and he was often careless about dates and details, as well as shading the character of the governors to suit his needs, but on the whole he was faithful to Dutch history after his burlesque fashion. His accuracy may not be so great as his comic pretense of accuracy, but ironically it is accurate enough.

In writing, Irving sought out a number of the serious accounts then available. For the history of New York itself he depended on William Smith's *History of the Province of New York, from the First Discovery to the Year 1732* (London, 1757). His most commonly employed contemporary source was Ebenezer Hazard's *Historical Collections . . . of State Papers, and Other Authentic Documents* (Philadelphia, 1794). But he also ransacked the colonial histories for information and for learned allusions: Pierre de Charlevoix' *Histoire et description générale de la Nouvelle France* (Paris, 1744 and an English translation of 1761), for instance, or John Ogilby's *America* (London, 1670), or that great compendium of voyages, Samuel Purchas' *Hakluytus Posthumus or Purchas His Pilgrimes* (London, 1625).

Irving made fun of his scholarship—the first books are aimed at ridiculing pedanticism, learned and cryptic footnotes, citation of odd sources, all the paraphernalia of the weighty historical scholarship of his day—and yet the hidden joke is that his knowledge is real. It is carefree and light, depending often on secondary sources, translations, and unscrupulous plagiarisms; yet his scholarship will more often than not stand up under investigation. A few of his footnotes, for instance, may be spurious; but most of them—ridiculous as they may appear in their then fashionably abbreviated form—are accurate. (Not that Irving had necessarily ever seen the book in question himself, but at least he had picked up the accurate reference somewhere.) Irving was never to be a scrupulous and careful scholar, even in his later serious history, but in his moderate and easygoing

way he was at least interested in getting at the truth, whether
the truth was intended to be amusing or not. For the history of
New York, his book was the begetter of more solemn and scrupulous histories by other men, yet Washington Irving for many
readers remains the only one known. Readers should be pleased
to discover they are not only being amused; they are indeed being instructed—the great classical combination of literary virtues.

VII

One particular form of history was always dear to Irving's
romantic nature. Men and events, battles and nations and governments might be of rational interest, but legend in all its
immediate appeal to the imagination was not so much an interest as an instinctive fascination. Wherever Irving traveled, he
seemed to absorb the local legends, and sooner or later he
would retell them, colored by his own fancy. He is probably
best known today for his legends of the Hudson River valley—
"Rip Van Winkle" and "The Legend of Sleepy Hollow" and
"Wolfert's Roost"—although in his own day he was equally
known for his reworking of European legend, sometimes in
whole books such as *The Alhambra* (1832). The relationship
between love of legend and the romantic mind is one that literary students can work out for themselves, bearing in mind that
the young Washington Irving lived in a period of transition between what literary historians somewhat vaguely call the "classic"
and the "romantic." Whatever the reason for the fascination of
legends for Irving, it was always there; and *Knickerbocker's History* is in part one of its results.

In it is a whole fabric of legend, woven of fact and fancy,
of myth and record. One of the constantly reiterated complaints
of the nineteenth-century literary mind—James Fenimore Cooper
in *Notions of the Americans* (1828), for example, or Henry
James in *Hawthorne* (1879)—was that America lacked a usable
past, the long past of an old civilization that could be exploited
for literary purposes. Whether the complaint was valid or not
does not matter; it seemed valid to the men of the time. But
Washington Irving did not simply complain, he did something
about it. He gave America a legendary past, "an antiquity," as
he was to say of his *History* in the preface of 1848, "extending

back into the regions of doubt and fable." He gathered the legends that did exist, combined them with the facts of history, and presented America with the new creation of an old past. Sir Walter Scott was still to discover the literary pleasures of the distant past in *Ivanhoe* (1820), or Victor Hugo in *Nôtre Dame de Paris* (1831), the past that they inherited with their nationalities; but Washington Irving created his own comic-romantic past in order to discover it. He is not only a literary exploiter but an inventor, and *Knickerbocker's History* in itself begins to take on something of a mythological character. The interpreter who wishes to approach it not only as legend but as deliberately conceived myth might find surprising and interesting results.

VIII

It is one of the pleasing anomalies of *Knickerbocker's History,* in fact, that it is a light-hearted comedy and a mock history that can be approached seriously as a work of literature. It is true that the first edition was rushed through the press in a jumble, apparently without any great care or attention by Irving. It is also true that in his "Author's Apology" Irving calls it a "hap-hazard production of my youth," begun as a "temporary jeu d'esprit." But it is equally true that Irving continually revised and reworked it for the rest of his life—hardly the actions of a man who wished a youthful mistake to slip silently out of sight. As Irving went on to *The Sketch Book* (1819-20) and to the other works of his long stay in Europe and after, he was never to do quite the same kind of thing again. He became increasingly more sober, more self-conscious, more "the authorized American author." Unfortunately—and it is part of the pathos of his life—he also toward the end began to grow dull. It can be argued that *Knickerbocker's History* is his strongest sustained work (perhaps he began to sense that himself), his one most consistently readable book today, and one that deserves greater analytical examination by the student of literature. The last three books on Peter Stuyvesant, with their unity, their effectiveness and their emotionally moving strength, should be enough to make the point. But even the first four books have their moments for the reader looking for something in addition to easy amusement.

One of Irving's real literary achievements in *Knickerbocker's History* is his tone, the original and unique effect of his prose style and his attitude toward his material and his reader. To attempt to describe it is inevitably unsatisfactory. Its combination of mockery and sentimentality, of satire and nostalgia, of humor and ironic solemnity and serious comment is Irving's own—and one that constitutes much of the attraction of the book. It is difficult to describe, because, like the character of the book itself, it is a natural outgrowth of the complex mind of young Washington Irving. A love of legend, a nostalgia for the past, a genuine interest in history, a pleasure in the life of the present, a naturally conservative bent, a satiric amusement at the follies of mankind combined with a lawyer's interest in the logic of politics, a youthful joy in jokes and mockery, a romantic concern with the imagination, a sensitive mind exposed to the literature of the world, a fascinated and yet sometimes reluctant membership in a new country in a new world creating a new literature, all combine in *Knickerbocker's History* to create a "salmagundi" that is still a century and a half later intriguing to the taste and satisfying to the appetite.

EDWIN T. BOWDEN

A NOTE ON THE TEXT

The text of *Knickerbocker's History* reprinted here is that of the second edition, published in New York and Philadelphia in 1812. The choice of text deserves a few words of explanation, particularly since the history of the text is a complex one of constant changes and revisions and since the bibliographies of Irving are sometimes misleading. After the first edition of 1809, Irving revised the text significantly at least three times and in a minor fashion several more times. In 1812 he gave it the first major revision, cutting (and carefully replacing) nearly ten thousand words.

In 1819 he made another series of revisions, not nearly so sweeping but still enough to change almost every chapter in one way or another. Most of the changes in that third edition take the form of deletions: a word here, a sentence there, a short paragraph occasionally. Book Three attracted the greatest number of deletions, losing in all nearly half a dozen pages. It was from this text that John Murray printed his London editions of 1820 that offered *Knickerbocker's History* to the English reading audience just then discovering and haling Irving's *Sketch Book*, published in England during the first half of that same year.

After 1819 only minor touches were given to the text until Irving made in 1848 his final major revision, printing the text that was to remain the commonly accepted one from then on. He reworked books Five, Six and Seven, the Peter Stuyvesant section, with particular care; he also smoothed out the expression of the entire history with—it is generally felt—all the propriety of middle age. His most important addition to the new version was "The Author's Apology" that is reprinted at the end of this volume. But even with that final revision completed, the text was not to be left entirely on its own. In 1886 the Grolier Club printed the book with further minor changes derived from Irving's 1848 manuscript, and Irving himself made a number of corrections and revisions for an edition of 1854.

It is the text of the 1812 edition, however, that is of immediate concern here. The 1809 printing had been hasty and careless,

19

and Irving went over it this time with closer attention: he corrected misprints, improved the punctuation and spelling, and brought the diction more nearly into accepted usage ("learned them" gives way to "taught them," for instance, although he retained "set" for "sit" and "lay" for "lie," as well as such misunderstandings as "hairbrained" for "harebrained.") In more important revision, he dropped many mocking classical and chivalric allusions, cut some of the long passages of comic world history, and—to the relief of the reader—shortened or cut entirely many of the duller, repetitive discussions of his problems as a historian. But in the most important revision, he added new material that is now some of the most enjoyed: the "Further Account of the Author" at the beginning; the account of the voyage of exploration and Oloffe's dream that is now chapters Four and Five of book Two; the satiric story of the growth of political parties, under the guise of the history of the Long Pipes and Short Pipes, in chapter Six of book Four. Most of these changes and additions were in the first four books; the Peter Stuyvesant section was changed less radically, and those changes that do appear seem aimed at making the writing more impersonal and at stressing unmistakably the mock-epic character of the section. The first third of chapter Six of book Six, for instance, was almost completely rewritten, apparently so that Irving could superimpose the concept of mock history on that of mock epic.

The second edition text, then, does vary noticeably from the first, but almost entirely for the better. If it loses a little of the crude vigor of the first, it more than makes up the difference by its new material and its greater readability. And unlike the 1848 text, it still has the youthful drive and daring and nerve of the first: there are still touches of saving vulgarity not yet lost to the coming Victorian taste, and there is still the willingness to satirize the age and laugh at the city. No one had yet convinced young Washington Irving, twenty-nine years old when he gave his revised text to the printer, that only certain modes and certain expressions were proper for a self-respecting American author. This was essentially the text too that the world was to know while Irving was building his reputation and gaining his name as America's first real contributor to world literature.

The editorial policy of this new edition—the first reprint in modern times of the 1812 text—is simple enough. The text itself is accurate, word for word. The only editorial changes are in spelling and punctuation, both designed to make the book easier and more pleasant for the modern reader. The spelling, except for proper names, has been brought into conformity with modern American practice. The punctuation is a more complicated matter. Irving wrote a conversational style that often is at odds with conventional punctuation: sentences are loose and rambling; sometimes a number of sentences are strung into one long logical unit tied together haphazardly by dashes. To impose strict, modern punctuation on such a style would destroy much of its effect as well as its charm or flavor. The editor has tried, therefore, to make a satisfactory compromise: he has retained the original—often odd—punctuation where it seems necessary; where the punctuation is simply the convention of a past age, he has substituted the present conventions. In practice, this policy led to retaining most of Irving's dashes and many of his semicolons (perhaps more than necessary, although that quickly becomes a matter of opinion), but dropping thousands of commas through the course of the book. The aim in all editorial changes was to offer an accurate text that retains the spirit and effect of the original, but one that presents the fewest hinderances to the modern reader.

SUGGESTIONS FOR FURTHER READING

(A brief, selective bibliography restricted to books of immediate interest and relevance.)

The most reliable edition of Irving's writings before 1850 is the "Author's Revised Edition" that he issued under his own supervision: *The Works of Washington Irving*, 15 vols. (New York, 1848-50). The edition of his complete works now accepted as standard is the "Author's Uniform Revised Edition," *The Works of Washington Irving*, 21 vols. (New York, 1860-61). There have been many later printings of the collected works, some stretching to forty volumes. In addition, most of his journals and notebooks have been published in scholarly editions. Several different volumes of selections for the beginning reader are now in print; an older one, *Washington Irving: Representative Selections*, "American Writers Series," ed. Henry A.

Pochmann (New York, 1934) is useful for its introduction, bibliography and notes. A verbatim reprint of the 1809 first edition of *A History of New York*, "American Authors Series," ed. Stanley T. Williams and Tremaine McDowell (New York, 1927) has a long and excellent introduction.

The definitive biography, and probably the single best and most useful book on Irving, is Stanley T. Williams, *The Life of Washington Irving*, 2 vols. (New York, 1935). Edward Wagenknecht, *Washington Irving: Moderation Displayed* (New York, 1962) offers further interpretation of Irving's character and personality. Van Wyck Brooks, *The World of Washington Irving* (New York, 1944) considers the times as well as the man. Good brief introductions are to be found in the chapter on Irving in *Literary History of the United States*, ed. Spiller, Thorp and others (New York, 1953) and in Lewis Leary's *Washington Irving*, "University of Minnesota Pamphlets on American Writers" (Minneapolis, 1963).

There are two separate bibliographies of Irving. William R. Langfeld and Philip C. Blackburn, *Washington Irving: a Bibliography* (New York, 1933) goes into considerable bibliographical detail about the first editions. Stanley T. Williams and Mary E. Edge, *A Bibliography of the Writings of Washington Irving: A Check List* (New York, 1936) is a listing of all editions. The definitive bibliography is the section on Irving in Jacob Blanck's uncompleted multi-volumed *Bibliography of American Literature* (New Haven, 1955-   ).

A HISTORY

OF

NEW YORK

FROM THE BEGINNING OF THE WORLD

TO THE END OF THE

DUTCH DYNASTY

CONTAINING

Among many Surprising and Curious Matters, the Unutterable Ponderings of WALTER THE DOUBTER, the Disastrous Projects of WILLIAM THE TESTY, and the chivalric achievements of PETER THE HEADSTRONG, the three Dutch Governors of NEW AMSTERDAM; being the only Authentic History of the Times that ever hath been published.

BY DIEDRICH KNICKERBOCKER

De waarheid die in duister lag,
Die komt met klaarheid aan den dag.

IN TWO VOLUMES.

VOL. I.

TO THE

NEW-YORK

HISTORICAL SOCIETY

This work is respectfully dedicated, as an humble and unworthy testimony of the profound veneration and exalted esteem of the Society's

Sincere well wisher,

and

Devoted Servant,

DIEDRICH KNICKERBOCKER

CONTENTS

BOOK II
Treating of the first settlement of the province of Nieuw Nederlandts.

BOOK III
In which is recorded the golden reign of Wouter Van Twiller.

BOOK IV
Containing the Chronicles of the reign of William the Testy.

BOOK V

Containing the first part of the reign of Peter Stuyvesant and his troubles with the Amphyctionic Council.

BOOK VI

Containing the second part of the reign of Peter the Headstrong—and his gallant achievements on the Delaware.

BOOK VII

*Containing the third part of the reign of Peter
the Headstrong—his troubles with the British
nation, and the decline and fall of the Dutch
dynasty.*

ACCOUNT OF THE AUTHOR

It was sometime, if I recollect right, in the early part of the fall of 1808 that a stranger applied for lodgings at the Independent Columbian Hotel in Mulberry Street, of which I am landlord. He was a small, brisk-looking old gentleman, dressed in a rusty black coat, a pair of olive velvet breeches, and a small cocked hat. He had a few gray hairs plaited and clubbed behind, and his beard seemed to be of some eight and forty hours growth. The only piece of finery which he bore about him was a bright pair of square silver shoe buckles, and all his baggage was contained in a pair of saddlebags which he carried under his arm. His whole appearance was something out of the common run; and my wife, who is a very shrewd body, at once set him down for some eminent country schoolmaster.

As the Independent Columbian Hotel is a very small house, I was a little puzzled at first where to put him; but my wife, who seemed taken with his looks, would needs put him in her best chamber, which is genteelly set off with the profiles of the whole family, done in black by those two great painters, Jarvis and Wood, and commands a very pleasant view of the new grounds on the Collect, together with the rear of the Poorhouse and Bridewell, and the full front of the Hospital, so that it is the cheerfullest room in the whole house.

During the whole time that he stayed with us we found him a very worthy good sort of an old gentleman, though a little queer in his ways. He would keep in his room for days together, and if any of the children cried or made a noise about his door, he would bounce out in a great passion, with his hands full of papers, and say something about "deranging his ideas"; which made my wife believe sometimes that he was not altogether *compos*. Indeed, there was more than one reason to make her think so, for his room was always covered with scraps of paper and old mouldy books, laying about at sixes and sevens, which he would never let anybody touch; for he said he had laid them all away in their proper places so that he might know where to find them; though for that matter, he was half his time worrying about the house in search of some book or writing which he had carefully put out of the way. I shall never forget what a pother he once made because my wife cleaned out his room when his back was turned and put everything to rights; for he swore he would never be able to get his papers in order again in a twelvemonth. Upon this my wife ventured to ask him what he did with so many books and papers? and he told her that he was "seeking for immortality"; which made her think more than ever that the poor old gentleman's head was a little cracked.

He was a very inquisitive body, and when not in his room was continually poking about town, hearing all the news and prying into everything that was going on: this was particularly the case about election time, when he did nothing but bustle about from poll to poll, attending all ward meetings and committee rooms; though I could never find that he took part with either side of the question. On the contrary, he would come home and rail at both parties with great wrath—and plainly proved one day, to the satisfaction of my wife and three old ladies who were drinking tea with her, that the two parties were like two rogues, each tugging at a skirt of the nation; and that in the end they would tear the very coat off its back and expose its nakedness. Indeed he was an oracle among the neighbors, who would collect around him to hear him talk of an afternoon as he smoked his pipe on the bench before the door; and I really believe he would have brought over the whole neighborhood to his own side of the question, if they could ever have found out what it was.

He was very much given to argue, or, as he called it, *philosophize,* about the most trifling matter, and, to do him justice, I never knew anybody that was a match for him, except it was a grave-looking gentleman who called now and then to see him and often posed him in an argument. But this is nothing surprising, as I have since found out this stranger is the city librarian, and of course must be a man of great learning; and I have my doubts if he had not some hand in the following history.

As our lodger had been a long time with us and we had never received any pay, my wife began to be somewhat uneasy and curious to find out who and what he was. She accordingly made bold to put the question to his friend, the librarian, who replied in his dry way that he was one of the *Literati;* which she supposed to mean some new party in politics. I scorn to push a lodger for his pay, so I let day after day pass on without dunning the old gentleman for a farthing; but my wife, who always takes these matters on herself, and is, as I said, a shrewd kind of a woman, at last got out of patience and hinted that she thought it high time "some people should have a sight of some people's money." To which the old gentleman replied, in a mighty touchy manner, that she need not make herself uneasy, for that he had a treasure thère (pointing to his saddlebags) worth her whole house put together. This was the only answer we could ever get from him; and as my wife, by some of those odd ways in which women find out everything, learnt that he was of very great connections, being related to the Knickerbockers of Scaghtikoke, and cousin-german to the Congressman of that name, she did not like to treat him uncivilly. What is more, she even offered, merely by way of making things easy, to let him live scot-free if he would teach the children their letters; and to try her best and get the neighbors to send their children also: but the old gentleman took it in such dudgeon, and seemed so affronted at being taken for a schoolmaster, that she never dared speak on the subject again.

About two months ago, he went out of a morning with a bundle in his hand—and has never been heard of since. All kinds of inquiries were made after him, but in vain. I wrote to his relations at Scaghtikoke, but they sent for answer that he had a great dispute with the Congressman about politics and left the place in a huff, and they had neither heard nor seen anything of him from that time to this. I must own I felt very much worried about the poor old gentleman, for I thought something bad must have happened to him, that he should be missing so long and never return to pay his bill. I therefore advertised him in the newspapers, and though my melancholy advertisement was published by several humane printers, yet I have never been able to learn anything satisfactory about him.

My wife now said it was high time to take care of ourselves and see if he had left any thing behind in his room that would pay us for his board and lodging. We found nothing, however, but some old books and musty writings and his saddlebags; which, being opened in the presence of the librarian, contained only a few articles of worn-out clothes and a large bundle of blotted paper. On looking over this, the librarian told us he had no doubt it was the treasure which the old gentleman had spoke about; as it proved to be a most excellent and faithful

HISTORY OF NEW YORK, which he advised us by all means to publish: assuring us that it would be so eagerly bought up by a discerning public that he had no doubt it would be enough to pay our arrears ten times over. Upon this we got a very learned schoolmaster, who teaches our children, to prepare it for the press, which he accordingly has done; and has, moreover, added to it a number of valuable notes of his own and an engraving of the city as it was at the time Mr. Knickerbocker writes about.

This, therefore, is a true statement of my reasons for having this work printed without waiting for the consent of the author: and I here declare that if he ever returns (though I much fear some unhappy accident has befallen him) I stand ready to account with him like a true and honest man. Which is all at present—

From the public's humble servant,
SETH HANDASIDE.

Independent Columbian Hotel,
New York.

The foregoing account of the author was prefixed to the first edition of this work. Shortly after its publication, a letter was received from him, by Mr. Handaside, dated at a small Dutch village on the banks of the Hudson, whither he had traveled for the purpose of inspecting certain ancient records. As this was one of those few and happy villages into which newspapers never find their way, it is not a matter of surprise that Mr. Knickerbocker should never have seen the numerous advertisements that were made concerning him; and that he should learn of the publication of his history by mere accident.

He expressed much concern at its premature appearance, as thereby he was prevented from making several important corrections and alterations; as well as from profiting by many curious hints which he had collected during his travels along the shores of the Tappan Sea and his sojourn at Haverstraw and Esopus.

Finding that there was no longer any immediate necessity for his return to New York, he extended his journey up to the residence of his relations at Scaghtikoke. On his way thither, he stopped for some days at Albany, for which city he is known to have entertained a great partiality. He found it, however, considerably altered, and was much concerned at the inroads and improvements which the Yankees were making, and the consequent decline of the good old Dutch manners. Indeed he was informed that these intruders were making sad innovations in all parts of the state; where they had given great trouble and vexation to the regular Dutch settlers by the introduction of turnpike gates and country schoolhouses. It is said also that Mr. Knickerbocker shook his head sorrowfully at noticing the gradual decay of the great Vander Heyden palace; but was highly indignant at finding that the ancient Dutch church which stood in the middle of the street had been pulled down since his last visit.

The fame of Mr. Knickerbocker's history having reached even to Albany, he received much flattering attention from its worthy burghers, some of whom, however, pointed out two or three very great errors he had fallen into, particularly that of suspending a lump of sugar over the Albany tea tables, which, they assured him, had been discontinued for some years past. Several families, moreover, were somewhat piqued that their ancestors had not been mentioned in his work, and showed great jealousy of their neighbors who had been thus distinguished; while the latter, it must be confessed, plumed themselves vastly thereupon; considering these recordings in the light of letters patent of nobility, establishing their claims to ancestry—which, in this republican country, is a matter of no little solicitude and vainglory.

It is also said that he enjoyed high favor and countenance from the governor, who once asked him to dinner and was seen two or three times to shake hands with him when they met in the street; which certainly was going great length, considering that they differed in politics. Indeed, certain of the governor's confidential friends, to whom he could venture to speak his mind freely on such matters, have assured us that he privately entertained a considerable good will for our author—nay, he even once went so far as to declare, and that openly too, and at his own table, just after dinner, that "Knickerbocker was a very well-meaning sort of an old gentleman, and no fool." From all which many have been led to suppose that had our author been of different politics, and written for the newspapers instead of wasting his talents on histories, he might have risen to some post of honor and profit: peradventure to be a notary public, or even a justice in the ten pound court.

Beside the honors and civilities already mentioned, he was much caressed by the literati of Albany; particularly Mr. John Cook, who entertained him very hospitably at his circulating library and reading room, where they used to drink Spa water and talk about the ancients. He found Mr. Cook a man after his own heart—of great literary research, and a curious collector of books. At parting, the latter, in testimony of friendship, made him a present of the two oldest works in his collection; which were the earliest edition of the Hiedelburgh Catechism, and Adrian Vander Donck's famous account of the New Netherlands: by the last of which Mr. Knickerbocker profited greatly in this his second edition.

Having passed some time very agreeably at Albany, our author proceeded to Scaghtikoke; where, it is but justice to say, he was received with open arms and treated with wonderful loving-kindness. He was much looked up to by the family, being the first historian of the name; and was considered almost as great a man as his cousin the Congressman—with whom, by the by, he became perfectly reconciled and contracted a strong friendship.

In spite, however, of the kindness of his relations and their great attention to his comforts, the old gentleman soon became restless and discontented. His history being published, he had no longer any business to occupy his thoughts, or any scheme to excite his hopes and anticipations. This, to a busy mind like his, was a truly deplorable situation; and had he not been a man of inflexible morals and regular habits, there would have been great danger of his taking to politics or drinking—both which pernicious vices we daily see men driven to by mere spleen and idleness.

It is true he sometimes employed himself in preparing a second edition of his history, wherein he endeavored to correct and improve many passages with which he was dissatisfied and to rectify some mistakes that had crept into it; for he was particularly anxious that his work should be noted for its authenticity; which, indeed, is the very life and soul of history.—But the glow of composition had departed—he had to leave many places untouched which he would fain have altered; and even where he did make alterations, he seemed always in doubt whether they were for the better or the worse.

After a residence of some time at Scaghtikoke, he began to feel a strong desire to return to New York, which he ever regarded with the warmest affection; not merely because it was his native city, but because he really considered it the very best city in the whole world. On his return, he entered into the full enjoyment of the advantages of a literary reputation. He was continually importuned to write advertisements, petitions, handbills, and productions of similar import; and, although he never meddled with the public papers, yet had he the credit of writing innumerable essays and smart things that appeared on all subjects and all sides of the question; in all which he was clearly detected "by his style."

He contracted, moreover, a considerable debt at the post office, in consequence of the numerous letters he received from authors and printers soliciting his subscription—he was applied to by every charitable society for yearly donations, which he gave very cheerfully, considering these applications as so many compliments. He was once invited to a great corporation dinner; and was even twice summoned to attend as a juryman at the court of quarter sessions. Indeed, so renowned did he become that he could no longer pry about, as formerly, in all holes and corners of the city, according to the bent of his humor, unnoticed and uninterrupted; but several times when he has been sauntering the streets on his usual rambles of observation, equipped with his cane and cocked hat, the little boys at play have been known to cry, "There goes Diedrich!"—at which the old gentleman seemed not a little pleased, looking upon these salutations in the light of the praises of posterity.

In a word, if we take into consideration all these various honors and distinctions, together with an exuberant eulogium passed on him in the Port Folio—(with which, we are told, the old gentleman was so much overpowered that he was sick for two or three days)—it must be confessed that few authors have ever lived to receive such illustrious rewards, or have so completely enjoyed in advance their own immortality.

After his return from Scaghtikoke, Mr. Knickerbocker took up his residence at a little rural retreat which the Stuyvesants had granted him on the family domain in gratitude for his honorable mention of their ancestor. It was pleasantly situated on the borders of one of the salt marshes beyond Corlear's Hook: subject, indeed, to be occasionally overflowed, and much infested in the summer time with mosquitoes; but otherwise very agreeable, producing abundant crops of salt grass and bulrushes.

Here, we are sorry to say, the good old gentleman fell dangerously ill of a fever, occasioned by the neighboring marshes. When he found his end approaching, he disposed of his worldly affairs, leaving the bulk of his fortune to the New-York Historical Society; his Hiedelburgh Catechism and Vander Donck's work to the city library; and his saddlebags to Mr. Handaside. He forgave all his enemies—that is to say, all that bore any enmity towards him; for as to himself, he declared he died in good will to all the world. And after dictating several kind messages to his relations at Scaghtikoke, as well as to certain of our most substantial Dutch citizens, he expired in the arms of his friend the librarian.

His remains were interred, according to his own request, in St. Mark's churchyard, close by the bones of his favorite hero, Peter Stuyvesant; and it is rumored that the Historical Society have it in mind to erect a wooden monument to his memory in the Bowling Green.

TO THE PUBLIC

"To rescue from oblivion the memory of former incidents, and to render a just tribute of renown to the many great and wonderful transactions of our Dutch progenitors, Diedrich Knickerbocker, native of the city of New York, produces this historical essay."* Like the great Father of History whose words I have just quoted, I treat of times long past, over which the twilight of uncertainty had already thrown its shadows, and the night of forgetfulness was about to descend forever. With great solicitude had I long beheld the early history of this venerable and ancient city gradually slipping from our grasp, trembling on the lips of narrative old age, and day by day dropping piecemeal into the tomb. In a little while, thought I, and those reverend Dutch burghers, who serve as the tottering monuments of good old times, will be gathered to their fathers; their children, engrossed by the empty pleasures or insignificant transactions of the present age, will neglect to treasure up the recollections of the past, and posterity shall search in vain for memorials of the days of the Patriarchs. The origin of our city will be buried in eternal oblivion, and even the names and achievements of Wouter Van Twiller, William Kieft, and Peter Stuyvesant be enveloped in doubt and fiction, like those of Romulus and Remus, of Charlemagne, King Arthur, Rinaldo, and Godfrey of Bologne.

Determined therefore to avert if possible this threatened misfortune, I industriously sat myself to work to gather together all the fragments of our infant history which still existed, and like my revered prototype, Herodotus, where no written records could be found, I have endeavored to continue the chain of history by well authenticated traditions.

In this arduous undertaking, which has been the whole business of a long and solitary life, it is incredible the number of learned authors I have consulted; and all to but little purpose. Strange as it may seem, though such multitudes of excellent works have been written about this country, there are none ex-

---

* Beloe's Herodotus.

41

tant which give any full and satisfactory account of the early history of New York, or of its three first Dutch governors. I have, however, gained much valuable and curious matter from an elaborate manuscript written in exceeding pure and classic Low Dutch, excepting a few errors in orthography, which was found in the archives of the Stuyvesant family. Many legends, letters, and other documents have I likewise gleaned in my researches among the family chests and lumber garrets of our respectable Dutch citizens; and I have gathered a host of well authenticated traditions from divers excellent old ladies of my acquaintance who requested that their names might not be mentioned. Nor must I neglect to acknowledge how greatly I have been assisted by that admirable and praiseworthy institution, the NEW-YORK HISTORICAL SOCIETY, to which I here publicly return my sincere acknowledgments.

In the conduct of this inestimable work I have adopted no individual model, but on the contrary have simply contented myself with combining and concentrating the excellencies of the most approved ancient historians. Like Xenophon, I have maintained the utmost impartiality and the strictest adherence to truth throughout my history. I have enriched it, after the manner of Sallust, with various characters of ancient worthies drawn at full length and faithfully colored. I have seasoned it with profound political speculations like Thucydides, sweetened it with the graces of sentiment like Tacitus, and infused into the whole the dignity, the grandeur and magnificence of Livy.

I am aware that I shall incur the censure of numerous very learned and judicious critics for indulging too frequently in the bold excursive manner of my favorite Herodotus. And to be candid, I have found it impossible always to resist the allurements of those pleasing episodes which, like flowery banks and fragrant bowers, beset the dusty road of the historian and entice him to turn aside and refresh himself from his wayfaring. But I trust it will be found that I have always resumed my staff and addressed myself to my weary journey with renovated spirits, so that both my readers and myself have been benefited by the relaxation.

Indeed, though it has been my constant wish and uniform endeavor to rival Polybius himself in observing the requisite unity of History, yet the loose and unconnected manner in which many of the facts herein recorded have come to hand rendered such an attempt extremely difficult. This difficulty was likewise increased by one of the grand objects contemplated in my work, which was to trace the rise of sundry customs and institutions in this best of cities, and to compare them, when in the germ of infancy, with what they are in the present old age of knowledge and improvement.

But the chief merit on which I value myself, and found my hopes for future regard, is that faithful veracity with which I have compiled this invaluable little work; carefully winnowing away the chaff of hypothesis and discarding the tares of fable, which are too apt to spring up and choke the seeds of truth and wholesome knowledge.—Had I been anxious to captivate the superficial throng who skim like swallows over the surface of literature; or had I been anxious to commend my writings to the pampered palates of literary epicures, I might have availed myself of the obscurity that overshadows the infant years of our city to introduce a thousand pleasing fictions. But I have scrupulously discarded many a pithy tale and marvellous adventure whereby the drowsy ear of summer indolence might be enthralled; jealously maintaining that fidelity, gravity, and dignity which should ever distinguish the historian. "For a writer of this class," observes an elegant critic, "must sustain the character of a wise man writing for the instruction of posterity; one who has studied to inform himself well, who has pondered his subject with care, and addresses himself to our judgment rather than to our imagination."

Thrice happy, therefore, is this our renowned city in having incidents worthy of swelling the theme of history; and doubly thrice happy is it in having such an historian as myself to relate them. For after all, gentle reader, cities *of themselves,* and, in fact, empires *of themselves,* are nothing without an historian. It is the patient narrator who records their prosperity as they rise—who blazons forth the splendor of their noontide meridian —who props their feeble memorials as they totter to decay—who gathers together their scattered fragments as they rot—and who piously at length collects their ashes into the mausoleum of his work, and rears a triumphal monument to transmit their renown to all succeeding ages.

What has been the fate of many fair cities of antiquity whose nameless ruins encumber the plains of Europe and Asia and awaken the fruitless inquiry of the traveler?—they have sunk

into dust and silence—they have perished from remembrance
for want of a historian! The philanthropist may weep over
their desolation—the poet may wander among their mouldering
arches and broken columns and indulge the visionary flights of
his fancy—but, alas! alas! the modern historian, whose pen, like
my own, is doomed to confine itself to dull matter of fact, seeks
in vain among their oblivious remains for some memorial that
may tell the instructive tale of their glory and their ruin.

"Wars, conflagrations, deluges," says Aristotle, "destroy nations, and with them all their monuments, their discoveries, and
their vanities—The torch of science has more than once been
extinguished and rekindled—A few individuals, who have escaped by accident, reunite the thread of generations."

The same sad misfortune which has happened to so many
ancient cities will happen again, and from the same sad cause,
to nine-tenths of those which now flourish on the face of the
globe. With most of them the time for recording their early
history is gone by; their origin, their foundation, together with
the early stages of their settlement, are forever buried in the
rubbish of years; and the same would have been the case with
this fair portion of the earth if I had not snatched it from
obscurity in the very nick of time, at the moment that those
matters herein recorded were about entering into the wide-
spread insatiable maw of oblivion—if I had not dragged them
out, as it were, by the very locks, just as the monster's adamantine fangs were closing upon them forever. And here have I,
as before observed, carefully collected, collated, and arranged
them, scrip and scrap, *"punt en punt, gat en gat,"* and commenced in this little work a history to serve as a foundation on
which other historians may hereafter raise a noble superstruc-
ture, swelling in process of time until *Knickerbocker's New
York* may be equally voluminous with *Gibbon's Rome,* or *Hume
and Smollet's England!*

And now indulge me for a moment while I lay down my pen,
skip to some little eminence at the distance of two or three
hundred years ahead; and, casting back a bird's eye glance over
the waste of years that is to roll between, discover myself—little
I!—at this moment the progenitor, prototype, and precursor of
of them all, posted at the head of this host of literary worthies,
with my book under my arm and New York on my back, pressing forward like a gallant commander to honor and immortality!

Such are the vainglorious imaginings that will now and then enter into the brain of the author—that irradiate, as with celestial light, his solitary chamber, cheering his weary spirits and animating him to persevere in his labors. And I have freely given utterance to these rhapsodies whenever they have occurred; not, I trust, from an unusual spirit of egotism, but merely that the reader may for once have an idea how an author thinks and feels while he is writing—a kind of knowledge very rare and curious, and much to be desired.

BOOK I
Containing divers ingenious theories and philosophic speculations, concerning the creation and population of the world, as connected with the history of New York.

CHAPTER I

Description of the World.

According to the best authorities, the world in which we dwell is a huge, opaque, reflecting, inanimate mass floating in the vast ethereal ocean of infinite space. It has the form of an orange, being an oblate spheroid, curiously flattened at opposite parts for the insertion of two imaginary poles which are supposed to penetrate and unite at the center; thus forming an axis on which the mighty orange turns with a regular diurnal revolution.

The transitions of light and darkness, whence proceed the alternations of day and night, are produced by this diurnal revolution successively presenting the different parts of the earth to the rays of the sun. The latter is, according to the best, that is to say the latest, accounts, a luminous or fiery body, of a prodigious magnitude, from which this world is driven by a centrifugal or repelling power, and to which it is drawn by a centripetal or attractive force, otherwise called the attraction of gravitation; the combination, or rather the counteraction of these two opposing impulses producing a circular and annual revolution. Hence result the different seasons of the year, viz. spring, summer, autumn and winter.

This I believe to be the most approved modern theory on the subject—though there be many philosophers who have entertained very different opinions; some too of them entitled to much deference from their great antiquity and illustrious characters. Thus it was advanced by some of the ancient sages that the earth was an extended plain supported by vast pillars; and by others, that it rested on the head of a snake or the back of a huge tortoise—but as they did not provide a resting place for either the pillars or the tortoise, the whole theory fell to the ground for want of proper foundation.

The Bramins assert that the heavens rest upon the earth, and the sun and moon swim therein like fishes in the water, moving from east to west by day and gliding along the edge of the horizon to their original stations during the night;* while, according to the Pauranicas of India, it is a vast plain encircled by seven oceans of milk, nectar, and other delicious liquids; that it is studded with seven mountains and ornamented in the center by a mountainous rock of burnished gold; and that a great dragon occasionally swallows up the moon, which accounts for the phenomena of lunar eclipses.†

Beside these and many other equally sage opinions, we have the profound conjectures of ABOUL-HASSAN-ALY, son of Al Khan, son of Aly, son of Abderrahman, son of Abdallah, son of Masoud-el-Hadheli, who is commonly called MASOUDI, and surnamed Cothbeddin, but who takes the humble title of Laheb-ar-rasoul, which means the companion of the ambassador of God. He has written an universal history entitled "Mouroudge-ed-dhahrab, or, the Golden Meadows and the Mines of Precious Stones."‡ In this valuable work he has related the history of the world from the creation down to the moment of writing; which was under the khaliphat of Mothi Billah, in the month Dgioumadi-el-aoual of the 336th year of the Hegira or flight of the Prophet. He informs us that the earth is a huge bird, Mecca and Medina constituting the head, Persia and India the right wing, the land of Gog the left wing, and Africa the tail. He informs us, moreover, that an earth has existed before the present (which he considers as a mere chicken of 7000 years), that it has undergone divers deluges, and that, according to the opinion of some well informed Brahmins of his acquaintance, it will be renovated every seventy thousandth hazarouam; each hazarouam consisting of 12,000 years.

These are a few of the many contradictory opinions of philosophers concerning the earth, and we find that the learned have had equal perplexity as to the nature of the sun. Some of the

* Faria y Souza. Mick. Lus, note b. 7.

† Sir W. Jones, Diss. Antiq. Ind. Zod.

‡ Mss. Bibliot. Roi. Fr.

ancient philosophers have affirmed that it is a vast wheel of brilliant fire;* the others that it is merely a mirror or sphere of transparent crystal;† and a third class, at the head of whom stands Anaxagoras, maintained that it was nothing but a huge ignited mass of iron or stone—indeed, he declared the heavens to be merely a vault of stone, and that the stars were stones whirled upwards from the earth and set on fire by the velocity of its revolutions.‡ But I give little attention to the doctrines of this philosopher, the people of Athens having fully refuted them by banishing him from their city; a concise mode of answering unwelcome doctrines, much resorted to in former days. Another sect of philosophers do declare that certain fiery particles exhale constantly from the earth, which concentrating in a single point of the firmament by day, constitute the sun, but being scattered and rambling about in the dark at night, collect in various points and form stars. These are regularly burnt out and extinguished, not unlike to the lamps in our streets, and require a fresh supply of exhalations for the next occasion.§

It is even recorded that at certain remote and obscure periods, in consequence of a great scarcity of fuel, the sun has been completely burnt out and sometimes not rekindled for a month at a time—a most melancholy circumstance, the very idea of which gave vast concern to Heraclitus, that worthy weeping philosopher of antiquity. In addition to these various speculations, it was the opinion of Herschel that the sun is a magnificent habitable abode; the light it furnishes arising from certain empyreal, luminous, or phosphoric clouds, swimming in its transparent atmosphere.‖

But we will not enter further at present into the nature of the sun, that being an inquiry not immediately necessary to the development of this history; neither will we embroil ourselves in any more of the endless disputes of philosophers

---

* Plutarch de placitis Philosoph. lib. ii. cap. 20.

† Achill. Tat. Isag. cap. 19. Ap. Petav. t. iii. p. 81. Stob. Eclog. Phys. lib. i. p. 56. Plut. de plac. phs.

‡ Diogenes Laertius in Anaxag. l. ii. sec. 8. Plat. Apol. t. i. p. 26. Plut. de Plac. Philo. Xenoph. Mem. l. iv. p. 815.

§ Aristot. Meteor. l. ii. c. 2. Idem Probl. sec. 15. Stob. Ecl. Phys. l. i. p. 55. Bruck. Hist. Phil. t. I. p. 1154, &c.

‖ Philos. Trans. 1795. p. 72. Idem. 1801. p. 265. Nich. Philos. Journ. I. p. 13.

touching the form of this globe, but content ourselves with the theory advanced in the beginning of this chapter, and will proceed to illustrate by experiment the complexity of motion therein ascribed to this our rotatory planet.

Professor Von Poddincoft (or Puddinghead, as the name may be rendered into English) was long celebrated in the university of Leyden for most profound gravity of deportment and his talent at going to sleep in the midst of examinations, to the infinite relief of his hopeful students who thereby worked their way through college with great ease and little study. In the course of one of his lectures, the learned professor, seizing a bucket of water, swung it round his head at arm's length; the impulse with which he threw the vessel from him being a centrifugal force, the retention of his arm operating as a centripetal power, and the bucket, which was a substitute for the earth, describing a circular orbit round about the globular head and ruby visage of Professor Von Poddingcoft, which formed no bad representation of the sun. All of these particulars were duly explained to the class of gaping students around him. He apprised them, moreover, that the same principle of gravitation which retained the water in the bucket restrains the ocean from flying from the earth in its rapid revolutions; and he further informed them that should the motion of the earth be suddenly checked, it would incontinently fall into the sun through the centripetal force of gravitation; a most ruinous event to this planet and one which would also obscure, though it most probably would not extinguish, the solar luminary. An unlucky stripling, one of those vagrant geniuses who seem sent into the world merely to annoy worthy men of the puddinghead order, desirous of ascertaining the correctness of the experiment, suddenly arrested the arm of the professor just at the moment that the bucket was in its zenith, which immediately descended with astonishing precision upon the philosophic head of the instructor of youth. A hollow sound and a red-hot hiss attended the contact, but the theory was in the amplest manner illustrated, for the unfortunate bucket perished in the conflict; but the blazing countenance of Professor Von Poddingcoft emerged from amidst the waters glowing fiercer than ever with unutterable indignation—whereby the students were marvelously edified and departed considerably wiser than before.

It is a mortifying circumstance, which greatly perplexes many a painstaking philosopher, that nature often refuses to second his most profound and elaborate efforts; so that often after having invented one of the most ingenious and natural theories imaginable, she will have the perverseness to act directly in the teeth of his system and flatly contradict his most favorite positions. This is a manifest and unmerited grievance, since it throws the censure of the vulgar and unlearned entirely upon the philosopher; whereas the fault is not to be ascribed to his theory, which is unquestionably correct, but to the waywardness of dame Nature, who with the proverbial fickleness of her sex is continually indulging in coquetries and caprices, and seems really to take pleasure in violating all philosophic rules and jilting the most learned and indefatigable of her adorers. Thus it happened with respect to the foregoing satisfactory explanation of the motion of our planet; it appears that the centrifugal force has long since ceased to operate, while its antagonist remains in undiminished potency: the world, therefore, according to the theory as it originally stood, ought in strict propriety to tumble into the sun—philosophers were convinced that it would do so, and awaited in anxious impatience the fulfilment of their prognostics. But the untoward planet pertinaciously continued her course, notwithstanding that she had reason, philosophy, and a whole university of learned professors opposed to her conduct. The philosophers took this in very ill part, and it is thought they would never have pardoned the slight and affront which they conceived put upon them by the world, had not a good-natured professor kindly officiated as a mediator between the parties and effected a reconciliation.

Finding the world would not accommodate itself to the theory, he wisely determined to accommodate the theory to the world: he therefore informed his brother philosophers that the circular motion of the earth round the sun was no sooner engendered by the conflicting impulses above described than it became a regular revolution, independent of the causes which gave it origin. His learned brethren readily joined in the opinion, being heartily glad of any explanation that would decently extricate them from their embarrassment—and ever since that memorable era the world has been left to take her own course and to revolve around the sun in such orbit as she thinks proper.

Cosmogony, or Creation of the World; with a multitude of excellent theories, by which the creation of a world is shown to be no such difficult matter as common folks would imagine.

Having thus briefly introduced my reader to the world, and given him some idea of its form and situation, he will naturally be curious to know from whence it came and how it was created. And, indeed, the clearing up of these points is absolutely essential to my history, inasmuch as if this world had not been formed, it is more than probable that this renowned island, on which is situated the city of New York, would never have had an existence. The regular course of my history, therefore, requires that I should proceed to notice the cosmogony or formation of this our globe.

And now I give my readers fair warning that I am about to plunge for a chapter or two into as complete a labyrinth as ever historian was perplexed withal: therefore I advise them to take fast hold of my skirts and keep close at my heels, venturing neither to the right nor to the left, lest they get bemired in a slough of unintelligible learning, or have their brains knocked out by some of those hard Greek names which will be flying about in all directions. But should any of them be too indolent or chicken-hearted to accompany me in this perilous undertaking, they had better take a short cut round and wait for me at the beginning of some smoother chapter.

Of the creation of the world we have a thousand contradictory accounts; and though a very satisfactory one is furnished us by divine revelation, yet every philosopher feels himself in honor bound to furnish us with a better. As an impartial historian, I consider it my duty to notice their several theories by which mankind have been so exceedingly edified and instructed.

Thus it was the opinion of certain ancient sages that the earth and the whole system of the universe was the deity himself;* a doctrine most strenuously maintained by Zenophanes and the whole tribe of Eleatics, as also by Strato and the sect of peripatetic philosophers. Pythagoras likewise inculcated the famous numerical system of the monad, dyad, and triad, and by means of his sacred quaternary elucidated the formation of the world, the arcana of nature, and the principles both of music and morals.† Other sages adhered to the mathematical system of squares and triangles; the cube, the pyramid, and the sphere; the tetrahedron, the octahedron, the icosahedron and the dodecahedron.‡ While others advocated the great elementary theory which refers the construction of our globe and all that it contains to the combinations of four material elements, air, earth, fire, and water; with the assistance of a fifth, an immaterial and vivifying principle.

Nor must I omit to mention the great atomic system taught by old Moschus before the siege of Troy; revived by Democritus of laughing memory; improved by Epicurus that king of good fellows; and modernized by the fanciful Descartes. But I decline inquiring whether the atoms of which the earth is said to be composed are eternal or recent; whether they are animate or inanimate; whether, agreeably to the opinion of the atheists, they were fortuitously aggregated, or, as the theists maintain, were arranged by a supreme intelligence.§ Whether in fact the earth be an insensate clod, or whether it be animated by a soul;|| which opinion was strenuously maintained by a host of philosophers, at the head of whom stands the great Plato, that temperate sage who threw the cold water of philosophy on the form of sexual intercourse and inculcated the doctrine of Platonic love—an exquisitely refined intercourse, but much better adapted to the ideal inhabitants of his imaginary island of Atlantis than to the sturdy race, composed of rebellious flesh

---

* Aristot. ap. Cic. lib. i. cap. 3.

† Aristot. Metaph. lib. i. c. 5. Idem de coelo l. 3. c. i. Rousseau mem. sur musique ancien. p. 39. Plutarch de plac. Philos. lib. i. cap. 3.

‡ Tim. Locr. ap. Plato. t. 3. p. 90.

§ Aristot. Nat. Auscult. l. 2. cap. 6. Aristoph. Metaph. lib. i. cap. 3. Cic. de Nat. deor. lib. i. cap. 10. Justin. Mart. orat. ad gent. p. 20.

|| Mosheim in Cudw. lib. i. cap. 4. Tim. de anim. mund. ap. Plat. lib. 3. Mem. de L'acad. des Belles Lettr. t. 32, p. 19, et al.

and blood, which populates the little matter of fact island we inhabit.

Besides these systems, we have, moreover, the poetical theogony of old Hesiod, who generated the whole universe in the regular mode of procreation; and the plausible opinion of others that the earth was hatched from the great egg of night, which floated in chaos and was cracked by the horns of the celestial bull. To illustrate this last doctrine, Burnet in his theory of the earth* has favored us with an accurate drawing and description both of the form and texture of this mundane egg; which is found to bear a marvellous resemblance to that of a goose. Such of my readers as take a proper interest in the origin of this our planet will be pleased to learn that the most profound sages of antiquity among the Egyptians, Chaldeans, Persians, Greeks, and Latins have alternately assisted at the hatching of this strange bird, and that their cacklings have been caught and continued in different tones and inflections from philosopher to philosopher unto the present day.

But while briefly noticing long celebrated systems of ancient sages, let me not pass over with neglect those of other philosophers; which, though less universal and renowned, have equal claims to attention and equal chance for correctness. Thus it is recorded by the Brahmins in the pages of their inspired Shastah that the angel Bistnoo, transforming himself into a great boar, plunged into the watery abyss and brought up the earth on his tusks. Then issued from him a mighty tortoise and a mighty snake; and Bistnoo placed the snake erect upon the back of the tortoise, and he placed the earth upon the head of the snake.†

The negro philosophers of Congo affirm that the world was made by the hands of angels, excepting their own country, which the Supreme Being constructed himself that it might be supremely excellent. And he took great pains with the inhabitants and made them very black and beautiful; and when he had finished the first man, he was well pleased with him and smoothed him over the face, and hence his nose and the nose of all his descendants became flat.

The Mohawk philosophers tell us that a pregnant woman

* Book i. ch. 5.
† Holwell. Gent. Philosophy.

fell down from heaven, and that a tortoise took her upon its
back, because every place was covered with water; and that the
woman, sitting upon the tortoise, paddled with her hands in
the water, and raked up the earth, whence it finally happened
that the earth became higher than the water.*

But I forbear to quote a number more of these ancient and
outlandish philosophers whose deplorable ignorance, in despite
of all their erudition, compelled them to write in languages
which but few of my readers can understand; and I shall proceed briefly to notice a few more intelligible and fashionable
theories of their modern successors.

And first I shall mention the great Buffon who conjectures
that this globe was originally a globe of liquid fire, scintillated
from the body of the sun by the percussion of a comet, as a
spark is generated by the collision of flint and steel. That at
first it was surrounded by gross vapors, which, cooling and con-
densing in process of time, constituted, according to their densi-
ties, earth, water, and air; which gradually arranged themselves,
according to their respective gravities, round the burning or
vitrified mass that formed their center.

Hutton, on the contrary, supposes that the waters at first
were universally paramount; and he terrifies himself with the
idea that the earth must be eventually washed away by the
force of rain, rivers, and mountain torrents until it is confounded with the ocean, or in other words, absolutely dissolves
into itself.—Sublime idea! far surpassing that of the tender-
hearted damsel of antiquity who wept herself into a fountain;
or the good dame of Narbonne in France who, for a volubility
of tongue unusual in her sex, was doomed to peel five hundred
thousand and thirty-nine ropes of onions, and actually ran out
at her eyes before half the hideous task was accomplished.

Whiston, the same ingenious philosopher who rivalled Ditton
in his researches after the longitude (for which the mischief-
loving Swift discharged on their heads a most savory stanza)
has distinguished himself by a very admirable theory respecting the earth. He conjectures that it was originally a *chaotic
comet,* which being selected for the abode of man was removed
from its eccentric orbit and whirled round the sun in its pres-

---

* Johannes Megapolensis, jun. Account of Maquaas or Mohawk Indians.
1644.

ent regular motion; by which change of direction order succeeded to confusion in the arrangement of its component parts. The philosopher adds that the deluge was produced by an uncourteous salute from the watery tail of another comet; doubtless through sheer envy of its improved condition: thus furnishing a melancholy proof that jealousy may prevail even among the heavenly bodies, and discord interrupt that celestial harmony of the spheres so melodiously sung by the poets.

But I pass over a variety of excellent theories, among which are those of Burnet and Woodward and Whitehurst; regretting extremely that my time will not suffer me to give them the notice they deserve—and shall conclude with that of the renowned Dr. Darwin. This learned Theban, who is as much distinguished for rhyme as reason, and for good natured credulity as serious research, and who has recommended himself wonderfully to the good graces of the ladies by letting them into all the gallantries, amours, debaucheries, and other topics of scandal of the court of Flora, has fallen upon a theory worthy of his combustible imagination. According to his opinion, the huge mass of chaos took a sudden occasion to explode, like a barrel of gun-powder, and in that act exploded the sun—which in its flight, by a similar convulsion, exploded the earth—which in like guise exploded the moon—and thus by a concatenation of explosions, the whole solar system was produced and set most systematically in motion!*

By the great variety of theories here alluded to, every one of which, if thoroughly examined, will be found surprisingly consistent in all its parts, my unlearned readers will perhaps be led to conclude that the creation of a world is not so difficult a task as they at first imagined. I have shown at least a score of ingenious methods in which a world could be constructed; and I have no doubt that had any of the philosophers above quoted the use of a good manageable comet, and the philosophical warehouse *chaos* at his command, he would engage to manufacture a planet as good or, if you would take his word for it, better than this we inhabit.

And here I cannot help noticing the kindness of providence in creating comets for the great relief of bewildered philosophers. By their assistance more sudden evolutions and transitions are

---

* Darw. Bot. Garden. Part I. Cant. i. l. 105.

effected in the system of nature than are wrought in a panto-mimic exhibition by the wonder-working sword of Harlequin. Should one of our modern sages, in his theoretical flights among the stars, ever find himself lost in the clouds and in danger of tumbling into the abyss of nonsense and absurdity, he has but to seize a comet by the beard, mount astride of its tail, and away he gallops in triumph, like an enchanter on his hippogriff or a Connecticut witch on her broomstick, "to sweep the cobwebs out of the sky."

It is an old and vulgar saying, about a "beggar on horseback," which I would not for the world have applied to these reverend philosophers; but I must confess that some of them, when they are mounted on one of those fiery steeds, are as wild in their curvettings as was Phaeton of yore when he aspired to manage the chariot of Phœbus. One drives his comet at full speed against the sun and knocks the world out of him with the mighty concussion; another, more moderate, makes his comet a kind of beast of burden, carrying the sun a regular supply of food and fagots—a third, of more combustible disposition, threatens to throw his comet like a bombshell into the world and blow it up like a powder magazine; while a fourth, with no great deli-cacy to this planet and its inhabitants, insinuates. that some day or other his comet—my modest pen blushes while I write it—shall absolutely turn tail upon our world and deluge it with water!—Surely, as I have already observed, comets were bounti-fully provided by providence for the benefit of philosophers, to assist them in manufacturing theories.

And now, having adduced several of the most prominent theories that occur to my recollection, I leave my judicious readers at full liberty to choose among them. They are all seri-ous speculations of learned men—all differ essentially from each other—and all have the same title to belief. It has ever been the task of one race of philosophers to demolish the works of their predecessors and elevate more splendid fantasies in their stead, which in their turn are demolished and replaced by the air castles of a succeeding generation. Thus it would seem that knowledge and genius, of which we make such great parade, consist but in detecting the errors and absurdities of those who have gone before, and devising new errors and absurdities to be detected by those who are to come after us. Theories are the mighty soap bubbles with which the grown up children of science amuse themselves—while the honest vulgar stand gazing in stupid admiration and dignify these learned vagaries with the name of wisdom!—Surely Socrates was right in his opinion that philosophers are but a soberer sort of madmen, busying themselves in things totally incomprehensible, or which, if they could be comprehended, would be found not worthy the trouble of discovery.

For my own part, until the learned have come to an agreement among themselves I shall content myself with the account handed down to us by Moses; in which I do but follow the example of our ingenious neighbors of Connecticut, who at their first settlement proclaimed that the colony should be governed by the laws of God—until they had time to make better.

One thing, however, appears certain—from the unanimous authority of the before-quoted philosophers, supported by the evidence of our own senses (which, though very apt to deceive us, may be cautiously admitted as additional testimony), it appears, I say, and I make the assertion deliberately, without fear of contradiction, that this globe really *was created* and that it is composed of *land and water*. It further appears that it is curiously divided and parceled out into continents and islands, among which I boldly declare the renowned ISLAND OF NEW YORK will be found by anyone who seeks for it in its proper place.

CHAPTER III

How that famous navigator, Noah, was shamefully nicknamed; and how he committed an unpardonable oversight in not having four sons. With the great trouble of philosophers caused thereby, and the discovery of America.

Noah, who is the first seafaring man we read of, begat three sons, Shem, Ham, and Japhet. Authors, it is true, are not wanting who affirm that the patriarch had a number of other children. Thus Berosus makes him father of the gigantic Titans, Methodius gives him a son called Jonithus or Jonicus (who was the first inventor of johnny cakes), and others have mentioned a son, named Thuiscon, from whom descended the Teutons or Teutonic, or in other words the Dutch nation.

I regret exceedingly that the nature of my plan will not permit me to gratify the laudable curiosity of my readers by investigating minutely the history of the great Noah. Indeed such an undertaking would be attended with more trouble than many people would imagine; for the good old patriarch seems to have been a great traveler in his day and to have passed under a different name in every country that he visited. The Chaldeans, for instance, give us his story, merely altering his name into Xisuthrus—a trivial alteration which, to an historian skilled in etymologies, will appear wholly unimportant. It appears likewise that he had exchanged his tarpaulin and quadrant among the Chaldeans for the gorgeous insignia of royalty, and appears as a monarch in their annals. The Egyptians celebrate him under the name of Osiris; the Indians as Menu; the Greek and Roman writers confound him with Ogyges, and the Theban with Deucalion and Saturn. But the Chinese, who deservedly rank among the most extensive and authentic historians, inasmuch as they have known the world much longer than any one else, declare that Noah was no other than Fohi; and what gives this assertion some air of credibility is that it is a fact, admitted by the most enlightened literati, that Noah traveled into China at the time of the building of the tower of Babel (probably to improve himself in the study of languages); and the learned Dr. Shackford gives us the additional information that the ark rested on a mountain on the frontiers of China.

From this mass of rational conjectures and sage hypotheses many satisfactory deductions might be drawn; but I shall content myself with the simple fact stated in the Bible, viz. that Noah begat three sons, Shem, Ham, and Japhet. It is astonishing on what remote and obscure contingencies the great affairs of this world depend, and how events the most distant, and to the common observer unconnected, are inevitably consequent the one to the other. It remains to the philosopher to discover these mysterious affinities, and it is the proudest triumph of his skill to detect and drag forth some latent chain of causation which at first sight appears a paradox to the inexperienced ob-

server. Thus many of my readers will doubtless wonder what
connection the family of Noah can possibly have with this history—and many will stare when informed that the whole history
of this quarter of the world has taken its character and course
from the simple circumstance of the patriarch's having but three
sons—but to explain.

Noah, we are told by sundry very credible historians, becoming sole surviving heir and proprietor of the earth in fee simple
after the deluge, like a good father portioned out his estate
among his children. To Shem he gave Asia; to Ham, Africa;
and to Japhet, Europe. Now it is a thousand times to be lamented that he had but three sons, for had there been a fourth,
he would doubtless have inherited America; which of course
would have been dragged forth from its obscurity on the occasion; and thus many a hard working historian and philosopher
would have been spared a prodigious mass of weary conjecture
respecting the first discovery and population of this country.
Noah, however, having provided for his three sons, looked in
all probability upon our country as mere wild unsettled land
and said nothing about it; and to this unpardonable taciturnity
of the patriarch may we ascribe the misfortune that America
did not come into the world as early as the other quarters of
the globe.

It is true, some writers have vindicated him from this mis-
conduct towards posterity and asserted that he really did discover America. Thus it was the opinion of Mark Lescarbot, a
French writer, possessed of that ponderosity of thought and profoundness of reflection so peculiar to his nation, that the immediate descendants of Noah peopled this quarter of the globe,
and that the old patriarch himself, who still retained a passion
for the seafaring life, superintended the transmigration. The
pious and enlightened father Charlevoix, a French Jesuit remarkable for his aversion to the marvelous, common to all
great travelers, is conclusively of the same opinion; nay, he
goes still further and decides upon the manner in which the
discovery was effected, which was by sea, and under the immediate direction of the great Noah. "I have already observed,"
exclaims the good father in a tone of becoming indignation,
"that it is an arbitrary supposition that the grandchildren of
Noah were not able to penetrate into the new world, or that
they never thought of it. In effect, I can see no reason that can

justify such a notion. Who can seriously believe that Noah and his immediate descendants knew less than we do, and that the builder and pilot of the greatest ship that ever was, a ship which was formed to traverse an unbounded ocean and had so many shoals and quicksands to guard against, should be ignorant of, or should not have communicated to his descendants, the art of sailing on the ocean?" Therefore they did sail on the ocean—therefore they sailed to America—therefore America was discovered by Noah!

Now all this exquisite chain of reasoning, which is so strikingly characteristic of the good father, being addressed to the faith rather than the understanding, is flatly opposed by Hans de Laet, who declares it a real and most ridiculous paradox to suppose that Noah ever entertained the thought of discovering America; and as Hans is a Dutch writer, I am inclined to believe he must have been much better acquainted with the worthy crew of the ark than his competitors, and of course possessed of more accurate sources of information. It is astonishing how intimate historians do daily become with the patriarchs and other great men of antiquity. As intimacy improves with time, and as the learned are particularly inquisitive and familiar in their acquaintance with the ancients, I should not be surprised if some future writers should gravely give us a picture of men and manners as they existed before the flood, far more copious and accurate than the Bible; and that, in the course of another century, the logbook of the good Noah should be as current among historians as the voyages of Captain Cook or the renowned history of Robinson Crusoe.

I shall not occupy my time by discussing the huge mass of additional suppositions, conjectures, and probabilities respecting the first discovery of this country, with which unhappy historians overload themselves in their endeavors to satisfy the doubts of an incredulous world. It is painful to see these laborious wights panting and toiling and sweating under an enormous burden at the very outset of their works, which, on being opened, turns out to be nothing but a mighty bundle of straw. As, however, by unwearied assiduity they seem to have established the fact to the satisfaction of all the world that this country *has been discovered,* I shall avail myself of their useful labors to be extremely brief upon this point.

I shall not therefore stop to inquire whether America was

first discovered by a wandering vessel of that celebrated Phœni-
cian fleet which, according to Herodotus, circumnavigated
Africa; or by that Carthaginian expedition which Pliny, the
naturalist, informs us discovered the Canary Islands; or whether
it was settled by a temporary colony from Tyre, as hinted by
Aristotle and Seneca. I shall neither inquire whether it was
first discovered by the Chinese, as Vossius with great shrewdness
advances; nor by the Norwegians in 1002, under Biorn; nor by
Behem, the German navigator, as Mr. Otto has endeavored to
prove to the Scavans of the learned city of Philadelphia.

Nor shall I investigate the more modern claims of the Welsh,
founded on the voyage of Prince Madoc in the eleventh century,
who having never returned, it has since been wisely concluded
that he must have gone to America, and that for a plain reason
—if he did not go there, where else could he have gone?—a
question which most socratically shuts out all further dispute.

Laying aside, therefore, all the conjectures above mentioned,
with a multitude of others equally satisfactory, I shall take for
granted the vulgar opinion that America was discovered on
the 12th of October, 1492, by Christovallo Colon, a Genoese
who has been clumsily nicknamed Columbus, but for what
reason I cannot discern. Of the voyages and adventures of this
Colon, I shall say nothing, seeing that they are already sufficiently known. Nor shall I undertake to prove that this country
should have been called Colonia, after his name, that being
notoriously self-evident.

Having thus happily got my readers on this side of the
Atlantic, I picture them to myself all impatience to enter upon
the enjoyment of the land of promise, and in full expectation
that I will immediately deliver it into their possession. But if
I do, may I ever forfeit the reputation of a regular bred historian! No—no—most curious and thrice learned readers (for
thrice learned ye are if ye have read all that has gone before,
and nine times learned shall ye be if ye read that which comes
after) we have yet a world of work before us. Think you the
first discoverers of this fair quarter of the globe had nothing to
do but go on shore and find a country ready laid out and cultivated like a garden wherein they might revel at their ease?
No such thing—they had forests to cut down, underwood to grub
up, marshes to drain, and savages to exterminate.

In like manner, I have sundry doubts to clear away, questions to resolve, and paradoxes to explain before I permit you to range at random; but these difficulties once overcome, we shall be enabled to jog on right merrily through the rest of our history. Thus my work shall, in a manner, echo the nature of the subject, in the same manner as the sound of poetry has been found by certain shrewd critics to echo the sense—this being an improvement in history which I claim the merit of having invented.

CHAPTER IV

Showing the great difficulty Philosophers have had in peopling America—And how the Aborigines came to be begotten by accident —to the great relief and satisfaction of the Author.

The next inquiry at which we arrive in the regular course of our history is to ascertain, if possible, how this country was originally peopled; a point fruitful of incredible embarrassments; for unless we prove that the Aborigines did absolutely come from somewhere, it will be immediately asserted in this age of scepticism that they did not come at all; and if they did not come at all, then was this country never populated—a conclusion perfectly agreeable to the rules of logic but wholly irreconcilable to every feeling of humanity, inasmuch as it must syllogistically prove fatal to the innumerable Aborigines of this populous region.

To avert so dire a sophism, and to rescue from logical annihilation so many millions of fellow creatures, how many wings of geese have been plundered! what oceans of ink have been benevolently drained! and how many capacious heads of learned historians have been addled and for ever confounded! I pause with reverential awe when I contemplate the ponderous tomes in different languages with which they have endeavored to solve this question, so important to the happiness of society but so involved in clouds of impenetrable obscurity. Historian after

historian has engaged in the endless circle of hypothetical argument, and after leading us a weary chase through octavos,
quartos, and folios, has let us out at the end of his work just
as wise as we were at the beginning. It was doubtless some philosophical wild goose chase of the kind that made the old poet
Macrobius rail in such a passion at curiosity, which he an-
athematizes most heartily as "an irksome agonizing care, a superstitious industry about unprofitable things, an itching humor
to see what is not to be seen and to be doing what signifies
nothing when it is done." But to proceed.

Of the claims of the children of Noah to the original population of this country I shall say nothing, as they have already
been touched upon in my last chapter. The claimants next in
celebrity are the descendants of Abraham. Thus Christoval
Colon (vulgarly called Columbus), when he first discovered the
gold mines of Hispaniola, immediately concluded, with a
shrewdness that would have done honor to a philosopher, that
he had found the ancient Ophir from whence Solomon procured
the gold for embellishing the temple at Jerusalem; nay, Colon
even imagined that he saw the remains of furnaces of veritable
Hebraic construction, employed in refining the precious ore.

So golden a conjecture, tinctured with such fascinating ex-
travagance, was too tempting not to be immediately snapped at
by the gudgeons of learning; and accordingly there were divers
profound writers ready to swear to its correctness and to bring
in their usual load of authorities and wise surmises wherewithal
to prop it up. Vetablus and Robertus Stephens declared nothing
could be more clear—Arius Montanus, without the least hesita-
tion, asserts that Mexico was the true Ophir and the Jews the
early settlers of the country. While Possevin, Becan, and several
other sagacious writers lug in a *supposed* prophecy of the fourth
book of Esdras, which being inserted in the mighty hypothesis,
like the keystone of an arch, gives it, in their opinion, perpetual
durability.

Scarce, however, have they completed their goodly superstruc-
ture than in trudges a phalanx of opposite authors, with Hans
de Laet, the great Dutchman, at their head, and at one blow
tumbles the whole fabric about their ears. Hans, in fact, con-
tradicts outright all the Israelitish claims to the first settlement
of this country, attributing all those equivocal symptoms and
traces of Christianity and Judaism, which have been said to be

found in divers provinces of the new world, to the *Devil* who has always affected to counterfeit the worship of the true Deity. "A remark," says the knowing old Padre d'Acosta, "made by all good authors who have spoken of the religion of nations newly discovered, and founded besides on the authority of the *fathers of the church.*"

Some writers again, among whom it is with great regret I am compelled to mention Lopez de Gomara and Juan de Leri, insinuate that the Canaanites, being driven from the land of promise by the Jews, were seized with such a panic that they fled without looking behind them, until stopping to take breath they found themselves safe in America. As they brought neither their national language, manners, nor features with them, it is supposed they left them behind in the hurry of their flight— I cannot give my faith to this opinion.

I pass over the supposition of the learned Grotius, who, being both an ambassador and a Dutchman to boot, is entitled to great respect, that North America was peopled by a strolling company of Norwegians and that Peru was founded by a colony from China—Manco or Mungo Capac, the first Incas, being himself a Chinese. Nor shall I more than barely mention that father Kircher ascribes the settlement of America to the Egyptians, Budbeck to the Scandinavians, Charron to the Gauls, Juffredus Petri to a skating party from Friesland, Milius to the Celtæ, Marinocus the Sicilian to the Romans, Le Compte to the Phœnicians, Postel to the Moors, Martin d'Angleria to the Abyssinians, together with the sage surmise of De Laet that England, Ireland, and the Orcades may contend for that honor.

Nor will I bestow any more attention or credit to the idea that America is the fairy region of Zipangri, described by that dreaming traveler, Marco Polo the Venetian; or that it comprises the visionary island of Atlantis, described by Plato. Neither will I stop to investigate the heathenish assertion of Paracelsus that each hemisphere of the globe was originally furnished with an Adam and Eve—or the more flattering opinion of Dr. Romayne, supported by many nameless authorities, that Adam was of the Indian race—or the startling conjecture of Buffon, Helvetius, and Darwin, so highly honorable to mankind, that the whole human species is accidentally descended from a remarkable family of monkeys!

This last conjecture, I must own, came upon me very sud-

denly and very ungraciously. I have often beheld the clown in
a pantomime, while gazing in stupid wonder at the extravagant
gambols of a harlequin, all at once electrified by a sudden stroke
of the wooden sword across his shoulders. Little did I think at
such times that it would ever fall to my lot to be treated with
equal discourtesy, and that while I was quietly beholding these
grave philosophers, emulating the eccentric transformations of
the hero of pantomime, they would on a sudden turn upon me
and my readers and with one hypothetical flourish metamor-
phose us into beasts! I determined from that moment not to
burn my fingers with any more of their theories, but content
myself with detailing the different methods by which they transported the descendants of these ancient and respectable monkeys
to this great field of theoretical warfare.

This was done either by migrations by land or transmigrations
by water. Thus Padre Joseph D'Acosta enumerates three passages
by land—first by the north of Europe, secondly by the north of
Asia, and thirdly by regions southward of the straits of Magellan.
The learned Grotius marches his Norwegians, by a pleasant
route, across frozen rivers and arms of the sea, through Iceland,
Greenland, Estotiland, and Naremberga. And various writers,
among whom are Angleria, De Hornn and Buffon, anxious for
the accommodation of these travelers, have fastened the two
continents together by a strong chain of deductions—by which
means they could pass over dry shod. But should even this fail,
Pinkerton, that industrious old gentleman who compiles books
and manufactures Geographies, has constructed a natural bridge
of ice, from continent to continent, at the distance of four or
five miles from Behring's straits—for which he is entitled to the
grateful thanks of all the wandering aborigines who ever did
or ever will pass over it.

It is an evil much to be lamented that none of the worthy
writers above quoted could ever commence his work without
immediately declaring hostilities against every writer who had
treated of the same subject. In this particular, authors may be
compared to a certain sagacious bird which in building its nest
is sure to pull to pieces the nests of all the birds in its neighborhood. This unhappy propensity tends grievously to impede the
progress of sound knowledge. Theories are at best but brittle
productions, and when once committed to the stream, they

should take care that, like the notable pots which were fellow voyagers, they do not crack each other.

For my part, when I beheld the sages I have quoted gravely accounting for unaccountable things, and discoursing thus wisely about matters forever hidden from their eyes, like a blind man describing the glories of light and the beauty and harmony of colors, I fell back in astonishment at the amazing extent of human ingenuity.

If, cried I to myself, these learned men can weave whole systems out of nothing, what would be their productions were they furnished with substantial materials?—if they can argue and dispute thus ingeniously about subjects beyond their knowledge, what would be the profundity of their observations did they but know what they were talking about! Should old Rhadamanthus, when he comes to decide upon their conduct while on earth, have the least idea of the usefulness of their labors, he will undoubtedly class them with those notorious wise men of Gotham who milked a bull, twisted a rope of sand, and wove a velvet purse from a sow's ear.

My chief surprise is that among the many writers I have noticed no one has attempted to prove that this country was peopled from the moon—or that the first inhabitants floated hither on islands of ice, as white bears cruise about the northern oceans—or that they were conveyed hither by balloons, as modern aeronauts pass from Dover to Calais—or by witchcraft, as Simon Magus posted among the stars—or after the manner of the renowned Scythian Abaris who, like the New England witches on full-blooded broomsticks, made most unheard of journeys on the back of a golden arrow given him by the Hyperborean Apollo.

But there is still one mode left by which this country could have been peopled, which I have reserved for the last because I consider it worth all the rest: it is—*by accident!* Speaking of the islands of Solomon, New Guinea, and New Holland, the profound father Charlevoix observes, "in fine, all these countries are peopled, and *it is possible* some have been so *by accident*. Now if it could have happened in that manner, why might it not have been at the *same time* and by the *same means* with *the other* parts of the globe?" This ingenious mode of deducing certain conclusions from possible premises is an improvement in syllogistic skill and proves the good father superior even to Archimedes, for he can turn the world without anything to rest his lever upon. It is only surpassed by the dexterity with which the sturdy old Jesuit in another place cuts the gordian knot—"Nothing," says he, "is more easy. The inhabitants of both hemispheres are certainly the descendants of the same father. The common father of mankind received an express order from Heaven to people the world, and *accordingly it has been peopled*. To bring this about, it was necessary to overcome all difficulties in the way, *and they have also been overcome!*" Pious logician! How does he put all the herd of laborious theorists to the blush, by explaining in five words what it has cost them volumes to prove they knew nothing about!

They have long been picking at the lock and fretting at the latch, but the honest father at once unlocks the door by bursting it open, and when he has it once ajar he is at full liberty to pour in as many nations as he pleases. This proves to a demonstration that a little piety is better then a cartload of philosophy, and is a practical illustration of that scriptural promise—"By faith ye shall move mountains."

From all the authorities here quoted, and a variety of others which I have consulted but which are omitted through fear of fatiguing the unlearned reader—I can only draw the following conclusions, which luckily, however, are sufficient for my purpose—First, that this part of the world has actually *been peopled* (Q. E. D.), to support which we have living proofs in the numerous tribes of Indians that inhabit it.—Secondly, that it has been peopled in five hundred different ways, as proved by a cloud of authors who from the positiveness of their assertions seem to have been eye-witnesses to the fact.—Thirdly, that the people of this country had a *variety of fathers*, which, as it may not be though much to their credit by the common run of readers, the less we say on the subject the better. The question therefore, I trust, is forever at rest.

In which the Author puts a mighty Question to the rout, by the assistance of the Man in the Moon—which not only delivers thousands of people from great embarrassment, but likewise concludes this introductory book.

The writer of a history may in some respects be likened unto an adventurous knight who, having undertaken a perilous enterprise by way of establishing his fame, feels bound in honor and chivalry to turn back for no difficulty nor hardship, and never to shrink or quail, whatever enemy he may encounter. Under this impression I resolutely draw my pen and fall to with might and main at those doughty questions and subtle paradoxes which, like fiery dragons and bloody giants, beset the entrance to my history and would fain repulse me from the very threshold. And at this moment a gigantic question has started up which I must needs take by the beard and utterly subdue before I can advance another step in my historic undertaking—but I trust this will be the last adversary I shall have to contend with, and that in the next book I shall be enabled to conduct my readers in triumph into the body of my work.

The question which has thus suddenly arisen is, what right had the first discoverers of America to land and take possession of a country without first gaining the consent of its inhabitants or yielding them an adequate compensation for their territory? —a question which has withstood many fierce assaults and has given much distress of mind to multitudes of kindhearted folk. And indeed until it be totally vanquished and put to rest, the worthy people of America can by no means enjoy the soil they inhabit with clear right and title, and quiet, unsullied consciences.

The first source of right by which property is acquired in a country is DISCOVERY. For as all mankind have an equal right to any thing which has never before been appropriated, so any

nation that discovers an uninhabited country and takes possession thereof is considered as enjoying full property and absolute, unquestionable empire therein.*

This proposition being admitted, it follows clearly that the
Europeans who first visited America were the real discoverers of
the same; nothing being necessary to the establishment of this
fact but simply to prove that it was totally uninhabited by man.
This would at first appear to be a point of some difficulty, for
it is well known that this quarter of the world abounded with
certain animals that walked erect on two feet, had something
of the human countenance, uttered certain unintelligible sounds
very much like language, in short, had a marvellous resemblance
to human beings. But the zealous and enlightened fathers who
accompanied the discoverers for the purpose of promoting the
kingdom of heaven by establishing fat monasteries and bishop-
rics on earth soon cleared up this point, greatly to the satisfaction of his holiness the Pope and of all Christian voyagers and
discoverers.

They plainly proved, and as there were no Indian writers
arose on the other side, the fact was considered as fully admitted
and established, that the two-legged race of animals before mentioned were mere cannibals, detestable monsters, and many of
them giants—which last description of vagrants have, since the
times of Gog, Magog, and Goliath, been considered as outlaws
and have received no quarter in either history, chivalry, or
song. Indeed, even the philosophic Bacon declared the Americans to be people proscribed by the laws of nature, inasmuch
as they had a barbarous custom of sacrificing men and feeding
upon man's flesh.

Nor are these all the proofs of their utter barbarism: among
many other writers of discernment, Ulloa tells us "their imbecility is so visible that one can hardly form an idea of them
different from what one has of the brutes. Nothing disturbs the
tranquillity of their souls, equally insensible to disasters and
to prosperity. Though half naked, they are as contented as a
monarch in his most splendid array. Fear makes no impression
on them, and respect as little."—All this is furthermore supported by the authority of M. Bouguer. "It is not easy," says
he, "to describe the degree of their indifference for wealth and

* Grotius. Puffendorf, b. 5. c. 4. Vattel, b. 1. c. 18, &c.

all its advantages. One does not well know what motives to propose to them when one would persuade them to any service. It is vain to offer them money; they answer that they are not hungry." And Vanegas confirms the whole, assuring us that "ambition they have none, and are more desirous of being thought strong than valiant. The objects of ambition with us, honor, fame, reputation, riches, posts and distinctions are unknown among them. So that this powerful spring of action, the cause of so much *seeming* good and *real* evil in the world, has no power over them. In a word, these unhappy mortals may be compared to children in whom the development of reason is not completed."

Now all these peculiarities, although in the unenlightened states of Greece they would have entitled their possessors to immortal honor, as having reduced to practice those rigid and abstemious maxims, the mere talking about which acquired certain old Greeks the reputation of sages and philosophers;—yet were they clearly proved in the present instance to betoken a most abject and brutified nature, totally beneath the human character. But the benevolent fathers, who had undertaken to turn these unhappy savages into dumb beasts by dint of argument, advanced still stronger proofs; for as certain divines of the sixteenth century, and among the rest Lullus, affirm—the Americans go naked and have no beards!—"They have nothing," says Lullus, "of the reasonable animal except the mask."—And even that mask was allowed to avail them but little, for it was soon found that they were of a hideous copper complexion—and being of a copper complexion, it was all the same as if they were negroes—and negroes are black, "and black," said the pious fathers, devoutly crossing themselves, "is the color of the Devil!" Therefore, so far from being able to own property, they had no right even to personal freedom, for liberty is too radiant a deity to inhabit such gloomy temples. All which circumstances plainly convinced the righteous followers of Cortes and Pizarro that these miscreants had no title to the soil that they infested— that they were a perverse, illiterate, dumb, beardless, *black seed* —mere wild beasts of the forests, and like them should either be subdued or exterminated.

From the foregoing arguments, therefore, and a variety of others equally conclusive which I forbear to enumerate, it was clearly evident that this fair quarter of the globe when first visited by Europeans was a howling wilderness, inhabited by nothing but wild beasts; and that the transatlantic visitors acquired an incontrovertible property therein, by the *right of discovery*.

This right being fully established, we now come to the next, which is the right acquired by *cultivation*. "The cultivation of the soil," we are told, "is an obligation imposed by nature on mankind. The whole world is appointed for the nourishment of its inhabitants: but it would be incapable of doing it, was it uncultivated. Every nation is then obliged by the law of nature to cultivate the ground that has fallen to its share. Those people, like the ancient Germans and modern Tartars, who having fertile countries disdain to cultivate the earth and choose to live by rapine, are wanting to themselves and *deserve to be exterminated as savage and pernicious beasts*."*

Now it is notorious that the savages knew nothing of agriculture when first discovered by the Europeans, but lived a most vagabond, disorderly, unrighteous life,—rambling from place to place and prodigally rioting upon the spontaneous luxuries of nature without tasking her generosity to yield them anything more; whereas it has been most unquestionably shown that heaven intended the earth should be ploughed and sown and manured and laid out into cities and towns and farms and country seats and pleasure grounds and public gardens, all which the Indians knew nothing about—therefore they did not improve the talents providence had bestowed on them—therefore they were careless stewards—therefore they had no right to the soil —therefore they deserved to be exterminated.

It is true the savages might plead that they drew all the benefits from the land which their simple wants required—they found plenty of game to hunt, which together with the roots and uncultivated fruits of the earth furnished a sufficient variety for their frugal repasts;—and that as heaven merely designed the earth to form the abode and satisfy the wants of man, so long as those purposes were answered, the will of heaven was accomplished.—But this only proves how undeserving they were of the blessings around them—they were so much the more savages for not having more wants; for knowledge is in some degree an increase of desires, and it is this superiority both in

---

* Vattel—B. i. ch. 17. See likewise Grotius, Puffendorf, etc.

the number and magnitude of his desires that distinguishes the man from the beast. Therefore the Indians, in not having more wants, were very unreasonable animals; and it was but just that they should make way for the Europeans who had a thousand wants to their one, and therefore would turn the earth to more account and by cultivating it more truly fulfil the will of heaven. Besides—Grotius and Lauterbach and Puffendorf and Titius, and many wise men beside who have considered the matter properly, have determined that the property of a country cannot be acquired by hunting, cutting wood or drawing water in it—nothing but precise demarcation of limits and the intention of cultivation can establish the possession. Now as the savages (probably from never having read the authors above quoted) had never complied with any of these necessary forms, it plainly followed that they had no right to the soil, but that it was completely at the disposal of the first comers, who had more knowledge, more wants, and more elegant, that is to say artificial, desires than themselves.

In entering upon a newly discovered, uncultivated country, therefore, the new comers were but taking possession of what, according to the aforesaid doctrine, was their own property— therefore in opposing them, the savages were invading their just rights, infringing the immutable laws of nature, and counteracting the will of heaven—therefore they were guilty of impiety, burglary, and trespass on the case—therefore they were hardened offenders against God and man—therefore they ought to be exterminated.

But a more irresistible right than either that I have mentioned, and one which will be the most readily admitted by my reader, provided he be blessed with bowels of charity and philanthropy, is the right acquired by *civilization*. All the world knows the lamentable state in which these poor savages were found: not only deficient in the comforts of life, but what is still worse, most piteously and unfortunately blind to the miseries of their situation. But no sooner did the benevolent inhabitants of Europe behold their sad condition than they immediately went to work to ameliorate and improve it. They introduced among them rum, gin, brandy, and the other comforts of life—and it is astonishing to read how soon the poor savages learnt to estimate these blessings—they likewise made known to them a thousand remedies by which the most inveterate diseases are alleviated and healed;

and that they might comprehend the benefits and enjoy the comforts of these medicines, they previously introduced among them the diseases which they were calculated to cure. By these and a variety of other methods was the condition of these poor savages wonderfully improved; they acquired a thousand wants of which they had before been ignorant; and as he has most sources of happiness who has most wants to be gratified, they were doubtlessly rendered a much happier race of beings.

But the most important branch of civilization, and which has most strenuously been extolled by the zealous and pious fathers of the Romish Church, is the introduction of the Christian faith. It was truly a sight that might well inspire horror to behold these savages stumbling among the dark mountains of paganism and guilty of the most horrible ignorance of religion. It is true, they neither stole nor defrauded; they were sober, frugal, continent, and faithful to their word; but though they acted right habitually, it was all in vain unless they acted so from precept. The newcomers therefore used every method to induce them to embrace and practise the true religion—except indeed that of setting them the example.

But notwithstanding all these complicated labors for their good, such was the unparalleled obstinacy of these stubborn wretches that they ungratefully refused to acknowledge the strangers as their benefactors and persisted in disbelieving the doctrines they endeavored to inculcate; most insolently alleging that from their conduct the advocates of Christianity did not seem to believe in it themselves. Was not this too much for human patience?—would not one suppose that the benign visitants from Europe, provoked at their incredulity and discouraged by their stiff-necked obstinacy, would for ever have abandoned their shores and consigned them to their original ignorance and misery?—But no—so zealous were they to effect the temporal comfort and eternal salvation of these pagan infidels that they even proceeded from the milder means of persuasion to the more painful and troublesome one of persecution—let loose among them whole troops of fiery monks and furious bloodhounds—purified them by fire and sword, by stake and fagot; in consequence of which indefatigable measures the cause of Christian love and charity was so rapidly advanced that in a very few years not one fifth of the number of unbelievers existed in South America that were found there at the time of its discovery.

What stronger right need the European settlers advance to the country than this? Have not whole nations of uninformed savages been made acquainted with a thousand imperious wants and indispensable comforts of which they were before wholly ignorant? Have they not been literally hunted and smoked out of the dens and lurking-places of ignorance and infidelity and absolutely scourged into the right path? Have not the temporal things, the vain baubles and filthy lucre of this world, which were too apt to engage their worldly and selfish thoughts, been benevolently taken from them; and have they not, instead thereof, been taught to set their affections on things above?—And finally, to use the words of a reverend Spanish father in a letter to his superior in Spain—"Can anyone have the presumption to say that these savage Pagans have yielded anything more than an inconsiderable recompense to their benefactors; in surrendering to them a little pitiful tract of this dirty sublunary planet in exchange for a glorious inheritance in the kingdom of Heaven!"

Here then are three complete and undeniable sources of right established, any one of which was more than ample to establish a property in the newly discovered regions of America. Now, so it has happened in certain parts of this delightful quarter of the globe that the right of discovery has been so strenuously asserted, the influence of cultivation so industriously extended, and the progress of salvation and civilization so zealously prosecuted, that what with their attendant wars, persecutions, oppressions, diseases, and other partial evils that often hang on the skirts of great benefits—the savage aborigines have, somehow or another, been utterly annihilated—and this all at once brings me to a fourth right, which is worth all the others put together— For the original claimants to the soil being all dead and buried, and no one remaining to inherit or dispute the soil, the Spaniards, as the next immediate occupants, entered upon the possession as clearly as the hangman succeeds to the clothes of the malefactor—and as they have Blackstone* and all the learned expounders of the law on their side, they may set all actions of ejectment at defiance—and this last right may be entitled the RIGHT BY EXTERMINATION, or in other words, the RIGHT BY GUN-POWDER.

But lest any scruples of conscience should remain on this head, and to settle the question of right for ever, his holiness Pope

---

* Bl. Com. B. II. c. 1.

Alexander VI issued a mighty bull by which he generously granted the newly discovered quarter of the globe to the Spaniards and Portuguese; who thus having law and gospel on their side, and being inflamed with great spiritual zeal, showed the Pagan savages neither favor nor affection, but prosecuted the work of discovery, colonization, civilization and extermination with ten times more fury than ever.

Thus were the European worthies who first discovered America clearly entitled to the soil; and not only entitled to the soil but likewise to the eternal thanks of these infidel savages for having come so far, endured so many perils by sea and land, and taken such unwearied pains for no other purpose but to improve their forlorn, uncivilized, and heathenish condition—for having made them acquainted with the comforts of life; for having introduced among them the light of religion; and finally —for having hurried them out of the world, to enjoy its reward!

But as argument is never so well understood by us selfish mortals as when it comes home to ourselves, and as I am particularly anxious that this question should be put to rest for ever, I will suppose a parallel case by way of arousing the candid attention of my readers.

Let us suppose, then, that the inhabitants of the moon by astonishing advancement in science and by a profound insight into that ineffable lunar philosophy, the mere flickerings of which have of late years dazzled the feeble optics and addled the shallow brains of the good people of our globe—let us suppose, I say, that the inhabitants of the moon by these means had arrived at such a command of their *energies,* such an enviable state of *perfectibility,* as to control the elements and navigate the boundless regions of space. Let us suppose a roving crew of these soaring philosophers in the course of an aerial voyage of discovery among the stars should chance to alight upon this outlandish planet.

And here I beg my readers will not have the uncharitableness to smile, as is too frequently the fault of volatile readers when perusing the grave speculations of philosophers. I am far from indulging in any sportive vein at present; nor is the supposition I have been making so wild as many may deem it. It has long been a very serious and anxious question with me, and many a time and oft in the course of my overwhelming cares and contrivances for the welfare and protection of this my native planet have I lain awake whole nights debating in my mind whether it were most probable we should first discover and civilize the moon, or the moon discover and civilize our globe. Neither would the prodigy of sailing in the air and cruising among the stars be a whit more astonishing and incomprehensible to us than was the European mystery of navigating floating castles through the world of waters to the simple savages. We have already discovered the art of coasting along the aerial shores of our planet by means of balloons, as the savages had of venturing along their sea coasts in canoes; and the disparity between the former and the aerial vehicles of the philosophers from the moon might not be greater than that between the bark canoes of the savages and the mighty ships of their discoverers. I might here pursue an endless chain of similar speculations; but as they would be unimportant to my subject, I abandon them to my reader, particularly if he be a philosopher, as matters well worthy his attentive consideration.

To return then to my supposition—let us suppose the aerial visitants I have mentioned possessed of vastly superior knowledge to ourselves; that is to say, possessed of superior knowledge in the art of extermination—riding on hippogriffs—defended with impenetrable armor—armed with concentrated sunbeams and provided with vast engines to hurl enormous moon-stones; in short, let us suppose them, if our vanity will permit the supposition, as superior to us in knowledge, and consequently in power, as the Europeans were to the Indians when they first discovered them. All this is very possible; it is only our self-sufficiency that makes us think otherwise; and I warrant the poor savages, before they had any knowledge of the white men armed in all the terrors of glittering steel and tremendous gunpowder, were as perfectly convinced that they themselves were the wisest, the most virtuous, powerful, and perfect of created beings, as are, at this present moment, the lordly inhabitants of old England, the volatile populace of France, or even the self-satisfied citizens of this most enlightened republic.

Let us suppose, moreover, that the aerial voyagers, finding this planet to be nothing but a howling wilderness, inhabited by us poor savages and wild beasts, shall take formal possession of it in the name of his most gracious and philosophic excellency, the man in the moon. Finding, however, that their numbers are incompetent to hold it in complete subjection, on account of the

ferocious barbarity of its inhabitants; they shall take our worthy
President, the King of England, the Emperor of Hayti, the
mighty Bonaparte, and the great King of Bantam, and returning
to their native planet shall carry them to court, as were the
Indian chiefs led about as spectacles in the courts of Europe.

Then making such obeisance as the etiquette of the court requires, they shall address the puissant man in the moon in, as
near as I can conjecture, the following terms:

"Most serene and mighty Potentate, whose dominions extend
as far as eye can reach, who rideth on the Great Bear, useth the
sun as a looking glass, and maintaineth unrivalled control over
tides, madmen, and sea crabs. We thy liege subjects have just
returned from a voyage of discovery, in the course of which we
have landed and taken possession of that obscure little dirty
planet which thou beholdest rolling at a distance. The five uncouth monsters, which we have brought into this august presence, were once very important chiefs among their fellow savages,
who are a race of beings totally destitute of the common attributes of humanity; and differing in everything from the inhabitants of the moon, inasmuch as they carry their heads upon
their shoulders instead of under their arms—have two eyes instead of one—are utterly destitute of tails, and of a variety of
unseemly complexions, particularly of a horrible whiteness—
instead of pea green.

"We have moreover found these miserable savages sunk into
a state of the utmost ignorance and depravity, every man shame-
lessly living with his own wife and rearing his own children,
instead of indulging in that community of wives enjoined by
the law of nature, as expounded by the philosophers of the
moon. In a word, they have scarcely a gleam of true philosophy
among them, but are, in fact, utter heretics, ignoramuses, and
barbarians. Taking compassion, therefore, on the sad condition
of these sublunary wretches, we have endeavored, while we remained on their planet, to introduce among them the light of
reason—and the comforts of the moon. We have treated them
to mouthfuls of moonshine and draughts of nitrous oxide, which
they swallowed with incredible voracity, particularly the females;
and we have likewise endeavored to instil into them the precepts
of lunar philosophy. We have insisted upon their renouncing
the contemptible shackles of religion and common sense, and
adoring the profound, omnipotent, and all perfect energy, and

the ecstatic, immutable, immovable perfection. But such was the unparalleled obstinacy of these wretched savages that they persisted in cleaving to their wives and adhering to their religion, and absolutely set at nought the sublime doctrines of the moon —nay, among other abominable heresies, they even went so far as blasphemously to declare that this ineffable planet was made of nothing more nor less than green cheese!"

At these words, the great man in the moon (being a very profound philosopher) shall fall into a terrible passion, and possessing equal authority over things that do not belong to him as did whilome his holiness the Pope, shall forthwith issue a formidable bull,—specifying, "That—whereas a certain crew of Lunatics have lately discovered and taken possession of a newly discovered planet called *the earth*—and that whereas it is inhabited by none but a race of two-legged animals that carry their heads on their shoulders instead of under their arms; cannot talk the lunatic language; have two eyes instead of one; are destitute of tails, and of a horrible whiteness instead of pea green—therefore, and for a variety of other excellent reasons—they are considered incapable of possessing any property in the planet they infest, and the right and title to it are confirmed to its original discoverers.—And furthermore, the colonists who are now about to depart to the aforesaid planet are authorized and commanded to use every means to convert these infidel savages from the darkness of Christianity and make them thorough and absolute lunatics."

In consequence of this benevolent bull, our philosophic benefactors go to work with hearty zeal. They seize upon our fertile territories, scourge us from our rightful possessions, relieve us from our wives, and when we are unreasonable enough to complain they will turn upon us and say—Miserable barbarians! ungrateful wretches!—have we not come thousands of miles to improve your worthless planet!—have we not fed you with moonshine—have we not intoxicated you with nitrous oxide—does not our moon give you light every night, and have you the baseness to murmur when we claim a pitiful return for all these benefits? But finding that we not only persist in absolute contempt of their reasoning and disbelief in their philosophy but even go so far as daringly to defend our property, their patience shall be exhausted and they shall resort to their superior powers of argument—hunt us with hippogriffs, transfix us with concentrated sunbeams, demolish our cities with, moon-stones; until having by main force converted us to the true faith, they shall graciously permit us to exist in the torrid deserts of Arabia or the frozen regions of Lapland, there to enjoy the blessings of civilization and the charms of lunar philosophy—in much the same manner as the reformed and enlightened savages of this country are kindly suffered to inhabit the inhospitable forests of the north or the impenetrable wildernesses of South America.

Thus, I hope, I have clearly proved and strikingly illustrated the right of the early colonists to the possession of this country —and thus is this gigantic question completely vanquished—so having manfully surmounted all obstacles and subdued all opposition, what remains but that I should forthwith conduct my readers into the city which we have been so long in a manner besieging?—But hold; before I proceed another step I must pause to take breath and recover from the excessive fatigue I have undergone in preparing to begin this most accurate of histories. And in this I do but imitate the example of a renowned Dutch tumbler of antiquity who took a start of three miles for the purpose of jumping over a hill, but having run himself out of breath by the time he reached the foot, sat himself quietly down for a few moments to blow and then walked over it at his leisure.

BOOK II
Treating of the first
settlement of the Province
of Nieuw Nederlandts.

CHAPTER I

*In which are contained divers reasons why a
man should not write in a hurry. Also of
Master Hendrick Hudson, his discovery of a
strange country—and how he was magnificently rewarded by the munificence of their
High Mightinesses.*

My great-grandfather by the mother's side, Hermanus Van
Clattercop, when employed to build the large stone church at
Rotterdam which stands about three hundred yards to your
left after you turn off from the Boomkeys, and which is so
conveniently constructed that all the zealous Christians of
Rotterdam prefer sleeping through a sermon there to any other
church in the city—my great-grandfather, I say, when employed
to build that famous church, did in the first place send to Delft
for a box of long pipes; then having purchased a new spitting-
box and a hundredweight of the best Virginia, he sat himself
down and did nothing for the space of three months but smoke
most laboriously. Then did he spend full three months more
in trudging on foot, and voyaging in trekschuit, from Rotterdam
to Amsterdam—to Delft—to Haerlem—to Leyden—to the Hague,
knocking his head and breaking his pipe against every church
in his road. Then did he advance gradually nearer and nearer
to Rotterdam, until he came in full sight of the identical spot
whereon the church was to be built. Then did he spend three
months longer in walking round it and round it, contemplating
it first from one point of view and then from another—now
would he be paddled by it on the canal—now would he peep
at it through a telescope from the other side of the Meuse—and
now would he take a bird's eye glance at it from the top of one

of those gigantic windmills which protect the gates of the city. The good folks of the place were on the tiptoe of expectation and impatience—notwithstanding all the turmoil of my great-grandfather, not a symptom of the church was yet to be seen; they even began to fear it would never be brought into the world, but that its great projector would lie down and die in labor of the mighty plan he had conceived. At length, having occupied twelve good months in puffing and paddling and talking and walking—having travelled over all Holland, and even taken a peep into France and Germany—having smoked five hundred and ninety-nine pipes and three hundredweight of the best Virginia tobacco—my great-grandfather gathered together all that knowing and industrious class of citizens who prefer attending to anybody's business sooner than their own; and having pulled off his coat and five pair of breeches, he advanced sturdily up and laid the corner stone of the church in the presence of the whole multitude—just at the commencement of the thirteenth month.

In a similar manner, and with the example of my worthy ancestor full before my eyes, have I proceeded in writing this most authentic history. The honest Rotterdammers no doubt thought my great-grandfather was doing nothing at all to the purpose while he was making such a world of prefatory bustle about the building of his church—and many of the ingenious inhabitants of this fair city will unquestionably suppose that all the preliminary chapters, with the discovery, population, and final settlement of America, were totally irrelevant and superfluous—and that the main business, the history of New York, is not a jot more advanced than if I had never taken up my pen. Never were wise people more mistaken in their conjectures; in consequence of going to work slowly and deliberately, the church came out of my grandfather's hands one of the most sumptuous, goodly, and glorious edifices in the known world —excepting that, like our magnificent capitol at Washington, it was began on so grand a scale that the good folks could not afford to finish more than the wing of it. So likewise, I trust, if ever I am enabled to finish this work on the plan I have commenced (of which, in simple truth, I sometimes have my doubts), it will be found that I have pursued the latest rules of my art as exemplified in the writings of all the great American historians, and wrought a very large history out of a small subject

—which, nowadays, is considered one of the great triumphs of historic skill. To proceed, then, with the thread of my story.

In the ever memorable year of our Lord, 1609, on a Saturday morning, the five and twentieth day of March, old style, did that "worthy and irrecoverable discoverer (as he has justly been called), Master Henry Hudson," set sail from Holland in a stout vessel called the Half Moon, being employed by the Dutch East India Company to seek a northwest passage to China.

Henry (or as the Dutch historians call him, Hendrick) Hudson was a seafaring man of renown who had learned to smoke tobacco under Sir Walter Raleigh and is said to have been the first to introduce it into Holland, which gained him much popularity in that country and caused him to find great favor in the eyes of their High Mightinesses, the lords states general, and also of the honorable West India Company. He was a short, square, brawny old gentleman with a double chin, a mastiff mouth, and a broad copper nose which was supposed in those days to have acquired its fiery hue from the constant neighborhood of his tobacco pipe.

He wore a true Andrea Ferrara, tucked in a leathern belt, and a commodore's cocked hat [on] one side of his head. He was remarkable for always jerking up his breeches when he gave out his orders, and his voice sounded not unlike the brattling of a tin trumpet—owing to the number of hard northwesters which he had swallowed in the course of his seafaring.

Such was Hendrick Hudson, of whom we have heard so much and know so little: and I have been thus particular in his description for the benefit of modern painters and statuaries, that they may represent him as he was and not, according to their common custom with modern heroes, make him look like Cæsar or Marcus Aurelius or the Apollo of Belvidere.

As chief mate and favorite companion, the commodore chose master Robert Juet of Limehouse in England. By some his name has been spelled *Chewit* and ascribed to the circumstance of his having been the first man that ever chewed tobacco; but this I believe to be a mere flippancy; more especially as certain of his progeny are living at this day who write their names Juet. He was an old comrade and early schoolmate of the great Hudson with whom he had often played truant and sailed chip boats in a neighboring pond when they were little boys—from whence it is said the commodore first derived his bias towards a seafaring life. Certain it is that the old people about Limehouse declared Robert Juet to be an unlucky urchin, prone to mischief, that would one day or other come to the gallows.

He grew up, as boys of that kind often grow up, a rambling, heedless varlet, tossed about in all quarters of the world—meeting with more perils and wonders than did Sinbad the Sailor, without growing a whit more wise, prudent or ill-natured. Under every misfortune he comforted himself with a quid of tobacco and the truly philosophic maxim that "it will be all the same thing a hundred years hence." He was skilled in the art of carving anchors and true lover's knots on the bulk heads and quarter railings, and was considered a great wit on board ship, in consequence of his playing pranks on everybody around, and now and then even making a wry face at old Hendrick when his back was turned.

To this universal genius are we indebted for many particulars concerning this voyage; of which he wrote a history at the request of the commodore, who had an unconquerable aversion to writing himself, from having received so many floggings about it when at school. To supply the deficiencies of master Juet's journal, which is written with true logbook brevity, I have availed myself of divers family traditions handed down from my great-great-grandfather who accompanied the expedition in the capacity of cabin boy.

From all that I can learn, few incidents worthy of remark happened in the voyage; and it mortifies me exceedingly that I have to admit so noted an expedition into my work without making any more of it—Oh! that I had the advantages of that most authentic writer of yore, Apollonius Rhodius, who in his account of the famous Argonautic expedition has the whole mythology at his disposal and elevates Jason and his compeers into heroes and demigods; although all the world knows them to have been a mere gang of sheep stealers on a marauding expedition—or that I had the privileges of Dan Homer and Dan Virgil to enliven my narration with giants and Lystrigonians; to entertain our honest mariners with an occasional concert of syrens and mermaids, and now and then with the raree show of honest old Neptune and his fleet of frolicsome cruisers. But alas! the good old times have long gone by when your waggish deities would descend upon this terraqueous globe in their own proper persons and play their pranks upon its wondering inhabitants.

Suffice it then to say, the voyage was prosperous and tranquil —the crew being a patient people, much given to slumber and vacuity, and but little troubled with the disease of thinking— a malady of the mind which is the sure breeder of discontent. Hudson had laid in abundance of gin and sauerkraut, and every man was allowed to sleep quietly at his post unless the wind blew. True it is, some slight dissatisfaction was shown on two or three occasions at certain unreasonable conduct of Commodore Hudson. Thus, for instance, he forbore to shorten sail when the wind was light and the weather serene, which was considered among the most experienced Dutch seamen as certain *weather breeders,* or prognostics that the weather would change for the worse. He acted, moreover, in direct contradiction to that ancient and sage rule of the Dutch navigators, who always took in sail at night—put the helm aport, and turned in—by which precaution they had a good night's rest—were sure of knowing where they were the next morning, and stood but little chance of running down a continent in the dark. He likewise prohibited the seamen from wearing more than five jackets and six pair of breeches, under pretence of rendering them more alert; and no man was permitted to go aloft and hand in sails with a pipe in his mouth, as is the invariable Dutch custom at the present day.—All these grievances, though they might ruffle for a moment the constitutional tranquillity of the honest Dutch tars, made but transient impression; they eat hugely, drank profusely, and slept immeasurably; and being under the especial guidance of providence, the ship was safely conducted to the coast of America; where, after sundry unimportant touchings and standings off and on, she at length, on the fourth day of September, entered that majestic bay which at this day expands its ample bosom before the city of New York and which had never before been visited by any European.*

---

* True it is—and I am not ignorant of the fact that in a certain apocryphal book of voyages compiled by one Hakluyt is to be found a letter written to Francis the first by one Giovanne, or John Verazzani, on which some writers are inclined to found a belief that this delightful bay had been visited nearly a century previous to the voyage of the enterprising Hudson. Now this (albeit it has met with the countenance of certain very judicious and learned men) I hold in utter disbelief, and that for various good and substantial reasons. —*First,* Because on strict examination it will be found that the description given by this Verazzani applies about as well to the bay of New York as it does to my nightcap.—*Secondly,* Because that this John Verazzani, for whom I already begin to feel a most bitter enmity, is a native of Florence; and

It has been traditionary in our family that when the great navigator was first blessed with a view of this enchanting island, he was observed, for the first and only time in his life, to exhibit strong symptoms of astonishment and admiration. He is said to have turned to master Juet and uttered these remarkable words while he pointed towards this paradise of the new world—"See! there!"—and thereupon, as was always his way when he was uncommonly pleased, he did puff out such clouds of dense tobacco smoke that in one minute the vessel was out of sight of land and master Juet was fain to wait until the winds dispersed this impenetrable fog.

It was indeed—as my great-great-grandfather used to say— though in truth I never heard him, for he died, as might be expected, before I was born—"It was indeed a spot on which the eye might have reveled forever, in ever new and never ending beauties." The island of Manna-hata spread wide before them, like some sweet vision of fancy or some fair creation of industrious magic. Its hills of smiling green swelled gently one above another, crowned with lofty trees of luxuriant growth; some pointing their tapering foliage towards the clouds, which were gloriously transparent; and others, loaded with a verdant burthen of clambering vines, bowing their branches to the earth that was covered with flowers. On the gentle declivities of the hills were scattered in gay profusion the dogwood, the sumach, and the wild brier, whose scarlet berries and white blossoms glowed brightly among the deep green of the surrounding foliage; and here and there a curling column of smoke rising from the little glens that opened along the shore seemed to promise the

---

everybody knows the crafty wiles of these losel Florentines by which they filched away the laurels from the brows of the immortal Colon (vulgarly called Columbus) and bestowed them on their officious townsman, Amerigo Vespucci—and I make no doubt they are equally ready to rob the illustrious Hudson of the credit of discovering this beauteous island, adorned by the city of New York, and placing it beside their usurped discovery of South America.—And *thirdly,* I award my decision in favor of the pretensions of Hendrick Hudson, inasmuch as his expedition sailed from Holland, being truly and absolutely a Dutch enterprise—and though all the proofs in the world were introduced on the other side, I would set them at nought as undeserving my attention. If these three reasons be not sufficient to satisfy every burgher of this ancient city—all I can say is, they are degenerate descendants from their venerable Dutch ancestors and totally unworthy the trouble of convincing. Thus, therefore, the title of Hendrick Hudson to his renowned discovery is fully vindicated.

weary voyagers a welcome at the hands of their fellow creatures. As they stood gazing with entranced attention on the scene before them, a red man, crowned with feathers, issued from one of these glens, and after contemplating in silent wonder the gallant ship as she sat like a stately swan swimming on a silver lake, sounded the war whoop and bounded into the woods like a wild deer, to the utter astonishment of the phlegmatic Dutchmen who had never heard such a noise or witnessed such a caper in their whole lives.

Of the transactions of our adventurers with the savages, and how the latter smoked copper pipes and ate dried currants; how they brought great store of tobacco and oysters; how they shot one of the ship's crew, and how he was buried, I shall say nothing, being that I consider them unimportant to my history. After tarrying a few days in the bay in order to refresh themselves after their seafaring, our voyagers weighed anchor to explore a mighty river which emptied into the bay. This river, it is said, was known among the savages by the name of the *Shatemuck;* though we are assured in an excellent little history published in 1674, by John Josselyn, Gent. that it was called the *Mohegan,** and master Richard Bloome, who wrote some time afterwards, asserts the same—so that I very much incline in favor of the opinion of these two honest gentlemen. Be this as it may, up this river did the adventurous Hendrick proceed, little doubting but it would turn out to be the much looked for passage to China!

The journal goes on to make mention of divers interviews between the crew and the natives in the voyage up the river, but as they would be impertinent to my history, I shall pass over them in silence, except the following dry joke played off by the old commodore and his schoolfellow Robert Juet which does such vast credit to their experimental philosophy that I cannot refrain from inserting it. "Our master and his mate determined to try some of the chiefe men of the countrey, whether they had any treacherie in them. So they tooke them downe into the cabin, and gave them so much wine and aqua vitæ that they were all merrie; and one of them had his wife with him, which sate so modestly, as any of our countrey women would do

---

* This river is likewise laid down in Ogilvy's map as Manhattan—Noordt—Montaigne and Mauritius River.

in a strange place. In the end, one of them was drunke, which had been aboarde of our ship all the time that we had beene there, and that was strange to them, for they could not tell how to take it."*

Having satisfied himself by this ingenious experiment that the natives were an honest, social race of jolly roysters who had no objection to a drinking bout and were very merry in their cups, the old commodore chuckled hugely to himself, and thrusting a double quid of tobacco in his cheek directed master Juet to have it carefully recorded for the satisfaction of all the natural philosophers of the university of Leyden—which done, he proceeded on his voyage with great self-complacency. After sailing, however, above a hundred miles up the river, he found the watery world around him began to grow more shallow and confined, the current more rapid, and perfectly fresh—phenomena not uncommon in the ascent of rivers but which puzzled the honest Dutchmen prodigiously. A consultation was therefore called, and having deliberated full six hours they were brought to a determination by the ship's running aground—whereupon they unanimously concluded that there was but little chance of getting to China in this direction. A boat, however, was despatched to explore higher up the river, which, on its return, confirmed the opinion—upon this the ship was warped off and put about with great difficulty, being, like most of her sex, exceedingly hard to govern; and the adventurous Hudson, according to the account of my great-great-grandfather, returned down the river— with a prodigious flea in his ear!

Being satisfied that there was little likelihood of getting to China, unless like the blind man he returned from whence he sat out and took a fresh start, he forthwith recrossed the sea to Holland, where he was received with great welcome by the honorable East India company, who were very much rejoiced to see him come back safe—with their ship; and at a large and respectable meeting of the first merchants and burgomasters of Amsterdam it was unanimously determined that as a munificent reward for the eminent services he had performed, and the important discovery he had made, the great river Mohegan should be called after his name!—and it continues to be called Hudson River unto this very day.

* Juet's Journ. Purch. Pil.

Containing an account of a mighty Ark which floated, under the protection of St. Nicholas, from Holland to Gibbet Island—the descent of the strange Animals therefrom—a great victory, and a description of the ancient village of Communipaw.

The delectable accounts given by the great Hudson and master Juet of the country they had discovered excited not a little talk and speculation among the good people of Holland.—Letters patent were granted by government to an association of merchants, called the West India Company, for the exclusive trade on Hudson River, on which they erected a trading house called Fort Aurania, or Orange, from whence did spring the great city of Albany. But I forbear to dwell on the various commercial and colonizing enterprises which took place—among which was that of Mynheer Adrian Block, who discovered and gave a name to Block Island, since famous for its cheese—and shall barely confine myself to that which gave birth to this renowned city.

It was some three or four years after the return of the immortal Hendrick that a crew of honest Low Dutch colonists set sail from the city of Amsterdam for the shores of America. It is an irreparable loss to history, and a great proof of the darkness of the age and the lamentable neglect of the noble art of book making, since so industriously cultivated by knowing sea captains and learned supercargoes, that an expedition so interesting and important in its results should be passed over in utter silence. To my great-great-grandfather am I again indebted for the few facts I am enabled to give concerning it—he having once more embarked for this country with a full determination, as he said, of ending his days here—and of begetting a race of Knickerbockers that should rise to be great men in the land.

The ship in which these illustrious adventurers set sail was

called the *Goede Vrouw,* or good woman, in compliment to the
wife of the president of the West India Company, who was
allowed by everybody (except her husband) to be a sweet-tem-
pered lady, when not in liquor. It was in truth a most gallant
vessel, of the most approved Dutch construction, and made by
the ablest ship carpenters of Amsterdam, who, it is well known,
always model their ships after the fair forms of their country-
women. Accordingly, it had one hundred feet in the beam, one
hundred feet in the keel, and one hundred feet from the bottom
of the sternpost to the taffarel. Like the beauteous model who
was declared to be the greatest belle in Amsterdam, it was full
in the bows, with a pair of enormous catheads, a copper bottom,
and withal a most prodigious poop!

The architect, who was somewhat of a religious man, far from
decorating the ship with pagan idols such as Jupiter, Neptune,
or Hercules (which heathenish abominations, I have no doubt,
occasion the misfortunes and shipwreck of many a noble vessel),
he, I say, on the contrary, did laudably erect for a head a goodly
image of St. Nicholas, equipped with a low, broad-brimmed
hat, a huge pair of Flemish trunk hose, and a pipe that reached
to the end of the bowsprit. Thus gallantly furnished, the staunch
ship floated sideways, like a majestic goose, out of the harbor of
the great city of Amsterdam, and all the bells that were not
otherwise engaged rung a triple bobmajor on the joyful occasion.

My great-great-grandfather remarks that the voyage was uncommonly prosperous, for, being under the especial care of the
ever-revered St. Nicholas, the Goede Vrouw seemed to be endowed with qualities unknown to common vessels. Thus she
made as much leeway as headway, could get along very nearly
as fast with the wind ahead as when it was a-poop—and was particularly great in a calm; in consequence of which singular advantages, she made out to accomplish her voyage in a very few
months and came to anchor at the mouth of the Hudson, a
little to the east of Gibbet Island.*

Here, lifting up their eyes, they beheld on what is at present
called the Jersey shore a small Indian village pleasantly embowered in a grove of spreading elms, and the natives all collected on the beach gazing in stupid admiration at the Goede

---

* So called because one Joseph Andrews, a pirate and murderer, was hanged
in chains on that island, the 23d May, 1769.

Vrouw. A boat was immediately despatched to enter into a treaty with them, and, approaching the shore, hailed them through a trumpet in the most friendly terms; but so horribly confounded were these poor savages at the tremendous and uncouth sound of the Low Dutch language that they one and all took to their heels, scampered over the Bergen hills, nor did they stop until they had buried themselves, head and ears, in the marshes on the other side, where they all miserably perished to a man—and their bones being collected, and decently covered by the Tammany Society of that day, formed that singular mound called RATTLESNAKE HILL which rises out of the center of the salt marshes a little to the east of the Newark Causeway.

Animated by this unlooked-for victory, our valiant heroes sprang ashore in triumph, took possession of the soil as conquerors in the name of their High Mightinesses the Lords States General, and marching fearlessly forward carried the village of COMMUNIPAW by storm, notwithstanding that it was vigorously defended by some half a score of old squaws and poppooses. On looking about them they were so transported with the excellencies of the place that they had very little doubt the blessed St. Nicholas had guided them thither as the very spot whereon to settle their colony. The softness of the soil was wonderfully adapted to the driving of piles; the swamps and marshes around them afforded ample opportunities for the constructing of dikes and dams; the shallowness of the shore was peculiarly favorable to the building of docks—in a word, this spot abounded with all the requisites for the foundation of a great Dutch city. On making a faithful report, therefore, to the crew of the Goede Vrouw, they one and all determined that this was the destined end of their voyage. Accordingly they descended from the Goede Vrouw, men, women and children, in goodly groups, as did the animals of yore from the ark, and formed themselves into a thriving settlement which they called by the Indian name COMMUNIPAW.

As all the world is doubtless perfectly acquainted with Communipaw, it may seem somewhat superfluous to treat of it in the present work; but my readers will please to recollect that notwithstanding it is my chief desire to satisfy the present age, yet I write likewise for posterity, and have to consult the understanding and curiosity of some half a score of centuries yet to come; by which time perhaps, were it not for this invaluable history, the great Communipaw, like Babylon, Carthage, Nineveh, and other great cities, might be perfectly extinct—sunk and forgotten in its own mud—its inhabitants turned into oysters,* and even its situation a fertile subject of learned controversy and hard-headed investigation among indefatigable historians. Let me then piously rescue from oblivion the humble relics of a place which was the egg from whence was hatched the mighty city of New York!

Communipaw is at present but a small village, pleasantly situated among rural scenery on that beauteous part of the Jersey shore which was known in ancient legends by the name of Pavonia† and commands a grand prospect of the superb bay of New York. It is within but half an hour's sail of the latter place, provided you have a fair wind, and may be distinctly seen from the city. Nay, it is a well known fact which I can testify from my own experience that on a clear still summer evening you may hear from the battery of New York the obstreperous peals of broad-mouthed laughter of the Dutch negroes at Communipaw, who, like most other negroes, are famous for their risible powers. This is peculiarly the case on Sunday evenings; when, it is remarked by an ingenious and observant philosopher who has made great discoveries in the neighborhood of this city, that they always laugh loudest—which he attributes to the circumstance of their having their holiday clothes on.

These negroes, in fact, like the monks in the dark ages, engross all the knowledge of the place, and being infinitely more adventurous and more knowing than their masters, carry on all the foreign trade; making frequent voyages to town in canoes loaded with oysters, buttermilk, and cabbages. They are great astrologers, predicting the different changes of weather almost as accurately as an almanac—they are moreover exquisite performers on three-stringed fiddles: in whistling they almost boast the far-famed powers of Orpheus his lyre, for not a horse or an ox in the place when at the plough or before the waggon will budge a foot until he hears the well-known whistle of his black driver and companion.—And from their amazing skill at cast-

---

* "Men by inaction degenerate into oysters." *Kaines.*

† Pavonia in the ancient maps is given to a tract of country extending from about Hoboken to Amboy.

ing up accounts upon their fingers, they are regarded with as much veneration as were the disciples of Pythagoras of yore when initiated into the sacred quaternary of numbers.

As to the honest burghers of Communipaw, like wise men and sound philosophers they never look beyond their pipes nor trouble their heads about any affairs out of their immediate neighborhood; so that they live in profound and enviable ignorance of all the troubles, anxieties, and revolutions of this distracted planet. I am even told that many among them do verily believe that Holland, of which they have heard so much from tradition, is situated somewhere on Long Island—that *Spiking-devil* and *the Narrows* are the two ends of the world—that the country is still under the dominion of their High Mightinesses, and that the city of New York still goes by the name of Nieuw Amsterdam. They meet every Saturday afternoon at the only tavern in the place, which bears as a sign a squareheaded likeness of the Prince of Orange; where they smoke a silent pipe by way of promoting social conviviality, and invariably drink a mug of cider to the success of Admiral Van Tromp, who they imagine is still sweeping the British channel with a broom at his masthead.

Communipaw, in short, is one of the numerous little villages in the vicinity of this most beautiful of cities, which are so many strongholds and fastnesses whither the primitive manners of our Dutch forefathers have retreated and where they are cherished with devout and scrupulous strictness. The dress of the original settlers is handed down inviolate from father to son—the identical broadbrimmed hat, broadskirted coat, and broadbottomed breeches continue from generation to generation, and several gigantic knee buckles of massy silver are still in wear that made such gallant display in the days of the patriarchs of Communipaw. The language likewise continues unadulterated by barbarous innovations; and so critically correct is the village schoolmaster in his dialect, that his reading of a Low Dutch psalm has much the same effect on the nerves as the filing of a handsaw.

CHAPTER III

In which is set forth the true art of making a bargain—together with the miraculous escape of a great Metropolis in a fog—and the biograhy of certain heroes of Communipaw.

Having in the trifling digression which concluded the last chapter discharged the filial duty which the city of New York owed to Communipaw, as being the mother settlement; and having given a faithful picture of it as it stands at present, I return with a soothing sentiment of self-approbation to dwell upon its early history. The crew of the Goede Vrouw being soon reinforced by fresh importations from Holland, the settlement went jollily on, increasing in magnitude and prosperity. The neighboring Indians in a short time became accustomed to the uncouth sound of the Dutch language, and an intercourse gradually took place between them and the newcomers. The Indians were much given to long talks, and the Dutch to long silence—in this particular, therefore, they accommodated each other completely. The chiefs would make long speeches about the big bull, the wabash, and the great spirit; to which the others would listen very attentively, smoke their pipes, and grunt *yah, myn-her*—whereat the poor savages were wonderously delighted. They instructed the new settlers in the best art of curing and smoking tobacco, while the latter, in return, made them drunk with true Hollands—and then learned them the art of making bargains.

A brisk trade for furs was soon opened: the Dutch traders were scrupulously honest in their dealings, and purchased by weight, establishing it as an invariable table of avoirdupois that the hand of a Dutchman weighed one pound and his foot two pounds. It is true the simple Indians were often puzzled by the great disproportion between bulk and weight, for let them place a bundle of furs, never so large, in one scale and a Dutchman put his hand or foot in the other, the bundle was sure to kick

94

the beam—never was a package of furs known to weigh more than two pounds in the market of Communipaw!

This is a singular fact—but I have it direct from my great-great-grandfather, who had risen to considerable importance in the colony, being promoted to the office of weighmaster on account of the uncommon heaviness of his foot.

The Dutch possessions in this part of the globe began now to assume a very thriving appearance and were comprehended under the general title of Nieuw Nederlandts, on account, as the sage Vander Donck observes, of their great resemblance to the Dutch Netherlands—which indeed was truly remarkable, excepting that the former were rugged and mountainous, and the latter level and marshy. About this time the tranquillity of the Dutch colonists was doomed to suffer a temporary interruption. In 1614, Captain Sir Samuel Argal, sailing under a commission from Dale, governor of Virginia, visited the Dutch settlements on Hudson River and demanded their submission to the English crown and Virginian dominion.—To this arrogant demand, as they were in no condition to resist it, they submitted for the time like discreet and reasonable men.

It does not appear that the valiant Argal molested the settlement of Communipaw; on the contrary, I am told that when his vessel first hove in sight the worthy burghers were seized with such a panic that they fell to smoking their pipes with astonishing vehemence; insomuch that they quickly raised a cloud which, combining with the surrounding woods and marshes, completely enveloped and concealed their beloved village and overhung the fair regions of Pavonia—So that the terrible Captain Argal passed on, totally unsuspicious that a sturdy little Dutch settlement lay snugly couched in the mud under cover of all this pestilent vapor. In commemoration of this fortunate escape, the worthy inhabitants have continued to smoke almost without intermission unto this very day; which is said to be the cause of the remarkable fog that often hangs over Communipaw of a clear afternoon.

Upon the departure of the enemy, our magnanimous ancestors took full six months to recover their wind, having been exceedingly discomposed by the consternation and hurry of affairs. They then called a council of safety to smoke over the state of the province. After six months more of mature deliberation, during which nearly five hundred words were spoken and almost as much tobacco was smoked as would have served a certain modern general through a whole winter's campaign of hard drinking, it was determined to fit out an armament of canoes and despatch them on a voyage of discovery; to search if per-adventure some more sure and formidable position might not be found where the colony would be less subject to vexatious visitations.

This perilous enterprise was entrusted to the superintendence of Mynheers Oloffe Van Kortlandt, Abraham Hardenbroeck, Jacobus Van Zandt, and Winant Ten Broeck—four indubitably great men, but of whose history, although I have made diligent inquiry, I can learn but little previous to their leaving Holland. Nor need this occasion much surprise; for adventurers, like prophets, though they make great noise abroad, have seldom much celebrity in their own countries; but this much is certain, that the overflowings and offscourings of a country are invariably composed of the richest parts of the soil. And here I cannot help remarking how convenient it would be to many of our great men and great families of doubtful origin, could they have the privilege of the heroes of yore, who, whenever their origin was involved in obscurity, modestly announced themselves descended from a god—and who never visited a foreign country but what they told some cock and bull stories about their being kings and princes at home. This venal trespass on the truth, though it has occasionally been played off by some pseudo marquis, baronet, and other illustrious foreigner in our land of good-natured credulity, has been completely discountenanced in this sceptical, matter of fact age—and I even question whether any tender virgin, who was accidentally and unaccountably enriched with a bantling, would save her character at parlor firesides and evening tea parties by ascribing the phenomenon to a swan, a shower of gold, or a river god.

Thus being denied the benefit of mythology and classic fable, I should have been completely at a loss as to the early biography of my heroes had not a gleam of light been thrown upon their origin from their names.

By this simple means have I been enabled to gather some particulars concerning the adventurers in question. Van Kort-landt, for instance, was one of those peripatetic philosophers who tax providence for a livelihood, and, like Diogenes, enjoy a free and unencumbered estate in sunshine. He was usually arrayed in garments suitable to his fortune, being curiously fringed and fangled by the hand of time; and was helmeted with an old fragment of a hat which had acquired the shape of a sugar loaf; and so far did he carry his contempt for the adventitious distinction of dress, that it is said the remnant of a shirt, which covered his back and dangled like a pocket handkerchief out of a hole in his breeches, was never washed except by the bountiful showers of heaven. In this garb was he usually to be seen, sunning himself at noonday with a herd of philosophers of the same sect, on the side of the great canal of Amsterdam. Like your nobility of Europe, he took his name of *Kortlandt* (or *lack land*) from his landed estate which lay somewhere in terra incognita.

Of the next of our worthies, might I have had the benefit of mythological assistance, the want of which I have just lamented —I should have made honorable mention as boasting equally illustrious pedigree with the proudest hero of antiquity. His name was *Van Zandt,* which being freely translated signifies *from the dirt,* meaning, beyond a doubt, that like Triptolemus, Themis, the Cyclops and the Titans, he sprung from dame Terra, or the earth! This supposition is strongly corroborated by his size, for it is well known that all the progeny of mother earth were of a gigantic stature; and Van Zandt, we are told, was a tall rawboned man above six feet high—with an astonishingly hard head. Nor is this origin of the illustrious Van Zandt a whit more improbable or repugnant to belief than what is related and universally admitted of certain of our greatest, or rather richest men; who, we are told with the utmost gravity, did originally spring from a dunghill!

Of the third hero but a faint description has reached to this time, which mentions that he was a sturdy, obstinate, burly, bustling little man; and from being usually equipped with an old pair of buckskins, was familiarly dubbed *Harden Broeck,* or *Tough Breeches.*

Ten Broeck completed this junto of adventurers. It is a singular but ludicrous fact, which, were I not scrupulous in recording the whole truth I should almost be tempted to pass over in silence, as incompatible with the gravity and dignity of history, that this worthy gentleman should likewise have been nicknamed from the most whimsical part of his dress. In fact, the smallclothes seems to have been a very important garment in the eyes of our venerated ancestors, owing in all probability to its really being the largest article of raiment among them. The name of *Ten Broeck,* or *Tin Broeck,* is indifferently translated into Ten Breeches and Tin Breeches—the High Dutch commentators incline to the former opinion, and ascribe it to his being the first who introduced into the settlement the ancient Dutch fashion of wearing ten pair of breeches. But the most elegant and ingenious writers on the subject declare in favor of Tin, or rather *Thin* Breeches; from whence they infer that he was a poor but merry rogue whose galligaskins were none of the soundest, and who was the identical author of that truly philosophical stanza:

> "Then why should we quarrel for riches,
>   Or any such glittering toys;
> A light heart and *thin pair of breeches*
>   Will go through the world, my brave boys!"

Such was the gallant junto chosen to conduct this voyage into unknown realms, and the whole was put under the superintending care and direction of Oloffe Van Kortlandt, who was held in great reverence among the sages of Communipaw for the variety and darkness of his knowledge. Having, as I before observed, passed a great part of his life in the open air among the peripatetic philosophers of Amsterdam, he had become amazingly well acquainted with the aspect of the heavens, and could as accurately determine when a storm was brewing or a squall rising as a dutiful husband can foresee from the brow of his spouse when a tempest is gathering about his ears. He was moreover a great seer of ghosts and goblins, and a firm believer in omens; but what especially recommended him to public confidence was his marvelous talent at dreaming, for there never was anything of consequence happened at Communipaw but what he declared he had previously dreamt it; being one of those infallible prophets that always predict a thing after it has come to pass.

This supernatural gift was as highly valued among the burghers of Pavonia as it was among the enlightened nations of antiquity. The wise Ulysses was more indebted to his sleeping than his waking moments for all his subtle achievements, and seldom undertook any great exploit without first soundly sleeping upon it, and the same may truly be said of the good Van Kortlandt, who was thence aptly denominated Oloffe the Dreamer.

This cautious commander having chosen the crews that should accompany him in the proposed expedition, exhorted them to repair to their homes, take a good night's rest, settle all family affairs, and make their wills before departing on this voyage into unknown realms. And indeed this last was a precaution always taken by our forefathers, even in after times when they became more adventurous and voyaged to Haverstraw or Kaatskill or Groodt Esopus or any other far country that lay beyond the great waters of the Tappaan Zee.

CHAPTER IV

How the heroes of Communipaw voyaged to Hell Gate, and how they were received there.

And now the rosy blush of morn began to mantle in the east, and soon the rising sun, emerging from amidst golden and purple clouds, shed his blithesome rays on the tin weathercocks of Communipaw. It was that delicious season of the year when nature, breaking from the chilling thraldom of old winter like a blooming damsel from the tyranny of a sordid old father, threw herself, blushing with ten thousand charms, into the arms of youthful spring. Every tufted copse and blooming grove resounded with the notes of hymeneal love. The very insects as they sipped the dew that gemmed the tender grass of the meadows joined in the joyous epithalamium—the virgin bud timidly put forth its blushes, "the voice of the turtle was heard in the land," and the heart of man dissolved away in tenderness. Oh! sweet Theocritus! had I thine oaten reed wherewith thou erst didst charm the gay Sicilian plains—Or oh! gentle Bion! thy pastoral pipe wherein the happy swains of the Lesbian isle so much delighted, then might I attempt to sing, in soft Bucolic or negligent Idyllium, the rural beauties of the scene—but having nothing save this jaded goose quill wherewith to wing my flight, I must fain resign all poetic disportings of the fancy and pursue my narrative in humble prose; comforting myself with the hope that though it may not steal so sweetly upon the imagination of my reader, yet may it commend itself with virgin modesty to his better judgment, clothed in the chaste and simple garb of truth.

No sooner did the first rays of cheerful Phœbus dart into the windows of Communipaw than the little settlement was all in motion. Forth issued from his castle the sage Van Kortlandt, and seizing a conch shell blew a far resounding blast that soon summoned all his lusty followers. Then did they trudge resolutely down to the water side, escorted by a multitude of relatives and friends who all went down, as the common phrase expresses it, "to see them off." And this shows the antiquity of those long family processions often seen in our city, composed of all ages, sizes, and sexes, laden with bundles and bandboxes, escorting some bevy of country cousins about to depart for home in a market boat.

The good Oloffe bestowed his forces in a squadron of three canoes and hoisted his flag on board a little round Dutch boat, shaped not unlike a tub, which had formerly been the jolly boat of the Goede Vrouw. And now, all being embarked, they bid farewell to the gazing throng upon the beach, who continued shouting after them, even when out of hearing, wishing them a happy voyage, advising them to take good care of themselves, not to get drowned—with an abundance other of those sage and invaluable cautions generally given by landsmen to such as go down to the sea in ships and adventure upon the deep waters. In the meanwhile the voyagers cheerily urged their course across the crystal bosom of the bay, and soon left behind them the green shores of ancient Pavonia.

And first they touched at two small islands which lie nearly opposite Communipaw and which are said to have been brought into existence about the time of the great irruption of the Hudson when it broke through the Highlands and made its way to the ocean.* For in this tremendous uproar of the waters, we are

---

* It is a matter long since established by certain of our philosophers—that is to say, having been often advanced and never contradicted, it has grown to be pretty nigh equal to a settled fact—that the Hudson was originally a lake

told that many huge fragments of rock and land were rent from
the mountains and swept down by this runaway river for sixty
or seventy miles; where some of them ran aground on the shoals
just opposite Communipaw and formed the identical islands in
question, while others drifted out to sea, and were never heard
of more! A sufficient proof of the fact is that the rock which
forms the bases of these islands is exactly similar to that of the
Highlands, and moreover one of our philosophers who has diligently compared the agreement of their respective surfaces has
even gone so far as to assure me, in confidence, that Gibbet
Island was originally nothing more nor less than a wart on
Anthony's nose.*

Leaving these wonderful little isles, they next coasted by Governor's Island, since terrible from its frowning fortress and grin-
ning batteries. They would by no means, however, land upon
this island, since they doubted much it might be the abode of
demons and spirits, which in those days did greatly abound
throughout this savage and pagan country.

Just at this time a shoal of jolly porpoises came rolling and
tumbling by, turning up their sleek sides to the sun and spouting
up the briny element in sparkling showers. No sooner did the
sage Oloffe mark this than he was greatly rejoiced. "This," exclaimed he, "if I mistake not, augurs well—the porpoise is a fat,
well-conditioned fish—a burgomaster among fishes—his looks betoken ease, plenty and prosperity—I greatly admire this round
fat fish, and doubt not but this is a happy omen of the success
of our undertaking." So saying, he directed his squadron to steer
in the track of these alderman fishes.

Turning, therefore, directly to the left, they swept up the
strait vulgarly called the East River. And here the rapid tide
which courses through this strait, seizing on the gallant tub in
which Commodore Van Kortlandt had embarked, hurried it
forward with a velocity unparalleled in a Dutch boat navigated

---

dammed up by the mountains of the Highlands. In process of time, however,
becoming very mighty and obstreperous, and the mountains waxing pursy,
dropsical, and weak in the back by reason of their extreme old age, it suddenly rose upon them and after a violent struggle effected its escape. This is
said to have come to pass in very remote time, probably before that rivers
had lost the art of running uphill. The foregoing is a theory in which I do
not pretend to be skilled, notwithstanding that I do fully give it my belief.

* A promontory in the Highlands.

by Dutchmen; insomuch that the good commodore, who had all his life long been accustomed only to the drowsy navigation of canals, was more than ever convinced that they were in the hands of some supernatural power and that the jolly porpoises were towing them to some fair haven that was to fulfil all their wishes and expectations.

Thus borne away by the resistless current, they doubled that boisterous point of land since called Corlear's Hook,* and leaving to the right the rich winding cove of the Wallabout, where our infant navy is nowadays put out to nurse, they drifted into a magnificent expanse of water surrounded by pleasant shores whose verdure was exceedingly refreshing to the eye. While the voyagers were looking around them on what they conceived to be a serene and sunny lake, they beheld at a distance a crew of painted savages, busily employed in fishing, who seemed more like the genii of this romantic region—their slender canoe lightly balanced like a feather on the undulating surface of the bay.

At sight of these the hearts of the heroes of Communipaw were not a little troubled. But as good fortune would have it, at the bow of the commodore's boat was stationed a very valiant man named Hendrick Kip (which being interpreted, means *chicken,* a name given him in token of his courage). No sooner did he behold these varlet heathens than he trembled with excessive valor, and although a good half mile distant, he seized a musquetoon that lay at hand, and turning away his head, fired it most intrepidly in the face of the blessed sun. The blundering weapon recoiled and gave the valiant Kip an ignominious kick that laid him prostrate with uplifted heels in the bottom of the boat. But such was the effect of this tremendous fire that the wild men of the woods, struck with consternation, seized hastily upon their paddles and shot away into one of the deep inlets of the Long Island shore.

This signal victory gave new spirits to the hardy voyagers, and in honor of the achievement they gave the name of the valiant Kip to the surrounding bay, and it has continued to be called KIP's BAY from that time to the present. The heart of the good Van Kortlandt—who, having no land of his own, was a great admirer of other people's—expanded at the sumptuous prospect

---

* Properly spelt *hoeck* (i. e., a point of land).

of rich unsettled country around him, and falling into a delicious reverie, he straightway began to riot in the possession of vast meadows of salt marsh and interminable patches of cabbages. From this delectable vision he was all at once awakened by the sudden turning of the tide, which would soon have hurried him from this land of promise had not the discreet navigator given signal to steer for shore; where they accordingly landed, hard by the rocky heights of Bellevue—that happy retreat where our jolly aldermen eat for the good of the city and fatten the turtle that are sacrificed on civic solemnities.

Here, seated on the green sward by the side of a small stream that ran sparkling among the grass, they refreshed themselves after the toils of the seas by feasting lustily on the ample stores which they had provided for this perilous voyage. Thus having well fortified their deliberative powers, they fell into an earnest consultation what was further to be done. This was the first council dinner ever eaten at Bellevue by Christian burghers, and here, as tradition relates, did originate the great family feud between the Hardenbroecks and the Tenbroecks which afterwards had a singular influence on the building of the city. The sturdy Hardenbroeck, whose eyes had been wonderously delighted with the salt marshes that spread their reeking bosoms along the coast at the bottom of Kip's Bay, counseled by all means to return thither and found the intended city. This was strenuously opposed by the unbending Ten Broeck, and many testy arguments passed between them. The particulars of this controversy have not reached us, which is ever to be lamented; this much is certain, that the sage Oloffe put an end to the dispute by determining to explore still further in the route which the mysterious porpoises had so clearly pointed out—whereupon the sturdy Tough Breeches abandoned the expedition, took possession of a neighboring hill, and in a fit of great wrath peopled all that tract of country which has continued to be inhabited by the Hardenbroecks unto this very day.

By this time the jolly Phœbus, like some wanton urchin sporting on the side of a green hill, began to roll down the declivity of the heavens; and now, the tide having once more turned in their favor, the resolute Pavonians again committed themselves to its discretion, and coasting along the western shores were borne towards the straits of Blackwell's Island.

And here the capricious wanderings of the current occasioned not a little marvel and perplexity to these illustrious mariners. Now would they be caught by the wanton eddies, and, sweeping round a jutting point, would wind deep into some romantic little cove that indented the fair island of Manna-hata; now were they hurried narrowly by the very bases of impending rocks mantled with the flaunting grape vine and crowned with groves that threw a broad shade on the waves beneath; and anon they were borne away into the midchannel and wafted along with a rapidity that very much discomposed the sage Van Kortlandt, who, as he saw the land swiftly receding on either side, began exceedingly to doubt that terra firma was giving them the slip.

Wherever the voyagers turned their eyes, a new creation seemed to bloom around. No signs of human thrift appeared to check the delicious wildness of nature, who here reveled in all her luxuriant variety. Those hills, now bristled like the fretful porcupine with rows of poplars (vain upstart plants! minions of wealth and fashion!), were then adorned with the vigorous natives of the soil: the lordly oak, the generous chestnut, the graceful elm —while here and there the tulip tree reared his majestic head, the giant of the forest.—Where now are seen the gay retreats of luxury—villas half buried in twilight bowers, whence the amorous flute oft breathes the sighings of some city swain—there the fish hawk built his solitary nest on some dry tree that overlooked his watery domain. The timid deer fed undisturbed along those shores now hallowed by the lover's moonlight walk and printed by the slender foot of beauty; and a savage solitude extended over those happy regions where now are reared the stately towers of the Joneses, the Schermerhornes and the Rhinelanders.

Thus gliding in silent wonder through these new and unknown scenes, the gallant squadron of Pavonia swept by the foot of a promontory that strutted forth boldly into the waves and seemed to frown upon them as they brawled against its base. This is the bluff well known to modern mariners by the name of Gracie's Point, from the fair castle which, like an elephant, it carries upon its back. And here broke upon their view a wild and varied prospect where land and water were beauteously intermingled, as though they had combined to heighten and set off each other's charms. To the right lay the sedgy point of Blackwell's Island, dressed in the fresh garniture of living green—beyond it stretched the pleasant coast of Sundswick and the small harbor well known by the name of Hallett's cove—a place infamous in latter days by reason of its being the haunt of pirates who infest these seas, robbing orchards and watermelon patches and insulting gentlemen navigators when voyaging in their pleasure boats. To the left a deep bay, or rather creek, gracefully receded between shores fringed with forests and forming a kind of vista through which were beheld the sylvan regions of Haerlem, Morrissania, and East Chester. Here the eye reposed with delight on a richly wooded country diversified by tufted knolls, shadowy intervals, and waving lines of upland swelling above each other; while over the whole the purple mists of spring diffused a hue of soft voluptuousness.

Just before them the grand course of the stream making a sudden bend wound among embowered promontories and shores of emerald verdure that seemed to melt into the wave. A character of gentleness and mild fertility prevailed around. The sun had just descended and the thin haze of twilight, like a transparent veil drawn over the bosom of virgin beauty, heightened the charms which it half concealed.

Ah! witching scenes of foul delusion! Ah! hapless voyagers, gazing with simple wonder on these Circean shores! Such, alas! are they, poor easy souls, who listen to the seductions of a wicked world—treacherous are its smiles! fatal its caresses! He who yields to its enticements launches upon a whelming tide and trusts his feeble bark among the dimpling eddies of a whirlpool! And thus it fared with the worthies of Pavonia, who, little mistrusting the guileful scene before them, drifted quietly on until they were aroused by an uncommon tossing and agitation of their vessels. For now the late dimpling current began to brawl around them and the waves to boil and foam with horrific fury. Awakened as if from a dream, the astonished Oloffe bawled aloud to put about, but his words were lost amid the roaring of the waters. And now ensued a scene of direful consternation—at one time they were borne with dreadful velocity among tumultuous breakers, at another hurried down boisterous rapids. Now they were nearly dashed upon the Hen and Chickens (infamous rocks! —more voracious than Scylla and her whelps); and anon they seemed sinking into yawning gulfs that threatened to entomb them beneath the waves. All the elements combined to produce a hideous confusion. The waters raged—the winds howled—and as they were hurried along, several of the astonished mariners beheld the rocks and trees of the neighboring shores driving through the air!

At length the mighty tub of Commodore Van Kortlandt was drawn into the vortex of that tremendous whirlpool called the Pot, where it was whirled about in giddy mazes until the senses of the good commander and his crew were overpowered by the horror of the scene and the strangeness of the revolution.

How the gallant squadron of Pavonia was snatched from the jaws of this modern Charybdis has never been truly made known, for so many survived to tell the tale, and, what is still more wonderful, told it in so many different ways, that there has ever prevailed a great variety of opinions on the subject.

As to the commodore and his crew, when they came to their senses they found themselves stranded on the Long Island shore. The worthy commodore, indeed, used to relate many and wonderful stories of his adventures in this time of peril, which, by his account, did far exceed those of the sage Ulysses in the straits of Charybdis. For he saw spectres flying in the air and heard the yelling of hobgoblins, and put his hand into the Pot when they were whirled around and found the water scalding hot, and beheld several uncouth looking beings seated on rocks and skimming it with huge ladles—but particularly he declared with great exultation that he saw the losel porpoises, which had betrayed them into this peril, some broiling on the Gridiron and others hissing in the Frying Pan!

These, however, were considered by many as mere phantasies of the commodore's imagination while he lay in a trance; especially as he was known to be given to dreaming; and the truth of them has never been clearly ascertained. It is certain, however, that to the accounts of Oloffe and his followers may be traced the various traditions handed down of this marvelous strait—as how the devil has been seen there, sitting astride of the Hog's Back and playing on the fiddle—how he broils fish there before a storm; and many other stories in which we must be cautious of putting too much faith. In consequence of all these terrific circumstances, the Pavonian commander gave this pass the name of *Helle-gat,* or as it has been interpreted, *Hell Gate,** which it continues to bear at the present day.

---

* This is a narrow strait in the Sound at the distance of six miles above New York. It is dangerous to shipping, unless under the care of skilful pilots, by reason of numerous rocks, shelves and whirlpools. These have received

CHAPTER V

How the heroes of Communipaw returned somewhat wiser than they went—and how the sage Oloffe dreamed a dream—and the dream that he dreamed.

The darkness of night had closed upon this disastrous day, and a doleful night was it to the shipwrecked Pavonians, whose ears were incessantly assailed with the raging of the elements and the howling of the hobgoblins that infested this perfidious strait. But when the morning dawned, the horrors of the preceding evening had passed away; rapids, breakers, and whirlpools had disappeared; the stream again ran smooth and dimpling, and having changed its tide, rolled gently back towards the quarter where lay their much regretted home.

The woebegone heroes of Communipaw eyed each other with rueful countenances; their squadron had been totally dispersed by the late disaster. Some were cast upon the western shore where, headed by one Ruleff Hopper, they took possession of all the country lying about the six mile stone; which is held by the Hoppers at this present writing.

The Waldrons were driven by stress of weather to a distant coast where, having with them a jug of genuine Hollands, they were enabled to conciliate the savages, setting up a kind of tavern; from whence, it is said, did spring the fair town of Haerlem in which their descendants have ever since continued

---

sundry appellations such as the Gridiron, Frying Pan, Hog's Back, Pot, &c. and are very violent and turbulent at certain times of tide. Certain wise men who instruct these modern days have softened the above characteristic name into *Hurl Gate*, which means nothing. I leave them to give their own etymology. The name as given by our author is supported by the map in Vander Donck's history, published in 1656—by Ogilvie's History of America, 1671— as also by a journal still extant, written in the 16th century, and to be found in Hazard's State Papers. And an old MS. written in French, speaking of various alterations in names about this city, observes, "De *Helle-gat* trou d'Enfer, ils ont fait *Hell Gate*, Porte d'Enfer."

to be reputable publicans. As to the Suydams, they were thrown upon the Long Island coast and may still be found in those parts. But the most singular luck attended the great Ten Broeck, who, falling overboard, was miraculously preserved from sinking by the multitude of his nether garments. Thus buoyed up, he floated on the waves like a merman until he landed safely on a rock, where he was found the next morning busily drying his many breeches in the sunshine.

I forbear to treat of the long consultation of our adventurers —how they determined that it would not do to found a city in this diabolical neighborhood—and how at length, with fear and trembling, they ventured once more upon the briny element and steered their course back for Communipaw. Suffice it, in simple brevity, to say that after toiling back through the scenes of their yesterday's voyage, they at length opened the southern point of Manna-hata and gained a distant view of their beloved Communipaw.

And here they were opposed by an obstinate eddy that resisted all the efforts of the exhausted mariners. Weary and dispirited, they could no longer make head against the power of the tide, or rather, as some will have it, of old Neptune, who, anxious to guide them to a spot whereon should be founded his stronghold in this western world, sent half a score of potent billows that rolled the tub of commodore Van Kortlandt high and dry on the shores of Manna-hata.

Having thus in a manner been guided by supernatural power to this delightsome island, their first care was to light a fire at the foot of a large tree that stood upon the point at present called the battery. Then gathering together great store of oysters which abounded on the shore, and emptying the contents of their wallets, they prepared and made a sumptuous council repast. The worthy Van Kortlandt was observed to be particularly zealous in his devotions to the trencher; for having the cares of the expedition especially committed to his care, he deemed it incumbent on him to eat profoundly for the public good. In proportion as he filled himself to the very brim with the dainty viands before him did the heart of this excellent Burgher rise up towards his throat, until he seemed crammed and almost choked with good eating and good nature. And at such times it is, when a man's heart is in his throat, that he may more truly be said to speak from it, and his speeches abound with kindness and good fellowship. Thus the worthy Oloffe having swallowed

the last possible morsel and washed it down with a fervent pota-
tion, felt his heart yearning and his whole frame in a manner
dilating with unbounded benevolence. Everything around him
seemed excellent and delightful; and laying his hands on each
side of his capacious periphery, and rolling his half-closed eyes
around on the beautiful diversity of land and water before him,
he exclaimed in a fat half-smothered voice, "What a charming
prospect!" The words died away in his throat—he seemed to
ponder on the fair scene for a moment—his eyelids heavily closed
over their orbs—his head drooped upon his bosom—he slowly
sunk upon the green turf, and a deep sleep stole gradually upon
him.

And the sage Oloffe dreamed a dream—and lo, the good St.
Nicholas came riding over the tops of the trees in that selfsame
wagon wherein he brings his yearly presents to children; and he
came and descended hard by where the heroes of Communipaw
had made their late repast. And the shrewd Van Kortlandt knew
him by his broad hat, his long pipe, and the resemblance which
he bore to the figure on the bow of the Goede Vrouw. And he lit
his pipe by the fire and he sat himself down and smoked; and as
he smoked the smoke from his pipe ascended into the air and
spread like a cloud overhead. And the sage Oloffe bethought
him, and he hastened and climbed up to the top of one of the
tallest trees, and saw that the smoke spread over a great extent
of country—and as he considered it more attentively, he fancied
that the great volume of smoke assumed a variety of marvelous
forms, where in dim obscurity he saw shadowed out palaces and
domes and lofty spires, all which lasted but a moment and then
faded away, until the whole rolled off and nothing but the green
woods were left. And when St. Nicholas had smoked his pipe,
he twisted it in his hatband, and laying his finger beside his nose
gave the astonished Van Kortlandt a very significant look; then
mounting his wagon he returned over the tree tops and disappeared.

And Van Kortlandt awoke from his sleep greatly instructed,
and he aroused his companions and related to them his dream;
and interpreted it, that it was the will of St. Nicholas that they
should settle down and build the city here. And that the smoke
of the pipe was a type how vast should be the extent of the
city; inasmuch as the volumes of its smoke should spread over
a vast extent of country. And they all with one voice assented
to this interpretation, excepting Mynher Ten Broeck who de-

clared the meaning to be that it should be a city wherein a little
fire should occasion a great smoke, or in other words, a very
vaporing little city—both which interpretations have strangely
come to pass!

The great object of their perilous expedition, therefore, being
thus happily accomplished, the voyagers returned merrily to
Communipaw where they were received with great rejoicings.
And here calling a general meeting of all the wise men and the
dignitaries of Pavonia, they related the whole history of their
voyage and of the dream of Oloffe Van Kortlandt. And the
people lifted up their voices and blessed the good St. Nicholas,
and from that time forth the sage Van Kortlandt was held in more
honor than ever for his great talent at dreaming, and was pronounced a most useful citizen and a right good man—when he
was asleep.

CHAPTER VI

*Containing an attempt at etymology—and of
the founding of the great city of New Amsterdam.*

The original name of the island wherein the squadron of Communipaw was thus propitiously thrown is a matter of some dispute, and has already undergone considerable vitiation—a melancholy proof of the instability of all sublunary things and the
vanity of all our hopes of lasting fame; for who can expect his
name will live to posterity when even the names of mighty
islands are thus soon lost in contradiction and uncertainty!

The name most current at the present day, and which is likewise countenanced by the great historian Vander Donck, is
MANHATTAN; which is said to have originated in a custom among
the squaws in the early settlement of wearing men's hats, as is
still done among many tribes. "Hence," as we are told by an
old governor who was somewhat of a wag and flourished almost
a century since and had paid a visit to the wits of Philadelphia,
"Hence arose the appellation of man-hat-on, first given to the

Indians and afterwards to the island"—a stupid joke!—but well enough for a governor.

Among the more venerable sources of information on this subject is that valuable history of the American possessions written by Master Richard Blome in 1687,* wherein it is called Manhadaes and Manahanent; nor must I forget the excellent little book, full of precious matter, of that authentic historian, John Josselyn, Gent.† who expressly calls it Manadaes.

Another etymology still more ancient, and sanctioned by the countenance of our ever to be lamented Dutch ancestors, is that found in certain letters still extant‡ which passed between the early governors and their neighboring powers wherein it is called indifferently Monhattoes, Munhatos and Manhattoes, which are evidently unimportant variations of the same name; for our wise forefathers sat little store by those niceties either in orthography or orthoepy which form the sole study and ambition of many learned men and women of this hypercritical age. This last name is said to be derived from the great Indian spirit Manetho; who was supposed to make this island his favorite abode on account of its uncommon delights. For the Indian traditions affirm that the bay was once a translucid lake, filled with silver and golden fish, in the midst of which lay this beautiful island, covered with every variety of fruits and flowers; but that the sudden irruption of the Hudson laid waste these blissful scenes, and Manetho took his flight beyond the great waters of Ontario.

These, however, are fabulous legends to which very cautious credence must be given; and although I am willing to admit the last quoted orthography of the name as very suitable for prose, yet is there another one founded on still more ancient and indisputable authority which I particularly delight in, seeing that it is at once poetical, melodious, and significant—and this is recorded in the before-mentioned voyage of the great Hudson written by master Juet; who clearly and correctly calls it MANNA-HATA—that is to say, the island of Manna, or in other words—"a land flowing with milk and honey!"

It having been solemnly resolved that the seat of empire

---

* This history is to be found in the library of the New York Historical Society.

† Idem.

‡ Vide Hazard's Col. Stat. Pap.

should be transferred from the green shores of Pavonia to this delectable island, a vast multitude embarked and migrated across the mouth of the Hudson under the guidance of Oloffe the Dreamer, who was appointed protector or patroon to the new settlement.

And here let me bear testimony to the matchless honesty and magnanimity of our worthy forefathers, who purchased the soil of the native Indians before erecting a single roof; a circumstance singular and almost incredible in the annals of discovery and colonization.

The first settlement was made on the southwest point of the island on the very spot where the good St. Nicholas had appeared in the dream. Here they built a mighty and impregnable fort and trading house, called FORT AMSTERDAM, which stood on that eminence at present occupied by the custom house, with the open space now called the bowling green in front.

Around this potent fortress was soon seen a numerous progeny of little Dutch houses with tiled roofs, all which seemed most lovingly to nestle under its walls like a brood of half-fledged chickens sheltered under the wings of the mother hen. The whole was surrounded by an enclosure of strong palisadoes to guard against any sudden irruption of the savages who wandered in hordes about the swamps and forests that extended over those tracts of country at present called Broadway, Wall Street, William Street, and Pearl Street.

No sooner was the colony once planted than it took root and throve amazingly, for it would seem that this thrice-favored island is like a munificent dunghill where every foreign weed finds kindly nourishment and soon shoots up and expands to greatness.

And now the infant settlement having advanced in age and stature, it was thought high time it should receive an honest Christian name, and it was accordingly called NEW AMSTERDAM. It is true there were some advocates for the original Indian name, and many of the best writers of the province did long continue to call it by the title of "The Manhattoes," but this was discountenanced by the authorities as being heathenish and savage. Besides, it was considered an excellent and praiseworthy measure to name it after a great city of the old world; as by that means it was induced to emulate the greatness and renown of its namesake—in the manner that little sniveling urchins are called after great statesmen, saints and worthies and renowned generals of yore, upon which they all industriously copy their examples and come to be very mighty men in their day and generation.

The thriving state of the settlement and the rapid increase of houses gradually awakened the good Oloffe from a deep lethargy into which he had fallen after the building of the fort. He now began to think it was time some plan should be devised on which the increasing town should be built. Summoning, therefore, his counselors and coadjutors together, they took pipe in mouth and forthwith sunk into a very sound deliberation on the subject.

At the very outset of the business an unexpected difference of opinion arose, and I mention it with much sorrowing, as being the first altercation on record in the councils of New Amsterdam. It was a breaking forth of the grudge and heartburning that had existed between those two eminent burghers, Mynhers Tenbroeck and Hardenbroeck, ever since their unhappy altercation on the coast of Bellevue. The great Hardenbroeck had waxed very wealthy and powerful from his domains, which embraced the whole chain of Apulean mountains that stretch along the gulf of Kip's Bay, and from part of which his descendants have been expelled in latter ages by the powerful clans of the Joneses and the Schermerhorns.

An ingenious plan for the city was offered by Mynher Tenbroeck, who proposed that it should be cut up and intersected by canals, after the manner of the most admired cities in Holland. To this Mynher Hardenbroeck was diametrically opposed, suggesting in place thereof that they should run out docks and wharfs by means of piles driven into the bottom of the river, on which the town should be built. By these means, said he triumphantly, shall we rescue a considerable space of territory from these immense rivers and build a city that shall rival Amsterdam, Venice, or any amphibious city in Europe. To this proposition Ten Broeck (or Ten Breeches) replied with a look of as much scorn as he could possibly assume. He cast the utmost censure upon the plan of his antagonist as being preposterous and against the very order of things, as he would leave to every true Hollander. "For what," said he, "is a town without canals? —it is like a body without veins and arteries, and must perish for want of a free circulation of the vital fluid."—Tough Breeches, on the contrary, retorted with a sarcasm upon his antagonist, who was somewhat of an arid, dry-boned habit; he remarked that as to the circulation of the blood being necessary to existence, Mynher Ten Breeches was a living contradiction to his own assertion; for everybody knew there had not a drop of blood circulated through his wind-dried carcass for good ten years, and yet there was not a greater busybody in the whole colony. Personalities have seldom much effect in making converts in argument—nor have I ever seen a man convinced of error by being convicted of deformity. At least such was not the case at present. Ten Breeches was very acrimonious in reply, and Tough Breeches, who was a sturdy little man and never gave up the last word, rejoined with increasing spirit—Ten Breeches had the advantage of the greatest volubility, but Tough Breeches had that invaluable coat of mail in argument called obstinacy—Ten Breeches had, therefore, the most mettle, but Tough Breeches the best bottom—so that though Ten Breeches made a dreadful clattering about his ears, and battered and belabored him with hard words and sound arguments, yet Tough Breeches hung on most resolutely to the last. They parted, therefore, as is usual in all arguments where both parties are in the right, without coming to any conclusion—but they hated each other most heartily for ever after, and a similar breach with that between the houses of Capulet and Montague did ensue between the families of Ten Breeches and Tough Breeches.

I would not fatigue my reader with these dull matters of fact, but that my duty as a faithful historian requires that I should be particular—and in truth, as I am now treating of the critical period when our city, like a young twig, first received the twists and turns that have since contributed to give it the present picturesque irregularity for which it is celebrated, I cannot be too minute in detailing their first causes.

After the unhappy altercation I have just mentioned, I do not find that anything further was said on the subject worthy of being recorded. The council, consisting of the largest and oldest heads in the community, met regularly once a week to ponder on this momentous subject.—But either they were deterred by the war of words they had witnessed, or they were naturally averse to the exercise of the tongue and the consequent exercise of the brains—certain it is, the most profound silence was maintained—the question as usual lay on the table—the members quietly smoked their pipes, making but few laws, without ever enforcing any, and in the meantime the affairs of the settlement went on—as it pleased God.

As most of the council were but little skilled in the mystery of combining pothooks and hangers, they determined most judiciously not to puzzle either themselves or posterity with voluminous records. The secretary, however, kept the minutes of the council with tolerable precision in a large vellum folio fastened with massy brass clasps; the journal of each meeting consisted but of two lines, stating in Dutch that "the council sat this day and smoked twelve pipes on the affairs of the colony." —By which it appears that the first settlers did not regulate their time by hours, but pipes, in the same manner as they measure distances in Holland at this very time; an admirably exact measurement, as a pipe in the mouth of a trueborn Dutchman is never liable to those accidents and irregularities that are continually putting our clocks out of order.

In this manner did the profound council of NEW AMSTERDAM smoke and doze and ponder from week to week, month to month, and year to year in what manner they should construct their infant settlement—meanwhile, the town took care of itself, and like a sturdy brat which is suffered to run about wild, unshackled by clouts and bandages and other abominations by which your notable nurses and sage old women cripple and disfigure the children of men, increased so rapidly in strength and magnitude that before the honest burgomasters had determined upon a plan, it was too late to put it in execution—whereupon they wisely abandoned the subject altogether.

CHAPTER VII

How the city of New Amsterdam waxed great under the protection of Oloffe the Dreamer.

There is something exceedingly delusive in thus looking back through the long vista of departed years and catching a glimpse of the fairy realms of antiquity that lie beyond. Like some goodly landscape melting into distance, they receive a thousand charms from their very obscurity, and the fancy delights to fill up their outlines with graces and excellencies of its own creation.

Thus beam on my imagination those happier days of our city, when as yet New Amsterdam was a mere pastoral town, shrouded in groves of sycamore and willows, and surrounded by trackless forests and wide spreading waters that seemed to shut out all the cares and vanities of a wicked world.

In those days did this embryo city present the rare and noble spectacle of a community governed without laws; and thus being left to its own course and the fostering care of providence, increased as rapidly as though it had been burthened with a dozen panniers full of those sage laws that are usually heaped on the backs of young cities—in order to make them grow. And in this particular I greatly admire the wisdom and sound knowledge of human nature displayed by the sage Oloffe the Dreamer and his fellow legislators. For my part I have not so bad an opinion of mankind as many of my brother philosophers. I do not think poor human nature so sorry a piece of workmanship as they would make it out to be; and as far as I have observed, I am fully satisfied that man, if left to himself, would about as readily go right as wrong. It is only this eternally sounding in his ears that it is his duty to go right that makes him go the very reverse. The noble independence of his nature revolts at this intolerable tyranny of law and the perpetual interference of officious morality which is ever besetting his path with finger posts and directions to "keep to the right, as the law directs"; and like a spirited urchin, he turns directly contrary, and gallops through mud and mire, over hedges and ditches, merely to show that he is a lad of spirit and out of his leading strings. And these opinions are amply substantiated by what I have above said of our worthy ancestors; who never being be-preached and be-lectured, and guided and governed by statutes and laws and bylaws, as are their more enlightened descendants, did one and all demean themselves honestly and peaceably, out of pure ignorance, or, in other words—because they knew no better.

Nor must I omit to record one of the earliest measures of this infant settlement, inasmuch as it shows the piety of our forefathers and that, like good Christians, they were always ready to serve God, after they had first served themselves. Thus, having quietly settled themselves down and provided for their own comfort, they bethought themselves of testifying their gratitude to the great and good St. Nicholas for his protecting care in guiding them to this delectable abode. To this end they built a fair and goodly chapel within the fort, which they consecrated to his name; whereupon he immediately took the town of New Amsterdam under his peculiar patronage, and he has ever since been, and I devoutly hope will ever be, the tutelar saint of this excellent city.

I am moreover told that there is a little legendary book somewhere extant, written in Low Dutch, which says that the image of this renowned saint, which whilome graced the bowsprit of the Goede Vrouw, was elevated in front of this chapel in the very center of what in modern days is called the Bowling Green. And the legend further treats of divers miracles wrought by the mighty pipe which the saint held in his mouth; a whiff of which was a sovereign cure for an indigestion—an invaluable relic in this colony of brave trenchermen. As, however, in spite of the most diligent search I cannot lay my hands upon this little book, I must confess that I entertain considerable doubt on the subject.

Thus benignly fostered by the good St. Nicholas, the burghers of New Amsterdam beheld their settlement increase in magnitude and population and soon become the metropolis of divers settlements and an extensive territory. Already had the disastrous pride of colonies and dependencies, those banes of a sound-hearted empire, entered into their imaginations; and Fort Aurania on the Hudson, Fort Nassau on the Delaware, and Fort Goede Hoep on the Connecticut River seemed to be the darling offspring of the venerable council.* Thus prosperously, to all appearance, did the province of New Netherlands advance in power; and the early history of its metropolis presents a fair page, unsullied by crime or calamity.

Hordes of painted savages still lurked about the tangled forests and rich bottoms of the unsettled part of the island—the hunter pitched his rude bower of skins and bark beside the rills that ran through the cool and shady glens, while here and there might be seen on some sunny knoll a group of Indian wigwams,

---

* The province about this time extended on the north to Fort Aurania, or Orange (now the city of Albany), situated about 160 miles up the Hudson river. Indeed the province claimed quite to the river St. Lawrence; but this claim was not much insisted on at the time, as the country beyond Fort Aurania was a perfect wilderness. On the south the province reached to Fort Nassau on the south river, since called the Delaware—and on the east it extended to the Varshe (or fresh) river, now the Connecticut. On this last frontier was likewise erected a fort and tradinghouse, much about the spot where at present is situated the pleasant town of Hartford. This was called Fort Goed Hoep (or Good Hope) and was intended as well for the purpose of trade as of defense.

whose smoke arose above the neighboring trees and floated in the transparent atmosphere. By degrees a mutual goodwill had grown up between these wandering beings and the burghers of New Amsterdam. Our benevolent forefathers endeavored as much as possible to ameliorate their situation by giving them gin, rum, and glass beads in exchange for their peltries; for it seems the kindhearted Dutchmen had conceived a great friendship for their savage neighbors, on account of their being pleasant men to trade with and little skilled in the art of making a bargain.

Now and then a crew of these half-human sons of the forests would make their appearance in the streets of New Amsterdam, fantastically painted and decorated with beads and flaunting feathers, sauntering about with an air of listless indifference— sometimes in the marketplace instructing the little Dutch boys in the use of the bow and arrow—at other times, inflamed with liquor, swaggering and whooping and yelling about the town like so many fiends, to the great dismay of all the good wives, who would hurry their children into the house, fasten the doors, and throw water upon the enemy from the garret windows. It is worthy of mention here that our forefathers were very particular in holding up these wild men as excellent domestic examples—and for reasons that may be gathered from the history of Master Ogilby, who tells us that "for the least offence the bridegroom soundly beats his wife and turns her out of doors and marries another, insomuch that some of them have every year a new wife." Whether this awful example had any influence or not, history does not mention; but it is certain that our grandmothers were miracles of fidelity and obedience.

True it is that the good understanding between our ancestors and their savage neighbors was liable to occasional interruptions, and I have heard my grandmother, who was a very wise old woman and well versed in the history of these parts, tell a long story, of a winter's evening, about a battle between the New Amsterdammers and the Indians which was known by the name of the *Peach War,* and which took place near a peach orchard in a dark glen which for a long while went by the name of Murderer's Valley.

The legend of this sylvan war was long current among the nurses, old wives, and other ancient chroniclers of the place; but time and improvement have almost obliterated both the tradition and the scene of battle; for what was once the blood-stained valley is now in the center of this populous city, and known by the name of *Dey Street*.

The accumulating wealth and consequence of New Amsterdam and its dependencies at length awakened the tender solicitude of the mother country; who finding it a thriving and opulent colony, and that it promised to yield great profit and no trouble, all at once became wonderfully anxious about its safety and began to load it with tokens of regard, in the same manner that your knowing people are sure to overwhelm rich relations with their affection and loving-kindness.

The usual marks of protection shown by mother countries to wealthy colonies were forthwith manifested—the first care always being to send rulers to the new settlement with orders to squeeze as much revenue from it as it will yield. Accordingly, in the year of our Lord 1629, Mynher WOUTER VAN TWILLER was appointed governor of the province of Nieuw Nederlandts, under the commission and control of their High Mightinesses, the Lords States General of the United Netherlands, and the privileged West India Company.

This renowned old gentleman arrived at New Amsterdam in the merry month of June, the sweetest month in all the year; when Dan Apollo seems to dance up the transparent firmament —when the robin, the thrush, and a thousand other wanton songsters make the woods to resound with amorous ditties, and the luxurious little boblincon revels among the clover blossoms of the meadows—all which happy coincidence persuaded the old dames of New Amsterdam, who were skilled in the art of fore-telling events, that this was to be a happy and prosperous administration.

But as it would be derogatory to the consequence of the first Dutch governor of the great province of Nieuw Nederlandts to be thus scurvily introduced at the end of a chapter, I will put an end to this second book of my history that I may usher him in with more dignity in the beginning of my next.

BOOK III
In which is recorded the golden reign of Wouter Van Twiller.

CHAPTER I

Of the renowned Wouter Van Twiller, his unparalleled virtues—as likewise his unutterable wisdom in the law case of Wandle Schoonhoven and Barent Bleecker—and the great admiration of the public thereat.

Grievous and very much to be commiserated is the task of the feeling historian who writes the history of his native land. If it fall to his lot to be the sad recorder of calamity or crime, the mournful page is watered with his tears—nor can he recall the most prosperous and blissful era without a melancholy sigh at the reflection that it has passed away forever! I know not whether it be owing to an immoderate love for the simplicity of former times, or to that certain tenderness of heart incident to all sentimental historians; but I candidly confess that I cannot look back on the happier days of our city, which I now describe, without a sad dejection of the spirits. With a faltering hand do I withdraw the curtain of oblivion that veils the modest merit of our venerable ancestors, and as their figures rise to my mental vision, humble myself before the mighty shades.

Such are my feelings when I revisit the family mansion of the Knickerbockers and spend a lonely hour in the chamber where hang the portraits of my forefathers, shrouded in dust like the forms they represent. With pious reverence do I gaze on the countenances of those renowned burghers who have preceded me in the steady march of existence—whose sober and temperate blood now meanders through my veins, flowing slower and slower in its feeble conduits until its current shall soon be stopped forever!

These, say I to myself, are but frail memorials of the mighty men who flourished in the days of the patriarchs; but who, alas, have long since mouldered in that tomb towards which my steps are insensibly and irresistibly hastening! As I pace the darkened chamber and lose myself in melancholy musings, the shadowy images around me almost seem to steal once more into existence—their countenances to assume the animation of life—their eyes to pursue me in every movement! Carried away by the delusions of fancy, I almost imagine myself surrounded by the shades of the departed and holding sweet converse with the worthies of antiquity! Ah, hapless Diedrich! born in a degenerate age, abandoned to the buffetings of fortune—a stranger and a weary pilgrim in thy native land—blest with no weeping wife nor family of helpless children; but doomed to wander neglected through those crowded streets and elbowed by foreign upstarts from those fair abodes where once thine ancestors held sovereign empire.

Let me not, however, lose the historian in the man nor suffer the doting recollections of age to overcome me while dwelling with fond garrulity on the virtuous days of the patriarchs—on those sweet days of simplicity and ease which never more will dawn on the lovely island of Manna-hata!

The renowned Wouter (or Walter) Van Twiller was descended from a long line of Dutch burgomasters who had successively dozed away their lives and grown fat upon the bench of magistracy in Rotterdam; and who had comported themselves with such singular wisdom and propriety that they were never either heard or talked of—which, next to being universally applauded, should be the object of ambition of all sage magistrates and rulers.

His surname of Twiller is said to be a corruption of the original *Twijfler,* which in English means *doubter;* a name admirably descriptive of his deliberative habits. For though he was a man shut up within himself like an oyster, and of such a profoundly reflective turn that he scarcely ever spoke except in monosyllables, yet did he never make up his mind on any doubtful point. This was clearly accounted for by his adherents, who affirmed that he always conceived every subject on so comprehensive a scale that he had not room in his head to turn it over and examine both sides of it, so that he always remained in doubt, merely in consequence of the astonishing magnitude of his ideas!

There are two opposite ways by which some men get into notice—one by talking a vast deal and thinking a little, and the other by holding their tongues and not thinking at all. By the first, many a vaporing superficial pretender acquires the reputation of a man of quick parts—by the other many a vacant dunderpate, like the owl, the stupidest of birds, comes to be complimented by a discerning world with all the attributes of wisdom. This, by the way, is a mere casual remark which I would not for the universe have it thought I apply to governor Van Twiller. On the contrary, he was a very wise Dutchman, for he never said a foolish thing—and of such invincible gravity that he was never known to laugh, or even to smile, through the course of a long and prosperous life. Certain, however, it is, there never was a matter proposed, however simple, and on which your common narrow-minded mortals would rashly determine at the first glance, but what the renowned Wouter put on a mighty mysterious vacant kind of look, shook his capacious head, and having smoked for five minutes with redoubled earnestness, sagely observed that "he had his doubts about the matter"—which in process of time gained him the character of a man slow of belief and not easily imposed on.

The person of this illustrious old gentleman was as regularly formed and nobly proportioned as though it had been moulded by the hands of some cunning Dutch statuary as a model of majesty and lordly grandeur. He was exactly five feet six inches in height, and six feet five inches in circumference. His head was a perfect sphere far excelling in magnitude that of the great Pericles (who was thence waggishly called *Schenocephalus,* or onion head)—indeed, of such stupendous dimensions was it that dame Nature herself, with all her sex's ingenuity, would have been puzzled to construct a neck capable of supporting it; wherefore she wisely declined the attempt and settled it firmly on the top of his backbone, just between the shoulders; where it remained as snuggly bedded as a ship of war in the mud of the Potowmac. His body was of an oblong form, particularly capacious at bottom; which was wisely ordered by providence, seeing that he was a man of sedentary habits and very averse to the idle labor of walking. His legs, though exceeding short, were sturdy in proportion to the weight they had to sustain; so that when erect he had not a little the appearance of a robustious beer barrel standing on skids. His face, that infallible index of the mind, presented a vast expanse, perfectly unfurrowed or deformed by any of those lines and angles which disfigure the human countenance with what is termed expression. Two small gray eyes twinkled feebly in the midst, like two stars of lesser magnitude in a hazy firmament; and his full-fed cheeks, which seemed to have taken toll of everything that went into his mouth, were curiously mottled and streaked with dusky red, like a Spitzenberg apple.

His habits were as regular as his person. He daily took his four stated meals, appropriating exactly an hour to each; he smoked and doubted eight hours, and he slept the remaining twelve of the four and twenty. Such was the renowned Wouter Van Twiller—a true philosopher, for his mind was either elevated above or tranquilly settled below the cares and perplexities of this world. He had lived in it for years without feeling the least curiosity to know whether the sun revolved round it, or it round the sun; and he had watched for at least half a century the smoke curling from his pipe to the ceiling without once troubling his head with any of those numerous theories by which a philosopher would have perplexed his brain in accounting for its rising above the surrounding atmosphere.

In his council he presided with great state and solemnity. He sat in a huge chair of solid oak hewn in the celebrated forest of the Hague, fabricated by an experienced Timmerman of Amsterdam, and curiously carved about the arms and feet into exact imitations of gigantic eagles' claws. Instead of a scepter he swayed a long Turkish pipe wrought with jasmin and amber, which had been presented to a stadtholder of Holland at the conclusion of a treaty with one of the petty Barbary powers.— In this stately chair would he sit, and this magnificent pipe would he smoke, shaking his right knee with a constant motion and fixing his eye for hours together upon a little print of Amsterdam which hung in a black frame against the opposite wall of the council chamber. Nay, it has even been said that when any deliberation of extraordinary length and intricacy was on the carpet, the renowned Wouter would absolutely shut his eyes for full two hours at a time, that he might not be disturbed by external objects—and at such times the internal commotion of his mind was evinced by certain regular guttural sounds which his admirers declared were merely the noise of conflict made by his contending doubts and opinions.

It is with infinite difficulty I have been enabled to collect these biographical anecdotes of the great man under consideration. The facts respecting him were so scattered and vague, and divers of them so questionable in point of authenticity, that I have had to give up the search after many and decline the admission of still more which would have tended to heighten the coloring of his portrait.

I have been the more anxious to delineate fully the person and habits of the renowned Van Twiller, from the consideration that he was not only the first but also the best governor that ever presided over this ancient and respectable province; and so tranquil and benevolent was his reign that I do not find throughout the whole of it a single instance of any offender being brought to punishment—a most indubitable sign of a merciful governor, and a case unparalleled, excepting in the reign of the illustrious King Log, from whom, it is hinted, the renowned Van Twiller was a lineal descendant.

The very outset of the career of this excellent magistrate, like that of Solomon, or to speak more appropriately, like that of the illustrious governor of Barataria, was distinguished by an example of legal acumen that gave flattering presage of a wise and equitable administration. The very morning after he had been solemnly installed in office, and at the moment that he was making his breakfast from a prodigious earthen dish filled with milk and Indian pudding, he was suddenly interrupted by the appearance of one Wandle Schoonhoven, a very important old burgher of New Amsterdam, who complained bitterly of one Barent Bleecker, inasmuch as he fraudulently refused to come to a settlement of accounts, seeing that there was a heavy balance in favor of the said Wandle. Governor Van Twiller, as I have already observed, was a man of few words; he was likewise a mortal enemy to multiplying writings—or being disturbed at his breakfast. Having listened attentively to the statement of Wandle Schoonhoven, giving an occasional grunt as he shovelled a mighty spoonful of Indian pudding into his mouth—either as a sign that he relished the dish or comprehended the story—he called unto him his constable, and pulling out of his breeches pocket a huge jackknife, despatched it after the defendant as a summons, accompanied by his tobacco box as a warrant.

This summonary process was as effectual in those simple days as was the seal ring of the great Haroun Alraschid among the true believers—The two parties being confronted before him, each produced a book of accounts written in a language and character that would have puzzled any but a high Dutch commentator or a learned decipherer of Egyptian obelisks to understand. The sage Wouter took them one after the other, and having poised them in his hands and attentively counted over the number of leaves, fell straightway into a very great doubt, and smoked for half an hour without saying a word; at length, laying his finger beside his nose and shutting his eyes for a moment, with the air of a man who has just caught a subtle idea by the tail, he slowly took his pipe from his mouth, puffed forth a column of tobacco smoke, and with marvelous gravity and solemnity pronounced—that having carefully counted over the leaves and weighed the books, it was found that one was just as thick and as heavy as the other—therefore it was the final opinion of the court that the accounts were equally balanced—therefore Wandle should give Barent a receipt, and Barent should give Wandle a receipt—and the constable should pay the costs.

This decision, being straightway made known, diffused general joy throughout New Amsterdam, for the people immediately perceived that they had a very wise and equitable magistrate to rule over them. But its happiest effect was that not another lawsuit took place throughout the whole of his administration—and the office of constable fell into such decay that there was not one of those losel scouts known in the province for many years. I am the more particular in dwelling on this transaction, not only because I deem it one of the most sage and righteous judgments on record, and well worthy the attention of modern magistrates, but because it was a miraculous event in the history of the renowned Wouter—being the only time he was ever known to come to a decision in the whole course of his life.

Containing some account of the Grand Council of New Amsterdam, as also divers especial good philosophical reasons why an alderman should be fat—with other particulars touching the state of the Province.

In treating of the early governors of the province, I must caution my readers against confounding them in point of dignity and power with those worthy gentlemen who are whimsically denominated governors in this enlightened republic—a set of unhappy victims of popularity, who are in fact the most dependent, henpecked beings in the community: doomed to bear the secret goadings and corrections of their own party, and the sneers and revilings of the whole world beside.—Set up like geese at Christmas holidays to be pelted and shot at by every whipster and vagabond in the land. On the contrary, the Dutch governors enjoyed that uncontrolled authority vested in all commanders of distant colonies or territories. They were in a manner absolute despots in their little domains, lording it, if so disposed, over both law and gospel, and accountable to none but the mother country; which it is well known is astonishingly deaf to all complaints against its governors, provided they discharge the main duty of their station—squeezing out a good revenue. This hint will be of importance to prevent my readers from being seized with doubt and incredulity whenever, in the course of this authentic history, they encounter the uncommon circumstance of a governor acting with independence and in opposition to the opinions of the multitude.

To assist the doubtful Wouter in the arduous business of legislation, a board of magistrates was appointed, which presided immediately over the police. This potent body consisted of a schout or bailiff, with powers between those of the present mayor and sheriff—five burgermeesters, who were equivalent to aldermen, and five schepens, who officiated as scrubs, subdevils, or

bottle holders to the burgermeesters, in the same manner as do
assistant aldermen to their principals at the present day; it being
their duty to fill the pipes of the lordly burgermeesters—hunt
the markets for delicacies for corporation dinners, and to discharge such other little offices of kindness as were occasionally
required. It was, moreover, tacitly understood, though not speci-
fically enjoined, that they should consider themselves as butts
for the blunt wits of the burgermeesters, and should laugh most
heartily at all their jokes; but this last was a duty as rarely called
in action in those days as it is at present, and was shortly re-
mitted in consequence of the tragical death of a fat little schepen-
—who actually died of suffocation in an unsucessful effort to
force a laugh at one of burgermeester Van Zandt's best jokes.

In return for these humble services they were permitted to say
yes and *no* at the council board and to have that enviable
privilege, the run of the public kitchen—being graciously permitted to eat and drink and smoke at all those snug junketings
and public gormandizings for which the ancient magistrates were
equally famous with their more modern successors. The post of
schepen, therefore, like that of assistant alderman, was eagerly
coveted by all your burghers of a certain description, who have
a huge relish for good feeding and an humble ambition to be
great men in a small way—who thirst after a little brief authority that shall render them the terror of the almshouse and the
bridewell—that shall enable them to lord it over obsequious
poverty, vagrant vice, outcast prostitution, and hunger-driven
dishonesty—that shall place in their hands the lesser but galling
scourge of the law, and give to their beck a hound-like pack of
catchpoles and bumbailiffs—tenfold greater rogues than the
culprits they hunt down!—My readers will excuse this sudden
warmth, which I confess is unbecoming of a grave historian—
but I have a mortal antipathy to catchpoles, bumbailiffs, and
little great men.

The ancient magistrates of this city corresponded with those
of the present time no less in form, magnitude, and intellect than
in prerogative and privilege. The burgomasters, like our aldermen, were generally chosen by weight—and not only the weight
of the body, but likewise the weight of the head. It is a maxim
practically observed in all honest, plain-thinking, regular cities
that an alderman should be fat—and the wisdom of this can be
proved to a certainty. That the body is in some measure an

image of the mind, or rather that the mind is moulded to the body, like melted lead to the clay in which it is cast, has been insisted on by many men of science who have made human nature their peculiar study—For as a learned gentleman of our own city observes, "there is a constant relation between the moral character of all intelligent creatures and their physical constitution—between their habits and the structure of their bodies." Thus we see that a lean, spare, diminutive body is generally accompanied by a petulant, restless, meddling mind—either the mind wears down the body by its continual motion; or else the body, not affording the mind sufficient house room, keeps it continually in a state of fretfulness, tossing and worrying about from the uneasiness of its situation. Whereas your round, sleek, fat, unwieldy periphery is ever attended by a mind like itself, tranquil, torpid, and at ease; and we may always observe that your well fed, robustious burghers are in general very tenacious of their ease and comfort; being great enemies to noise, discord, and disturbance—and surely none are more likely to study the public tranquillity than those who are so careful of their own.—Who ever hears of fat men heading a riot or herding together in turbulent mobs?—no—no—it is your lean, hungry men who are continually worrying society and setting the whole community by the ears.

The divine Plato, whose doctrines are not sufficiently attended to by philosophers of the present age, allows to every man three souls—one immortal and rational, seated in the brain, that it may overlook and regulate the body—a second consisting of the surly and irascible passions, which, like belligerent powers, lie encamped around the heart—a. third mortal and sensual, destitute of reason, gross and brutal in its propensities, and enchained in the belly, that it may not disturb the divine soul by its ravenous howlings. Now, according to this excellent theory, what can be more clear than that your fat alderman is most likely to have the most regular and well conditioned mind. His head is like a huge spherical chamber, containing a prodigious mass of soft brains whereon the rational soul lies softly and snugly couched, as on a feather bed; and the eyes, which are the windows of the bed chamber, are usually half closed, that its slumberings may not be disturbed by external objects. A mind thus comfortably lodged and protected from disturbance is manifestly most likely to perform its functions with regularity and ease. By dint of good feeding, moreover, the mortal and malignant soul, which is confined in the belly, and which by its raging and roaring puts the irritable soul in the neighbor-hood of the heart in an intolerable passion, and thus renders men crusty and quarrelsome when hungry, is completely paci-fied, silenced, and put to rest—whereupon a host of honest good-fellow qualities and kindhearted affections, which had lain per-due, slily peeping out of the loopholes of the heart, finding this Cerberus asleep, do pluck up their spirits, turn out one and all in their holiday suits, and gambol up and down the diaphragm—disposing their possessor to laughter, good humor, and a thousand friendly offices towards his fellow mortals.

As a board of magistrates formed on this model think but very little, they are the less likely to differ and wrangle about favorite opinions—and as they generally transact business upon a hearty dinner, they are naturally disposed to be lenient and indulgent in the administration of their duties. Charlemagne was conscious of this, and therefore (a pitiful measure, for which I can never forgive him) ordered in his cartularies that no judge should hold a court of justice except in the morning on an empty stomach—a rule which, I warrant, bore hard upon all the poor culprits in his kingdom. The more enlightened and humane gen-eration of the present day have taken an opposite course, and have so managed that the aldermen are the best fed men in the community; feasting lustily on the fat things of the land, and gorging so heartily oysters and turtles that in process of time they acquire the activity of the one and the form, the waddle, and the green fat of the other. The consequence is, as I have just said; these luxurious feastings do produce such a dulcet equanimity and repose of the soul, rational and irrational, that their transac-tions are proverbial for unvarying monotony—and the profound laws which they enact in their dozing moments, amid the labors of digestion, are quietly suffered to remain as dead letters and never enforced when awake. In a word, your fair round-bellied burgomaster, like a full fed mastiff, dozes quietly at the house door, always at home and always at hand to watch over its safety—but as to electing a lean, meddling candidate to the office, as has now and then been done, I would as lief put a grey-hound to watch the house or a race horse to drag an ox-wagon.

The burgomasters, then, as I have already mentioned, were wisely chosen by weight, and the schepens, or assistant aldermen, were appointed to attend upon them and *help them eat;* but the latter, in the course of time, when they had been fed and fattened into sufficient bulk of body and drowsiness of brain, became very eligible candidates for the burgomasters' chairs, having fairly eaten themselves into office, as a mouse eats his way into a comfortable lodgment in a goodly, blue nosed, skimmed milk, New England cheese.

Nothing could equal the profound deliberations that took place between the renowned Wouter and these his worthy compeers, unless it be the sage divans of some of our modern corporations. They would sit for hours smoking and dozing over public affairs without speaking a word to interrupt that perfect stillness so necessary to deep reflection.—Under the sober sway of Wouter Van Twiller and these his worthy coadjutors, the infant settlement waxed vigorous apace, gradually emerging from the swamps and forests, and exhibiting that mingled appearance of town and country customary in new cities, and which at this day may be witnessed in the city of Washington; that immense metropolis which makes so glorious an appearance on paper.

It was a pleasing sight in those times to behold the honest burgher, like a patriarch of yore, seated on the bench at the door of his whitewashed house, under the shade of some gigantic sycamore or overhanging willow. Here would he smoke his pipe of a sultry afternoon, enjoying the soft southern breeze and listening with silent gratulation to the clucking of his hens, the cackling of his geese, and the sonorous grunting of his swine; that combination of farmyard melody which may truly be said to have a silver sound, inasmuch as it conveys a certain assurance of profitable marketing.

The modern spectator who wanders through the streets of this populous city can scarcely form an idea of the different appearance they presented in the primitive days of the Doubter. The busy hum of multitudes, the shouts of revelry, the rumbling equipages of fashion, the rattling of accursed carts, and all the spirit-grieving sounds of brawling commerce, were unknown in the settlement of New Amsterdam. The grass grew quietly in the highways—the bleating sheep and frolicsome calves sported about the verdant ridge where now the Broadway loungers take their morning stroll—the cunning fox or ravenous wolf skulked in the woods where now are to be seen the dens of Gomez and his righteous fraternity of moneybrokers—and flocks of vociferous geese cackled about the fields where now the great Tammany wigwam and the patriotic tavern of Martling echo with the wranglings of the mob.

In these good times did a true and enviable equality of rank and property prevail, equally removed from the arrogance of wealth and the servility and heartburnings of repining poverty —and what in my mind is still more conducive to tranquillity and harmony among friends, a happy equality of intellect was likewise to be seen. The minds of the good burghers of New Amsterdam seemed all to have been cast in one mould, and to be those honest, blunt sort of minds which, like certain manufactures, are made by the gross and considered as exceedingly good for common use.

Thus it happens that your true dull minds are generally preferred for public employ, and especially promoted to city honors; your keen intellects, like razors, being considered too sharp for common service. I know that it is common to rail at the unequal distribution of riches as the great source of jealousies, broils, and heartbreakings, whereas for my part, I verily believe it is the sad inequality of intellect that prevails that embroils communities more than anything else; and I have remarked that your knowing people who are so much wiser than anybody else are eternally keeping society in a ferment. Happily for New Amsterdam, nothing of the kind was known within its walls—the very words of learning, education, taste, and talents were unheard of—a bright genius was an animal unknown; a bluestocking lady would have been regarded with as much wonder as a horned frog or a fiery dragon. No man, in fact, seemed to know more than his neighbor, nor any man to know much more than an honest man ought to know who has nobody's business to mind but his own; the parson and the council clerk were the only men that could read in the community, and the sage Van Twiller always signed his name with a cross.

Thrice happy and ever to be envied little Burgh! existing in all the security of harmless insignificance—unnoticed and unenvied by the world, without ambition, without vain glory, without riches, without learning, and all their train of carking cares —and as of yore, in the better days of man, the deities were wont to visit him on earth and bless his rural habitations, so we are told, in the sylvan days of New Amsterdam the good St. Nicholas would often make his appearance in his beloved city of a holiday afternoon, riding jollily among the tree tops or over the roofs of the houses, now and then drawing forth magnificent presents from his breeches pockets and dropping them down the chimneys of his favorites. Whereas in these degenerate days of iron and brass he never shows us the light of his countenance nor ever visits us, save one night in the year; when he rattles down the chimneys of the descendants of the patriarchs, confining his presents merely to the children in token of the degeneracy of the parents.

Such are the comfortable and thriving effects of a fat government. The province of the New Netherlands, destitute of wealth, possessed a sweet tranquillity that wealth could never purchase. It seemed indeed as if old Saturn had again commenced his reign and renewed the days of primeval simplicity. For the golden age, says Ovid, was totally destitute of gold, and for that very reason was called the golden age; that is, the happy and fortunate age—because the evils produced by the precious metals, such as avarice, covetousness, theft, rapine, usury, banking, note shaving, lottery insuring, and the whole catalogue of crimes and grievances were then unknown. In the iron age there was abundance of gold; on that very account it was called the iron age, because of the hardships, the labors, the dissensions, and the wars occasioned by the thirst of gold.

The genial days of Wouter Van Twiller, therefore, may truly be termed the golden age of our city. There were neither public commotions nor private quarrels; neither parties, nor sects, nor schisms; neither prosecutions, nor trials, nor punishments; nor were there counselors, attorneys, catchpoles, or hangmen. Every man attended to what little business he was lucky enough to have, or neglected it if he pleased, without asking the opinion of his neighbor.—In those days nobody meddled with concerns above his comprehension, nor thrust his nose into other people's affairs; nor neglected to correct his own conduct and reform his own character in his zeal to pull to pieces the characters of others—but in a word, every respectable citizen eat when he was not hungry, drank when he was not thirsty, and went regular to bed when the sun set and the fowls went to roost, whether he were sleepy or not; all which tended so remarkably to the population of the settlement that I am told every dutiful wife throughout New Amsterdam made a point of always enriching her husband with at least one child a year, and very often a brace—this superabundance of good things clearly constituting the true luxury of life, according to the favorite Dutch maxim that "more than enough constitutes a feast." Everything therefore went on exactly as it should do, and, in the usual words employed by historians to express the welfare of a country, "the profoundest *tranquillity* and *repose* reigned throughout the province."

CHAPTER III

How the town of New Amsterdam arose out of mud, and came to be marvelously polished and polite—together with a picture of the manners of our great-great-grandfathers.

Manifold are the tastes and dispositions of the enlightened literati who turn over the pages of history. Some there be whose hearts are brimful of the yeast of courage, and whose bosoms do work and swell and foam with untried valor, like a barrel of new cider or a trainband captain fresh from under the hands of his tailor. This doughty class of readers can be satisfied with nothing but bloody battles and horrible encounters; they must be continually storming forts, sacking cities, springing mines, marching up to the muzzles of cannon, charging bayonet through every page, and revelling in gunpowder and carnage. Others, who are of a less martial but equally ardent imagination, and who, withal, are a little given to the marvelous, will dwell with wonderous satisfaction on descriptions of prodigies, unheard of events, hairbreadth escapes, hardy adventures, and all those astonishing narrations that just amble along the boundary line of possibility.—A third class, who, not to speak slightly of them, are of a lighter turn and skim over the records of past times as they do over the edifying pages of a novel, merely for relaxation and innocent amusement, do singularly delight in treasons, executions, Sabine rapes, Tarquin outrages, conflagrations, murders, and all the other catalogue of hideous crimes that, like cayenne in cookery, do give a pungency and flavor to the dull detail of history—while a fourth class, of more philosophic habits, do generally pore over the musty chronicles of time to investigate the operations of the human mind and watch the gradual changes in men and manners effected by the progress of knowledge, the vicissitudes of events, or the influence of situation.

If the three first classes find but little wherewithal to solace themselves in the tranquil reign of Wouter Van Twiller, I entreat them to exert their patience for a while and bear with the tedious picture of happiness, prosperity, and peace which my duty as a faithful historian obliges me to draw; and I promise them that as soon as I can possibly light upon anything horrible, uncommon, or impossible, it shall go hard but I will make it afford them entertainment. This being premised, I turn with great complacency to the fourth class of my readers, who are men or, if possible, women after my own heart; grave, philosophical, and investigating; fond of analyzing characters, of taking a start from first causes, and so hunting a nation down through all the mazes of innovation and improvement. Such will naturally be anxious to witness the first development of the newly hatched colony and the primitive manners and customs prevalent among its inhabitants during the halcyon reign of Van Twiller or the Doubter.

I will not grieve their patience, however, by describing minutely the increase and improvement of New Amsterdam. Their own imaginations will doubtless present to them the good burghers, like so many painstaking and persevering beavers, slowly and surely pursuing their labors—they will behold the prosperous transformation from the rude log hut to the stately Dutch mansion with brick front, glazed windows, and tiled roof —from the tangled thicket to the luxuriant cabbage garden—and from the skulking Indian to the ponderous burgomaster. In a word, they will picture to themselves the steady, silent, and undeviating march to prosperity incident to a city destitute of pride or ambition, cherished by a fat government, and whose citizens do nothing in a hurry.

The sage council, as has been mentioned in a preceding chapter, not being able to determine upon any plan for the building of their city—the cows, in a laudable fit of patriotism, took it under their particular charge, and as they went to and from pasture established paths through the bushes, on each side of which the good folks built their houses; which is one cause of the rambling and picturesque turns and labyrinths which distinguish certain streets of New York at this very day.

Some, it must be noted, who were strenuous partisans of Mynher Ten Breeches (or Ten Broeck), vexed that his plan of digging canals was not adopted, made a compromise with their inclinations by establishing themselves on the margins of those creeks and inlets which meandered through various parts of the ground laid out for improvement. To these may be particularly ascribed the first settlement of Broad Street, which originally was built along a creek that ran up to what at present is called Wall Street. The lower part soon became very busy and populous; and a ferry house* was in process of time established at the head of it; being at that day called "the head of inland navigation."

The disciples of Mynher Tough Breeches, on the other hand, no less enterprising, and more industrious than their rivals, stationed themselves along the shore of the river and labored with unexampled perseverance in making little docks and dikes, from which originated that multitude of mud traps with which this city is fringed. To these docks would the old burghers repair, just at those hours when the falling tide had left the beach uncovered, that they might snuff up the fragrant effluvia of mud and mire; which they observed had a true wholesome smell and reminded them of the canals of Holland. To the indefatigable labors and praiseworthy example of this latter class of projectors we are indebted for the acres of artificial ground on which several of our streets in the vicinity of the rivers are built; and which, if we may credit the assertions of several learned physicians of this city, have been very efficacious in producing the yellow fever.

The houses of the higher class were generally constructed of wood, excepting the gable end, which was of small black and yellow Dutch bricks and always faced on the street, as our an-

---

* This house has been several times repaired, and at present is a small yellow brick house, No. 23 Broad Street, with the gable end to the street, surmounted with an iron rod on which, until within three or four years, a little iron ferry boat officiated as weathercock.

cestors, like their descendants, were very much given to outward
show and were noted for putting the best leg foremost. The
house was always furnished with abundance of large doors and
small windows on every floor; the date of its erection was curiously designated by iron figures on the front; and on the top
of the roof was perched a fierce little weathercock to let the
family into the important secret, which way the wind blew.
These, like the weathercocks on the tops of our steeples, pointed
so many different ways that every man could have a wind to
his mind; and you would have thought old Eolus had set all
his bags of wind adrift, pell mell, to gambol about this windy
metropolis—the most staunch and loyal citizens, however, always
went according to the weathercock on the top of the governor's
house, which was certainly the most correct, as he had a trusty
servant employed every morning to climb up and point it whichever way the wind blew.

In those good days of simplicity and sunshine, a passion for
cleanliness was the leading principle in domestic economy and
the universal test of an able housewife—a character which formed
the utmost ambition of our unenlightened grandmothers. The
front door was never opened except on marriages, funerals, new
year's days, the festival of St. Nicholas, or some such great occasion.—It was ornamented with a gorgeous brass knocker, curiously wrought, sometimes in the device of a dog and sometimes
of a lion's head, and was daily burnished with such religious
zeal that it was ofttimes worn out by the very precautions taken
for its preservation. The whole house was constantly in a state
of inundation, under the discipline of mops and brooms and
scrubbing brushes; and the good housewives of those days were
a kind of amphibious animal, delighting exceedingly to be
dabbling in water—insomuch that an historian of the day gravely
tells us that many of his townswomen grew to have webbed
fingers like unto a duck; and some of them, he had little doubt,
could the matter be examined into, would be found to have the
tails of mermaids—but this I look upon to be a mere sport of
fancy, or, what is worse, a wilful misrepresentation.

The grand parlor was the sanctum sanctorum, where the
passion for cleaning was indulged without control. In this sacred
apartment no one was permitted to enter excepting the mistress
and her confidential maid, who visited it once a week for the

purpose of giving it a thorough cleaning and putting things to rights—always taking the precaution of leaving their shoes at the door and entering devoutly on their stocking feet. After scrubbing the floor, sprinkling it with fine white sand, which was curiously stroked into angles and curves and rhomboids with a broom—after washing the windows, rubbing and polishing the furniture, and putting a new bunch of evergreens in the fireplace—the window shutters were again closed to keep out the flies, and the room carefully locked up until the revolution of time brought round the weekly cleaning day.

As to the family, they always entered in at the gate, and most generally lived in the kitchen. To have seen a numerous household assembled around the fire, one would have imagined that he was transported back to those happy days of primeval simplicity which float before our imaginations like golden visions. The fireplaces were of a truly patriarchal magnitude, where the whole family, old and young, master and servant, black and white, nay, even the very cat and dog, enjoyed a community of privilege, and had each a prescriptive right to a corner. Here the old burgher would set in perfect silence, puffing his pipe, looking in the fire with half-shut eyes, and thinking of nothing for hours together; the goede vrouw on the opposite side would employ herself diligently in spinning her yarn or knitting stockings. The young folks would crowd around the hearth, listening with breathless attention to some old crone of a negro, who was the oracle of the family and who, perched like a raven in a corner of the chimney, would croak forth for a long winter afternoon a string of incredible stories about New England witches—grisly ghosts—horses without heads—and hair-breadth escapes and bloody encounters among the Indians.

In those happy days a well regulated family always rose with the dawn, dined at eleven, and went to bed at sundown. Dinner was invariably a private meal, and the fat old burghers showed incontestable symptoms of disapprobation and uneasiness at being surprised by a visit from a neighbor on such occasions. But though our worthy ancestors were thus singularly averse to giving dinners, yet they kept up the social bands of intimacy by occasional banquetings, called teaparties.

As this is the first introduction of those delectable orgies which have since become so fashionable in this city, I am conscious my fair readers will be very curious to receive information on the subject. Sorry am I that there will be but little in my description calculated to excite their admiration. I can neither delight them with accounts of suffocating crowds, nor brilliant drawing rooms, nor towering feathers, nor sparkling diamonds, nor immeasurable trains. I can detail no choice anecdotes of scandal, for in those primitive times the simple folk were either too stupid or too good-natured to pull each other's characters to pieces—nor can I furnish any whimsical anecdotes of brag—how one lady cheated, or another bounced into a passion; for as yet there was no junto of dulcet old dowagers who met to win each other's money and lose their own tempers at a card table.

These fashionable parties were generally confined to the higher classes, or noblesse, that is to say, such as kept their own cows and drove their own wagons. The company commonly assembled at three o'clock and went away about six, unless it was in winter time, when the fashionable hours were a little earlier, that the ladies might get home before dark. I do not find that they ever treated their company to iced creams, jellies, or syllabubs; or regaled them with musty almonds, mouldy raisins, or sour oranges, as is often done in the present age of refinement.—Our ancestors were fond of more sturdy, substantial fare. The tea table was crowned with a huge earthen dish well stored with slices of fat pork, fried brown, cut up into morsels, and swimming in gravy. The company being seated around the genial board, and each furnished with a fork, evinced their dexterity in launching at the fattest pieces in this mighty dish —in much the same manner as sailors harpoon porpoises at sea, or our Indians spear salmon in the lakes. Sometimes the table was graced with immense apple pies or saucers full of preserved peaches and pears; but it was always sure to boast an enormous dish of balls of sweetened dough, fried in hog's fat, and called doughnuts, or oly koeks—a delicious kind of cake, at present scarce known in this city excepting in genuine Dutch families.

The tea was served out of a majestic delft teapot ornamented with paintings of fat little Dutch shepherds and shepherdesses tending pigs—with boats sailing in the air, and houses built in the clouds, and sundry other ingenious Dutch fantasies. The beaux distinguished themselves by their adroitness in replenishing this pot from a huge copper teakettle which would have made the pigmy macaronies of these degenerate days sweat merely to look at it. To sweeten the beverage, a lump of sugar was laid beside each cup—and the company alternately nibbled and sipped with great decorum, until an improvement was introduced by a shrewd and economic old lady, which was to suspend a large lump directly over the teatable by a string from the ceiling, so that it could be swung from mouth to mouth—an ingenious expedient which is still kept up by some families in Albany; but which prevails without exception in Communipaw, Bergen, Flat Bush, and all our uncontaminated Dutch villages.

At these primitive teaparties the utmost propriety and dignity of deportment prevailed. No flirting nor coquetting—no gambling of old ladies, nor hoyden chattering and romping of young ones—no self-satisfied struttings of wealthy gentlemen with their brains in their pockets—nor amusing conceits and monkey divertisements of smart young gentlemen with no brains at all. On the contrary, the young ladies seated themselves demurely in their rush-bottomed chairs and knit their own woollen stockings; nor ever opened their lips, excepting to say *yah Mynher* or *yah ya Vrouw* to any question that was asked them; behaving in all things like decent, well educated damsels. As to the gentlemen, each of them tranquilly smoked his pipe and seemed lost in contemplation of the blue and white tiles with which the fireplaces were decorated, wherein sundry passages of scripture were piously portrayed—Tobit and his dog figured to great advantage; Haman swung conspicuously on his gibbet; and Jonah appeared most manfully bouncing out of the whale, like Harlequin through a barrel of fire.

The parties broke up without noise and without confusion. They were carried home by their own carriages, that is to say, by the vehicles nature had provided them, excepting such of the wealthy as could afford to keep a wagon. The gentlemen gallantly attended their fair ones to their respective abodes and took leave of them with a hearty smack at the door; which, as it was an established piece of etiquette, done in perfect simplicity and honesty of heart, occasioned no scandal at that time, nor should it at the present—if our great-grandfathers approved of the custom, it would argue a great want of reverence in their descendants to say a word against it.

CHAPTER IV

Containing further particulars of the Golden Age, and what constituted a fine Lady and Gentleman in the days of Walter the Doubter.

In this dulcet period of my history, when the beauteous island of Manna-hata presented a scene, the very counterpart of those glowing pictures drawn of the golden reign of Saturn, there was, as I have before observed, a happy ignorance, an honest simplicity prevalent among its inhabitants, which, were I even able to depict, would be but little understood by the degenerate age for which I am doomed to write. Even the female sex, those arch innovators upon the tranquillity, the honesty, and gray-beard customs of society, seemed for a while to conduct themselves with incredible sobriety and comeliness, and, indeed, behaved almost as if they had not been sent into the world to bother mankind, baffle philosophy, and confound the universe.

Their hair, untortured by the abominations of art, was scrupulously pomatumed back from their foreheads with a candle and covered with a little cap of quilted calico which fitted exactly to their heads. Their petticoats of linsey-woolsey were striped with a variety of gorgeous dyes, rivaling the many-colored robes of Iris—though I must confess these gallant garments were rather short, scarce reaching below the knee; but then they made up in the number, which generally equalled that of the gentlemen's smallclothes; and what is still more praiseworthy, they were all of their own manufacture—of which circumstance, as may well be supposed, they were not a little vain.

These were the honest days in which every woman staid at home, read the Bible, and wore pockets—aye, and that too of a goodly size, fashioned with patchwork into many curious devices, and ostentatiously worn on the outside. These, in fact, were convenient receptacles, where all good housewives carefully stored away such things as they wished to have at hand; by which means they often came to be incredibly crammed—and I remember there was a story current when I was a boy that the lady of Wouter Van Twiller once had occasion to empty her right pocket in search of a wooden ladle, and the utensil was discovered lying among some rubbish in one corner—but we must not give too much faith to all these stories; the anecdotes of these remote periods being very subject to exaggeration.

Besides these notable pockets, they likewise wore scissors and pincushions suspended from their girdles by red ribbons, or among the more opulent and showy classes, by brass and even silver chains—indubitable tokens of thrifty housewives and industrious spinsters. I cannot say much in vindication of the shortness of the petticoats; it doubtless was introduced for the purpose of giving the stockings a chance to be seen, which were generally of blue worsted, with magnificent red clocks—or perhaps to display a well-turned ankle and a neat, though serviceable, foot; set off by a high-heeled leathern shoe with a large and splendid silver buckle. Thus we find that the gentle sex, in all ages, have shown the same disposition to infringe a little upon the laws of decorum in order to betray a lurking beauty or gratify an innocent love of finery.

From the sketch here given it will be seen that our good grandmothers differed considerably in their ideas of a fine figure from their scantily dressed descendants of the present day. A fine lady, in those times, waddled under more clothes, even on a fair summer's day, than would have clad the whole bevy of a modern ballroom. Nor were they the less admired by the gentlemen in consequence thereof. On the contrary, the greatness of a lover's passion seemed to increase in proportion to the magnitude of its object—and a voluminous damsel, arrayed in a dozen of petticoats, was declared by a Low Dutch sonneteer of the province to be radiant as a sunflower and luxuriant as a full-blown cabbage. Certain it is that in those days the heart of a lover could not contain more than one lady at a time; whereas the heart of a modern gallant has often room enough to accommodate half a dozen.—The reason of which I conclude to be that either the hearts of the gentlemen have grown larger or the persons of the ladies smaller—this, however, is a question for physiologists to determine.

But there was a secret charm in these petticoats which, no doubt, entered into the consideration of the prudent gallants.

The wardrobe of a lady was in those days her only fortune; and she who had a good stock of petticoats and stockings was as absolutely an heiress as is a Kamschatka damsel with a store of bearskins, or a Lapland belle with a plenty of reindeer. The ladies, therefore, were very anxious to display these powerful attractions to the greatest advantage; and the best rooms in the house instead of being adorned with caricatures of dame Nature in water colors and needlework, were always hung round with abundance of homespun garments, the manufacture and the property of the females—a piece of laudable ostentation that still prevails among the heiresses of our Dutch villages. Such were the beauteous belles of the ancient city of New Amsterdam, rivaling in primeval simplicity of manners the renowned and courtly dames so loftily sung by Dan Homer—who tells us that the princess Nausicaa washed the family linen, and the fair Penelope wove her own petticoats.

The gentlemen, in fact, who figured in the circles of the gay world in these ancient times corresponded in most particulars with the beauteous damsels whose smiles they were ambitious to deserve. True it is, their merits would make but a very inconsiderable impression upon the heart of a modern fair; they neither drove their curricles nor sported their tandems, for as yet those gaudy vehicles were not even dreamt of—neither did they distinguish themselves by their brilliancy at the table and their consequent rencontres with watchmen, for our forefathers were of too pacific a disposition to need those guardians of the night, every soul throughout the town being in full snore before nine o'clock. Neither did they establish their claims to gentility at the expense of their tailors—for as yet those offenders against the pockets of society and the tranquillity of all aspiring young gentlemen were unknown in New Amsterdam; every good housewife made the clothes of her husband and family, and even the goede vrouw of Van Twiller himself thought it no disparagement to cut out her husband's linsey-woolsey galligaskins.

Not but what there were some two or three youngsters who manifested the first dawnings of what is called fire and spirit; who held all labor in contempt; skulked about docks and marketplaces; loitered in the sunshine; squandered what little money they could procure at hustle cap and chuck farthing; swore, boxed, fought cocks, and raced their neighbors' horses—in short, who promised to be the wonder, the talk, and abomination of the town, had not their stylish career been unfortunately cut short by an affair of honor with a whipping post.

Far other, however, was the truly fashionable gentleman of those days—his dress, which served for both morning and evening, street and drawing room, was a linsey-woolsey coat, made, perhaps, by the fair hands of the mistress of his affections, and gallantly bedecked with abundance of large brass buttons.—Half a score of breeches heightened the proportions of his figure—his shoes were decorated by enormous copper buckles—a low-crowned broad-brimmed hat overshadowed his burly visage, and his hair dangled down his back, in a prodigious queue of eel skin.

Thus equipped, he would manfully sally forth with pipe in mouth to besiege some fair damsel's obdurate heart—not such a pipe, good reader, as that which Acis did sweetly tune in praise of his Galatea, but one of true delft manufacture, and furnished with a charge of fragrant Cow Pen tobacco. With this would he resolutely set himself down before the fortress, and rarely failed in the process of time to smoke the fair enemy into a surrender upon honorable terms.

Such was the happy reign of Wouter Van Twiller, celebrated in many a long-forgotten song as the real golden age, the rest being nothing but counterfeit copper-washed coin. In that delightful period, a sweet and holy calm reigned over the whole province. The burgomaster smoked his pipe in peace—the substantial solace of his domestic cares, after her daily toils were done, sat soberly at the door with her arms crossed over her apron of snowy white, without being insulted by ribald street-walkers or vagabond boys—those unlucky urchins who do so infest our streets, displaying under the roses of youth the thorns and briars of iniquity. Then it was that the lover with ten breeches and the damsel with petticoats of half a score indulged in all the innocent endearments of virtuous love, without fear and without reproach—for what had that virtue to fear which was defended by a shield of good linsey-woolseys, equal at least to the seven bull hides of the invincible Ajax.

Ah blissful and never to be forgotten age! when everything was better than it has ever been since or ever will be again—when Buttermilk Channel was quite dry at low water—when the shad in the Hudson were all salmon—and when the moon shone with a pure and resplendent whiteness instead of that melancholy yellow light which is the consequence of her sickening at the abominations she every night witnesses in this degenerate city!

Happy would it have been for New Amsterdam could it always have existed in this state of blissful ignorance and lowly simplicity: but alas! the days of childhood are too sweet to last! Cities, like men, grow out of them in time and are doomed alike to grow into the bustle, the cares, and miseries of the world. Let no man congratulate himself, when he beholds the child of his bosom or the city of his birth increasing in magnitude and importance—let the history of his own life teach him the dangers of the one, and this history of Manna-hata convince him of the calamities of the other.

CHAPTER V

In which the reader is beguiled into a delectable walk, which ends very differently from what it commenced.

In the year of our Lord one thousand eight hundred and four, on a fine afternoon in the glowing month of September, I took my customary walk upon the battery, which is at once the pride and bulwark of this ancient and impregnable city of New York. I remember well the season, for it immediately preceded that remarkably cold winter in which our sagacious corporation, in a freak of economical philanthropy, pulled to pieces, at an expense of several hundred dollars, the wooden ramparts which had cost them several thousand; and distributed the rotten fragments, which were worth considerably less than nothing, among the shivering poor of the city—never, since the fall of the walls of Jericho, or the heaven-built battlements of Troy, had there been known such a demolition—nor did it go unpunished; multitudes were blinded in vain attempts to smoke themselves warm with this charitable substitute for firewood, and an epidemic complaint of sore eyes was moreover produced which has since recurred every winter, particularly among those who undertake to burn rotten logs—who warm themselves with the charity of others—or who use patent chimneys.

On the year and month just designated did I take my accustomed walk of meditation on that same battery, which, though at present no battery, furnishes the most delightful walk and commands the noblest prospect in the whole known world. The ground on which I trod was hallowed by recollections of the past, and as I slowly wandered through the long alley of poplars which, like so many birch brooms standing on end, diffused a melancholy and lugubrious shade, my imagination drew a contrast between the surrounding scenery and what it was in the classic days of our forefathers. Where the government house by name, but the custom house by occupation, proudly reared its brick walls and wooden pillars, there whilome stood the low but substantial red-tiled mansion of the renowned Wouter Van Twiller. Around it the mighty bulwarks of Fort Amsterdam frowned defiance to every absent foe; but, like many a whiskered warrior and gallant militia captain, confined their martial deeds to frowns alone—alas! those threatening bulwarks had long since been sapped by time, and like the walls of Carthage, presented no traces to the enquiring eye of the antiquarian. The mud breastworks had long been levelled with the earth and their site converted into the green lawns and leafy alleys of the battery; where the gay apprentice sported his Sunday coat, and the laborious mechanic, relieved from the dirt and drudgery of the week, poured his weekly tale of love into the half-averted ear of the sentimental chambermaid. The capacious bay still presented the same expansive sheet of water, studded with islands, sprinkled with fishing boats, and bounded by shores of picturesque beauty. But the dark forests which once clothed these shores had been violated by the savage hand of cultivation, and their tangled mazes and impenetrable thickets had degenerated into teeming orchards and waving fields of grain. Even Governor's Island, once a smiling garden appertaining to the sovereigns of the province, was now covered with fortifications inclosing a tremendous blockhouse—so that this once peaceful island resembled a fierce little warrior in a big cocked hat, breathing gunpowder and defiance to the world!

For some time did I indulge in this pensive train of thought; contrasting in sober sadness the present day with the hallowed years behind the mountains; lamenting the melancholy progress of improvement, and praising the zeal with which our worthy burghers endeavor to preserve the wrecks of venerable customs, prejudices and errors from the overwhelming tide of modern innovation—when by degrees my ideas took a different turn, and I insensibly awakened to an enjoyment of the beauties around me.

It was one of those rich autumnal days which heaven particularly bestows upon the beauteous island of Manna-hata and its vicinity—not a floating cloud obscured the azure firmament —the sun, rolling in glorious splendor through his ethereal course, seemed to expand his honest Dutch countenance into an unusual expression of benevolence as he smiled his evening salutation upon a city which he delights to visit with his most bounteous beams—the very winds seemed to hold in their breaths in mute attention lest they should ruffle the tranquillity of the hour—and the waveless bosom of the bay presented a polished mirror in which nature beheld herself and smiled.—The standard of our city, which like a choice handkerchief is reserved for days of gala hung motionless on the flagstaff which forms the handle to a gigantic churn; and even the tremulous leaves of the poplar and the aspen, which like the tongues of the immortal sex are seldom still, ceased to vibrate to the breath of heaven. Everything seemed to acquiesce in the profound repose of nature.—The formidable eighteen-pounders slept in the embrazures of the wooden batteries, seemingly gathering fresh strength to fight the battles of their country on the next 4th of July—the solitary drum on Governor's Island forgot to call the garrison to their *shovels*—the evening gun had not yet sounded its signal for all the regular, well-meaning poultry throughout the country to go to roost; and the fleet of canoes at anchor between Gibbet Island and Communipaw slumbered on their rakes and suffered the innocent oysters to lie for a while unmolested in the soft mud of their native banks!—My own feelings sympathised with the contagious tranquillity, and I should infallibly have dozed upon one of those fragments of benches which our benevolent magistrates have provided for the benefit of convalescent loungers, had not the extraordinary inconvenience of the couch set all repose at defiance.

In the midst of this soothing slumber of the soul, my attention was attracted to a black speck peering above the western horizon just in the rear of Bergen steeple—gradually it augments and overhangs the would-be-cities of Jersey, Harsimus and Hoboken, which, like three jockeys, are starting on the course of existence and jostling each other at the commencement of the race. Now it skirts the long shore of ancient Pavonia, spreading its wide shadows from the high settlements at Weehawk quite to the lazaretto and quarantine erected by the sagacity of our police for the embarrassment of commerce—now it climbs the serene vault of heaven, cloud rolling over cloud like successive billows, shrouding the orb of day, darkening the vast expanse, and bearing thunder and hail and tempest in its bosom. The earth seems agitated at the confusion of the heavens—the late waveless mirror is lashed into furious waves that roll in hollow murmurs to the shore—the oyster boats that erst sported in the placid vicinity of Gibbet Island now hurry affrighted to the shore—the late dignified, unbending poplar writhes and twists before the merciless blast—descending torrents of drenching rain and sounding hail deluge the battery walks—the gates are thronged by 'prentices, servant maids, and little Frenchmen, with their pocket handkerchiefs over their hats, scampering from the storm —the late beauteous prospect presents one scene of anarchy and wild uproar, as though old Chaos had resumed his reign and was hurling back into one vast turmoil the conflicting elements of nature. Fancy to yourself, oh reader! the awful combat sung by old Hesiod of Jupiter and the Titans—fancy to yourself the long rebellowing artillery of heaven, streaming at the heads of the gigantic sons of earth.—In short, fancy to yourself all that has ever been said or sung of tempest, storm and hurricane—and you will save me the trouble of describing it.

Whether I fled from the fury of the storm or remained boldly at my post, as our gallant trainband captains who march their soldiers through the rain without flinching, are points which I leave to the conjecture of the reader. It is possible he may be a little perplexed also to know the reason why I introduced this most tremendous and unheard of tempest to disturb the serenity of my work. On this latter point I will gratuitously instruct his ignorance. The panorama view of the battery was given merely to gratify the reader with a correct description of that celebrated place and the parts adjacent—secondly, the storm was played off, partly to give a little bustle and life to this tranquil part of my work and to keep my drowsy readers from falling asleep, and partly to serve as a preparation, or rather an overture, to the tempestuous times that are about to assail the pacific province of Nieuw-Nederlandts and that overhang the slumbrous administration of the renowned Wouter Van Twiller. It is thus the experienced playwright puts all the fiddles, the French horns, the kettle drums and trumpets of his orchestra in requisition to usher in one of those horrible and brimstone uproars called melodrames—and it is thus he discharges his thunder, his lightning, his rosin and saltpeter preparatory to the raising of a ghost or the murdering of a hero.—We will now proceed with our history.

Whatever may be advanced by philosophers to the contrary, I am of opinion that, as to nations, the old maxim that "honesty is the best policy" is a sheer and ruinous mistake. It might have answered well enough in the honest times when it was made; but in these degenerate days if a nation pretends to rely merely upon the justice of its dealings it will fare something like an honest man among thieves, who, unless he have something more than his honesty to depend upon, stands but a poor chance of profiting by his company. Such at least was the case with the guileless government of the New Netherlands, which, like a worthy unsuspicious old burgher, quietly settled itself down into the city of New Amsterdam as into a snug elbowchair—and fell into a comfortable nap—while in the meantime its cunning neighbors stepped in and picked its pockets. Thus may we ascribe the commencement of all the woes of this great province, and its magnificent metropolis, to the tranquil security, or to speak more accurately, to the unfortunate honesty of its government. But as I dislike to begin an important part of my history towards the end of a chapter; and as my readers, like myself, must doubtless be exceedingly fatigued with the long walk we have taken and the tempest we have sustained—I hold it meet we shut up the book, smoke a pipe, and having thus refreshed our spirits, take a fair start in the next chapter.

CHAPTER VI

Faithfully describing the ingenious people of Connecticut and thereabouts—Showing, moreover, the true meaning of liberty of conscience, and a curious device among these sturdy barbarians to keep up a harmony of intercourse and promote population.

That my readers may the more fully comprehend the extent of the calamity at this very moment impending over the honest, unsuspecting province of Nieuw Nederlandts and its dubious governor, it is necessary that I should give some account of a horde of strange barbarians bordering upon the eastern frontier.

Now so it came to pass that many years previous to the time of which we are treating, the sage cabinet of England had adopted a certain national creed, a kind of public walk of faith, or rather a religious turnpike, in which every loyal subject was directed to travel to Zion—taking care to pay the *toll gatherers* by the way.

Albeit a certain shrewd race of men, being very much given to indulge their own opinions on all manner of subjects (a propensity exceedingly obnoxious to your free governments of Europe), did most presumptuously dare to think for themselves in matters of religion, exercising what they considered a natural and unextinguishable right—the liberty of conscience.

As, however, they possessed that ingenuous habit of mind which always thinks aloud, which in a manner rides cock-a-hoop on the tongue and is for ever galloping into other people's ears, it naturally followed that their liberty of conscience likewise implied *liberty of speech,* which being freely indulged, soon put the country in a hubbub and aroused the pious indignation of the vigilant fathers of the church.

The usual methods were adopted to reclaim them that in those days were considered so efficacious in bringing back stray sheep to the fold; that is to say, they were coaxed, they were admonished, they were menaced, they were buffeted—line upon line, precept upon precept, lash upon lash, here a little and there a great deal, were exhausted without mercy, and without success; until at length the worthy pastors of the church, wearied out by their unparalleled stubbornness, were driven in the excess of their tender mercy to adopt the scripture text, and literally "heaped live embers on their heads."

Nothing, however, could subdue that invincible spirit of independence which has ever distinguished this singular race of people, so that rather than submit to such horrible tyranny they one and all embarked for the wilderness of America where they might enjoy unmolested the inestimable luxury of talking. No sooner did they land on this loquacious soil than, as if they had caught the disease from the climate, they all lifted up their voices at once and for the space of one whole year did keep up such a joyful clamor that we are told they frightened every bird and beast out of the neighborhood, and so completely dumbfounded certain fish which abound on their coast that they have been called *dumbfish* ever since.

From this simple circumstance, unimportant as it may seem, did first originate that renowned privilege so loudly boasted of throughout this country—which is so eloquently exercised in newspapers, pamphlets, ward meetings, pothouse committees and congressional deliberations—which establishes the right of talking without ideas and without information—of misrepresenting public affairs—of decrying public measures—of aspersing great characters and destroying little ones; in short, that grand palladium of our country, the *liberty of speech.*

The simple aborigines of the land for a while contemplated these strange folk in utter astonishment, but discovering that they wielded harmless though noisy weapons and were a lively, ingenious, good-humored race of men, they became very friendly and sociable, and gave them the name of *Yanokies,* which in the Mais-Tchusaeg (or Massachusett) language signifies *silent men* —a waggish appellation since shortened into the familiar epithet of Yankees, which they retain unto the present day.

True it is, and my fidelity as an historian will not allow me to pass it over in silence, that the zeal of these good people to maintain their rights and privileges unimpaired did for a while betray them into errors which it is easier to pardon than defend. Having served a regular apprenticeship in the school of persecution, it behoved them to show that they had become proficients in the art. They accordingly employed their leisure hours in banishing, scourging, or hanging divers heretical papists, quakers, and anabaptists for daring to abuse the *liberty of conscience;* which they now clearly proved to imply nothing more than that every man should think as he pleased in matters of religion—*provided* he thought *right;* for otherwise it would be giving a latitude to damnable heresies. Now as they (the majority) were perfectly convinced that *they alone* thought right, it consequently followed that whoever thought different from them thought wrong—and whoever thought wrong, and obstinately persisted in not being convinced and converted, was a flagrant violator of the inestimable liberty of conscience, and a corrupt and infectious member of the body politic, and deserved to be lopped off and cast into the fire.

Now I'll warrant there are hosts of my readers ready at once to lift up their hands and eyes with that virtuous indignation with which we always contemplate the faults and errors of our neighbors, and to exclaim at these well-meaning but mistaken people for inflicting on others the injuries they had suffered themselves—for indulging the preposterous idea of convincing the mind by tormenting the body, and establishing the doctrine of charity and forbearance by intolerant persecution.—But, in simple truth, what are we doing at this very day, and in this very enlightened nation, but acting upon the very same principle in our political controversies. Have we not within but a few years released ourselves from the shackles of a government which cruelly denied us the privilege of governing ourselves and using in full latitude that invaluable member, the tongue? and are we not at this very moment striving our best to tyrannize over the opinions, tie up the tongues, or ruin the fortunes of one another? What are our great political societies but mere political inquisitions—our pothouse committees but little tribunals of denunciation—our newspapers but mere whipping-posts and pillories where unfortunate individuals are pelted with rotten eggs—and our council of appointment but a grand *auto da fé* where culprits are annually sacrificed for their political heresies?

Where then is the difference in principle between our measures and those you are so ready to condemn among the people

I am treating of? There is none; the difference is merely circumstantial.—Thus we *denounce* instead of banishing—we *libel* instead of scourging—we *turn out of office* instead of hanging—and where they burnt an offender in *propria persona,* we either tar and feather or *burn him in effigy*—this political persecution being, somehow or other, the grand palladium of our liberties and an incontrovertible proof that this is *a free country!*

But notwithstanding the fervent zeal with which this holy war was prosecuted against the whole race of unbelievers, we do not find that the population of this new colony was in any wise hindered thereby; on the contrary, they multiplied to a degree which would be incredible to any man unacquainted with the marvelous fecundity of this growing country.

This amazing increase may indeed be partly ascribed to a singular custom prevalent among them, and which was probably borrowed from the ancient republic of Sparta; where we are told the young ladies, either from being great romps and hoydens, or else, like many modern heroines, very fond of meddling with matters that did not appertain to their sex, used frequently to engage with the men in wrestling and other athletic exercises of the gymnasium. The custom to which I allude was vulgarly known by the name of *bundling*—a superstitious rite observed by the young people of both sexes, with which they usually terminated their festivities, and which was kept up with religious strictness by the more bigoted and vulgar part of the community. This ceremony was likewise, in those primitive times, considered as an indispensable preliminary to matrimony; their courtships commencing where ours usually finish—by which means they acquired that intimate acquaintance with each other's good qualities before marriage which has been pronounced by philosophers the sure basis of a happy union. Thus early did this cunning and ingenious people display a shrewdness at making a bargain which has ever since distinguished them—and a strict adherence to the good old vulgar maxim about "buying a pig in a poke."

To this sagacious custom, therefore, do I chiefly attribute the unparalleled increase of the yanokie or yankee tribe; for it is a certain fact, well authenticated by court records and parish registers, that wherever the practice of bundling prevailed there was an amazing number of sturdy brats annually born unto the state without the licence of the law or the benefit of clergy; and it is truly astonishing that the learned Malthus in his treatise on population has entirely overlooked this singular fact. Neither did the irregularity of their birth operate in the least to their disparagement. On the contrary, they grew up a long-sided, raw-boned, hardy race of whoreson whalers, woodcutters, fishermen and pedlers and strapping corn-fed wenches; who by their united efforts tended marvelously towards populating those notable tracts of country called Nantucket, Piscataway, and Cape Cod.

CHAPTER VII

How these singular barbarians turned out to be notorious squatters. How they built air castles, and attempted to initiate the Nederlanders in the mystery of bundling.

In the last chapter I have given a faithful and unprejudiced account of the origin of that singular race of people inhabiting the country eastward of the Nieuw Nederlandts; but I have yet to mention certain peculiar habits which rendered them exceedingly obnoxious to our ever-honored Dutch ancestors.

The most prominent of these was a certain rambling propensity with which, like the sons of Ishmael, they seem to have been gifted by heaven, and which continually goads them on to shift their residence from place to place, so that a Yankee farmer is in a constant state of migration; *tarrying* occasionally here and there, clearing lands for other people to enjoy, building houses for others to inhabit, and in a manner may be considered the wandering Arab of America.

His first thought, on coming to the years of manhood, is to *settle* himself in the world—which means nothing more nor less than to begin his rambles. To this end he takes unto himself for a wife some dashing country heiress; that is to say, a buxom rosy-cheeked wench, passing rich in red ribbons, glass beads, and mock tortoise-shell combs, with a white gown and morocco shoes

for Sunday, and deeply skilled in the mystery of making apple
sweetmeats, long sauce, and pumpkin pie.

Having thus provided himself, like a true pedler, with a heavy
knapsack wherewith to regale his shoulders through the journey
of life, he literally sets out on the peregrination. His whole family, household furniture, and farming utensils are hoisted into
a covered cart; his own and his wife's wardrobe packed up in a
firkin—which done, he shoulders his axe, takes staff in hand,
whistles "Yankee Doodle," and trudges off to the woods, as con-
fident of the protection of providence, and relying as cheerfully
upon his own resources, as did ever a patriarch of yore when he
journeyed into a strange country of the Gentiles. Having buried
himself in the wilderness, he builds himself a log hut, clears
away a corn field and potato patch, and, providence smiling
upon his labors, is soon surrounded by a snug farm and some
half a score of flaxen-headed urchins, who, by their size, seem
to have sprung all at once out of the earth, like a crop of toad-
stools.

But it is not the nature of this most indefatigable of specu-
lators to rest contented with any state of sublunary enjoyment
—*improvement* is his darling passion, and having thus improved
his lands, the next care is to provide a mansion worthy the residence of a landholder. A huge palace of pine boards immediately
springs up in the midst of the wilderness, large enough for a
parish church, and furnished with windows of all dimensions,
but so rickety and flimsy withal that every blast gives it a fit of
the ague.

By the time the outside of this mighty air castle is completed,
either the funds or the zeal of our adventurer are exhausted, so
that he barely manages to half finish one room within, where
the whole family burrow together—while the rest of the house
is devoted to the curing of pumpkins or storing of carrots and
potatoes, and is decorated with fanciful festoons of wilted peaches
and dried apples. The outside, remaining unpainted, grows
venerably black with time; the family wardrobe is laid under
contribution for old hats, petticoats, and breeches to stuff into
the broken windows, while the four winds of heaven keep up
a whistling and howling about this aerial palace and play as
many unruly gambols as they did of yore in the cave of old
Eolus.

The humble log hut, which whilome nestled this *improving* family snugly within its narrow but comfortable walls, stands hard by in ignominious contrast, degraded into a cowhouse or pig sty; and the whole scene reminds one forcibly of a fable, which I am surprised has never been recorded, of an aspiring snail who quit his humble habitation, which he filled with great respectability, to crawl into the empty shell of a lobster—where he would no doubt have resided with great style and splendor, the envy and hate of all the painstaking snails of his neighborhood, had he not accidentally perished with cold in one corner of his stupendous mansion.

Being thus completely settled and, to use his own words, "to rights," one would imagine that he would begin to enjoy the comforts of his situation, to read newspapers, talk politics, neglect his own business and attend to the affairs of the nation, like a useful and patriotic citizen; but now it is that his wayward disposition begins again to operate. He soon grows tired of a spot where there is no longer any room for improvement—sells his farm, air castle, petticoat windows and all, reloads his cart, shoulders his axe, puts himself at the head of his family, and wanders away in search of new lands—again to fell trees, again to clear corn fields, again to build a shingle palace, and again to sell off and wander.

Such were the people of Connecticut, who bordered upon the eastern frontier of Nieuw Nederlandts, and my readers may easily imagine what obnoxious neighbors this light-hearted but restless tribe must have been to our tranquil progenitors. If they cannot, I would ask them if they have ever known one of our regular well-organized Dutch families whom it hath pleased Heaven to afflict with the neighborhood of a French boarding house? The honest old burgher cannot take his afternoon's pipe on the bench before his door but he is persecuted with the scraping of fiddles, the chattering of women, and the squalling of children—he cannot sleep at night for the horrible melodies of some amateur who chooses to serenade the moon and display his terrible proficiency in *execution* by playing demi-semiquavers in alt on the clarionet, the hautboy, or some other soft-toned instrument—nor can he leave the street door open but his house is defiled by the unsavory visits of a troop of pug dogs who even sometimes carry their loathsome ravages into the sanctum sanctorum, the parlor!

If my readers have ever witnessed the sufferings of such a family so situated, they may form some idea how our worthy ancestors were distressed by their mercurial neighbors of Connecticut.

Gangs of these marauders, we are told, penetrated into the New Netherland settlements and threw whole villages into consternation by their unparalleled volubility and their intolerable inquisitiveness—two evil habits hitherto unknown in those parts, or only known to be abhorred; for our ancestors were noted as being men of truly Spartan taciturnity, and who neither knew nor cared aught about anybody's concerns but their own. Many enormities were committed on the highways, where several unoffending burghers were brought to a stand and tortured with questions and guesses, which outrages occasioned as much vexation and heartburning as does the modern right of search on the high seas.

Great jealousy did they likewise stir up by their intermeddling and successes among the divine sex; for being a race of brisk, likely, pleasant-tongued varlets, they soon seduced the light affections of the simple damsels from their ponderous Dutch gallants. Among other hideous customs, they attempted to introduce among them that of *bundling,* which the Dutch lasses of the Nederlandts, with that eager passion for novelty and foreign fashions natural to their sex, seemed very well inclined to follow, but that their mothers, being more experienced in the world and better acquainted with men and things, strenuously discountenanced all such outlandish innovations.

But what chiefly operated to embroil our ancestors with these strange folk was an unwarrantable liberty which they occasionally took of entering in hordes into the territories of the New Netherlands and settling themselves down, without leave or licence, to *improve* the land in the manner I have before noticed. This unceremonious mode of taking possession of *new land* was technically termed *squatting,* and hence is derived the appellation of *squatters;* a name odious in the ears of all great landholders, and which is given to those enterprising worthies who seize upon land first and take their chance to make good their title to it afterwards.

All these grievances, and many others which were constantly accumulating, tended to form that dark and portentous cloud which, as I observed in a former chapter, was slowly gathering over the tranquil province of New Netherlands. The pacific cabinet of Van Twiller, however, as will be perceived in the sequel, bore them all with a magnanimity that redounds to their immortal credit—becoming by passive endurance inured to this increasing mass of wrongs; like the sage old woman of Ephesus who, by dint of carrying about a calf from the time it was born, continued to carry it without difficulty when it had grown to be an ox.

CHAPTER VIII

How the Fort Goed Hoop was fearfully beleaguered—how the renowned Wouter fell into a profound doubt, and how he finally evaporated.

By this time my readers must fully perceive what an arduous task I have undertaken—collecting and collating with painful minuteness the chronicles of past times, whose events almost defy the powers of research—exploring a little kind of Herculaneum of history which had lain nearly for ages buried under the rubbish of years and almost totally forgotten—raking up the limbs and fragments of disjointed facts and endeavouring to put them scrupulously together, so as to restore them to their original form and connection—now lugging forth the character of an almost forgotten hero, like a mutilated statue —now deciphering a half-defaced inscription, and now lighting upon a mouldering manuscript which, after painful study, scarce repays the trouble of perusal.

In such case how much has the reader to depend upon the honor and probity of his author, lest, like a cunning antiquarian, he either impose upon him some spurious fabrication of his own for a precious relic from antiquity—or else dress up the dismembered fragment with such false trappings that it is scarcely possible to distinguish the truth from the fiction with which it is enveloped. This is a grievance which I have more than once had to lament in the course of my wearisome researches among the works of my fellow historians, who have strangely disguised and distorted the facts respecting this country; and particularly respecting the great province of New Netherlands, as will be perceived by any who will take the trouble to compare their romantic effusions, tricked out in the meretricious gauds of fable, with this authentic history.

I have had more vexations of the kind to encounter in those parts of my history which treat of the transactions on the eastern border than in any other, in consequence of the troops of historians who have infested those quarters and have shown the honest people of Nieuw Nederlandts no mercy in their works. Among the rest, Mr. Benjamin Trumbull arrogantly declares that "the Dutch were always mere intruders."—Now to this I shall make no other reply than to proceed in the steady narration of my history, which will contain not only proofs that the Dutch had clear title and possession in the fair valleys of the Connecticut, and that they were wrongfully dispossessed thereof—but likewise that they have been scandalously maltreated ever since by the misrepresentations of the crafty historians of New England. And in this I shall be guided by a spirit of truth and impartiality and a regard to immortal fame—for I would not wittingly dishonor my work by a single falsehood, misrepresentation or prejudice, though it should gain our forefathers the whole country of New England.

It was at an early period of the province, and previous to the arrival of the renowned Wouter, that the cabinet of Nieuw Nederlandts purchased the lands about the Connecticut and established for their superintendence and protection a fortified

post on the banks of the river, which was called Fort Goed
Hoop and was situated hard by the present fair city of Hartford. The command of this important post, together with the
rank, title, and appointment of commissary, were given in
charge to the gallant Jacobus Van Curlet, or, as some historians
will have it, Van Curlis—a most doughty soldier of that stomachful class of which we have such numbers on parade days—
who are famous for eating all they kill. He was of a very soldierlike appearance, and would have been an exceeding tall
man had his legs been in proportion to his body; but the latter
being long, and the former uncommonly short, it gave him
the uncouth appearance of a tall man's body mounted upon a
little man's legs. He made up for this turnspit construction
of body by throwing his legs to such an extent when he
marched that you would have sworn he had on the identical
seven league boots of the far-famed Jack the giant killer; and
so astonishingly high did he tread on any great military occasion that his soldiers were ofttimes alarmed lest he should
trample himself under foot.

But notwithstanding the erection of this fort and the appointment of this ugly little man of war as a commander, the intrepid
Yankees continued those daring interlopings which I have
hinted at in my last chapter; and taking advantage of the character which the cabinet of Wouter Van Twiller soon acquired
for profound and phlegmatic tranquillity—did audaciously invade the territories of the Nieuw Nederlandts and *squat* themselves down within the very jurisdiction of Fort Goed Hoop.

On beholding this outrage, the long-bodied Van Curlet proceeded as became a prompt and valiant officer. He immediately
protested against these unwarrantable encroachments, in Low
Dutch by way of inspiring more terror, and forthwith despatched a copy of the protest to the governor at New Amsterdam, together with a long and bitter account of the aggressions
of the enemy. This done, he ordered his men one and all to be
of good cheer—shut the gate of the fort, smoked three pipes,
went to bed, and awaited the result with a resolute and intrepid
tranquillity that greatly animated his adherents and no doubt

struck sore dismay and affright into the hearts of the enemy.

Now it came to pass that about this time the renowned Wouter Van Twiller, full of years and honors and council dinners, had reached that period of life and faculty which, according to the great Gulliver, entitles a man to admission into the ancient order of Struldbruggs. He employed his time in smoking his Turkish pipe amid an assemblage of sages equally enlightened and nearly as venerable as himself, and who for their silence, their gravity, their wisdom, and their cautious averseness to coming to any conclusion in business are only to be equalled by certain profound corporations which I have known in my time. Upon reading the protest of the gallant Jacobus Van Curlet, therefore, his excellency fell straightway into one of the deepest doubts that ever he was known to encounter; his capacious head gradually drooped on his chest,* he closed his eyes and inclined his ear to one side, as if listening with great attention to the discussion that was going on in his belly, which all who knew him declared to be the huge courthouse or council chamber of his thoughts; forming to his head what the House of Representatives do to the Senate. An inarticulate sound, very much resembling a snore, occasionally escaped him—but the nature of this internal cogitation was never known, as he never opened his lips on the subject to man, woman, or child. In the meantime, the protest of Van Curlet laid quietly on the table, where it served to light the pipes of the venerable sages assembled in council; and in the great smoke which they raised, the gallant Jacobus, his protest, and his mighty Fort Goed Hoop were soon as completely beclouded and forgotten as is a question of emergency swallowed up in the speeches and resolutions of a modern session of Congress.

There are certain emergencies when your profound legislators and sage deliberative councils are mightily in the way of a nation; and when an ounce of hairbrained decision is worth a

---

* Perplexed with vast affairs of state and town,
  His great head being overset, hangs down.
  Teleclides, in Pericles

pound of sage doubt and cautious discussion. Such at least
was the case at present; for while the renowned Wouter Van
Twiller was daily battling with his doubts, and his resolution
growing weaker and weaker in the contest, the enemy pushed
further and further into his territories and assumed a most
formidable appearance in the neighborhood of Fort Goed
Hoop. Here they founded the mighty town of *Pyquag*, or, as
it has since been called, *Weathersfield*, a place which, if we
may credit the assertions of that worthy historian, John Josselyn, gent. "hath been infamous by reason of the witches
therein."—And so daring did these men of Pyquag become that
they extended those plantations of onions, for which their town
is illustrious, under the very noses of the garrison of Fort Goed
Hoop—insomuch that the honest Dutchmen could not look
toward that quarter without tears in their eyes.

This crying injustice was regarded with proper indignation
by the gallant Jacobus Van Curlet. He absolutely trembled
with the amazing violence of his choler and the exacerbations
of his valor; which seemed to be the more turbulent in their
workings from the length of the body in which they were
agitated. He forthwith proceeded to strengthen his redoubts,
heighten his breastworks, deepen his fosse, and fortify his position with a double row of abbatis; after which valiant precautions, he with unexampled intrepidity despatched a fresh
courier with tremendous accounts of his perilous situation.
Never did the modern hero, who immortalized himself at the
second Sabine war, show greater valor in the art of letter writing or distinguish himself more gloriously upon paper than
the heroic Van Curlet.

The courier chosen to bear these alarming despatches was
a fat, oily little man, as being least liable to be worn out or
to lose leather on the journey; and to insure his speed, he was
mounted on the fleetest wagon horse in the garrison, remarkable for his length of limb, largeness of bone, and hardness of
trot; and so tall that the little messenger was obliged to climb
on his back by means of his tail and crupper. Such extraordinary speed did he make that he arrived at Fort Amsterdam

in little less than a month, though the distance was full two hundred pipes, or about 120 miles.

The extraordinary appearance of this portentous stranger would have thrown the whole town of New Amsterdam into a quandary had the good people troubled themselves about anything more than their domestic affairs. With an appearance of great hurry and business, and smoking a short traveling pipe, he proceeded on a long swing trot through the muddy lanes of the metropolis, demolishing whole batches of dirt pies which the little Dutch children were making in the road; and for which kind of pastry the children of this city have ever been famous.—On arriving at the governor's house, he climbed down from his steed in great trepidation; roused the gray-headed doorkeeper, old Skaats, who, like his lineal descendant and faithful representative, the venerable crier of our court, was nodding at his post—rattled at the door of the council chamber, and startled the members as they were dozing over a plan for establishing a public market.

At that very moment a gentle grunt, or rather a deep-drawn snore, was heard from the chair of the governor; a whiff of smoke was at the same instant observed to escape from his lips, and a light cloud to ascend from the bowl of his pipe. The council of course supposed him engaged in deep sleep for the good of the community, and according to custom in all such cases established, every man bawled out "silence!" in order to maintain tranquillity; when, of a sudden, the door flew open and the little courier straddled into the apartment, cased to the middle in a pair of Hessian boots which he had got into for the sake of expedition. In his right hand he held forth the ominous despatches, and with his left he grasped firmly the waistband of his galligaskins, which had unfortunately given way in the exertion of descending from his horse. He stumped resolutely up to the governor, and with more hurry than perspicuity delivered his message. But fortunately his ill tidings came too late to ruffle the tranquillity of this most tranquil of rulers. His venerable excellency had just breathed and smoked his last—his lungs and his pipe having been exhausted together, and his peaceful soul having escaped in the last whiff that curled from his tobacco pipe.—In a word, the renowned Walter the Doubter, who had so often slumbered with his contemporaries, now slept with his fathers, and Wilhelmus Kieft governed in his stead.

BOOK IV
Containing the chronicles
of the reign of
William the Testy.

CHAPTER I

Showing the nature of history in general; containing furthermore the universal acquirements of William the Testy, and how a man may learn so much as to render himself good for nothing.

When the lofty Thucydides is about to enter upon his description of the plague that desolated Athens, one of his modern commentators* assures the reader that the history "is now going to be exceeding solemn, serious, and pathetic"; and hints, with that air of chuckling gratulation with which a good dame draws forth a choice morsel from a cupboard to regale a favorite, that this plague will give his history a most agreeable variety.

In like manner did my heart leap within me when I came to the dolorous dilemma of Fort Good Hope, which I at once perceived to be the forerunner of a series of great events and entertaining disasters. Such are the true subjects for the historic pen. For what is history, in fact, but a kind of Newgate Calendar, a register of the crimes and miseries that man has inflicted on his fellow man? It is a huge libel on human nature, to which we industriously add page after page, volume after volume, as if we were building up a monument to the honor rather than the infamy of our species. If we turn over the pages of these chronicles that man has written of himself, what are the characters dignified by the appellation of great and held up to the admiration of posterity?—Tyrants, robbers, conquerors, renowned only for the magnitude of their misdeeds and the

* Smith's Thucyd. Vol. I.

stupendous wrongs and miseries they have inflicted on mankind—warriors who have hired themselves to the trade of
blood, not from motives of virtuous patriotism or to protect
the injured and defenceless, but merely to gain the vaunted
glory of being adroit and successful in massacring their fellow
beings! What are the great events that constitute a glorious
era?—The fall of empires—the desolation of happy countries—
splendid cities smoking in their ruins—the proudest works of
art tumbled in the dust—the shrieks and groans of whole nations ascending unto heaven!

It is thus the historians may be said to thrive on the miseries
of mankind; they are like the birds of prey that hover over
the field of battle to fatten on the mighty dead. It was observed by a great projector of inland lock navigation that
rivers, lakes and oceans were only formed to feed canals. In like
manner I am tempted to believe that plots, conspiracies, wars,
victories and massacres are ordained by providence only as food
for the historian.

It is a source of great delight to the philosopher in studying
the wonderful economy of nature to trace the mutual dependencies of things, how they are created reciprocally for each
other, and how the most noxious and apparently unnecessary
animal has its uses. Thus those swarms of flies which are so
often execrated as useless vermin are created for the sustenance
of spiders—and spiders, on the other hand, are evidently made
to devour flies. So those heroes who have been such pests
in the world were bounteously provided as themes for the poet
and the historian, while the poet and historian were destined
to record the achievements of heroes!

These and many similar reflections naturally arose in my
mind as I took up my pen to commence the reign of William
Kieft: for now the stream of our history, which hitherto has
rolled in a tranquil current, is about to depart forever from
its peaceful haunts and brawl through many a turbulent and
rugged scene. Like some sleek ox, which having fed and fattened in a rich cloverfield, lies sunk in luxurious repose and
will bear repeated taunts and blows before it heaves its unwieldy limbs and clumsily arouses from its slumbers; so the
province of the Nieuw Nederlandts, having long thrived and
grown corpulent under the prosperous reign of the Doubter,
was reluctantly awakened to a melancholy conviction that by

patient sufferance its grievances had become so numerous and aggravating that it was preferable to repel than endure them. The reader will now witness the manner in which a peaceful community advances towards a state of war; which it is too apt to approach as a horse does a drum, with much prancing and parade but with little progress—and too often with the wrong end foremost.

WILHELMUS KIEFT, who in 1634 ascended the *Gubernatorial* chair (to borrow a favorite, though clumsy, appellation of modern phraseologists), was in form, feature and character the very reverse of Wouter Van Twiller, his renowned predecessor. He was of very respectable descent, his father being Inspector of Windmills in the ancient town of Saardam; and our hero, we are told, made very curious investigations into the nature and operations of those machines when a boy, which is one reason why he afterwards came to be so ingenious a governor. His name according to the most ingenious etymologists was a corruption of *Kyver,* that is to say, a *wrangler* or *scolder,* and expressed the hereditary disposition of his family; which for nearly two centuries had kept the windy town of Saardam in hot water and produced more tartars and brimstones than any ten families in the place—and so truly did Wilhelmus Kieft inherit this family endowment that he had scarcely been a year in the discharge of his government before he was universally known by the appellation of WILLIAM THE TESTY.

He was a brisk, waspish, little old gentleman who had dried and withered away, partly through the natural process of years and partly from being parched and burnt up by his fiery soul; which blazed like a vehement rush-light in his bosom, constantly inciting him to most valorous broils, altercations and misadventures. I have heard it observed by a profound and philosophical judge of human nature that if a woman waxes fat as she grows old, the tenure of her life is very precarious, but if haply she withers, she lives for ever—such likewise was the case with William the Testy who grew tougher in proportion as he dried. He was some such a little Dutchman as we may now and then see stumping briskly about the streets of our city in a broad-skirted coat with buttons nearly as large as the shield of Ajax, an old-fashioned cocked hat stuck on the back of his head, and a cane as high as his chin. His visage was broad but his features sharp; his nose turned up with a most petulant curl; his cheeks, like the regions of Terra del Fuego, were scorched into a dusky red—doubtless in consequence of the neighborhood of two fierce little gray eyes through which his torrid soul beamed as fervently as a tropical sun blazing through a pair of burning-glasses. The corners of his mouth were curiously modelled into a kind of fretwork, not a little resembling the wrinkled proboscis of an irritable pug dog—in a word, he was one of the most positive, restless, ugly, little men that ever put himself in a passion about nothing.

Such were the personal endowments of William the Testy, but it was the sterling riches of his mind that raised him to dignity and power. In his youth he had passed with great credit through a celebrated academy at the Hague noted for producing finished scholars with a despatch unequalled except by certain of our American colleges, which seem to manufacture bachelors of arts by some patent machine. Here he skirmished very smartly on the frontiers of several of the sciences, and made so gallant an inroad in the dead languages as to bring off captive a host of Greek nouns and Latin verbs, together with divers pithy saws and apophthegms, all which he constantly paraded in conversation and writing with as much vainglory as would a triumphant general of yore display the spoils of the countries he had ravaged. He had, moreover, puzzled himself considerably with logic, in which he had advanced so far as to attain a very familiar acquaintance, by name at least, with the whole family of syllogisms and dilemmas; but what he chiefly valued himself on was his knowledge of metaphysics, in which, having once upon a time ventured too deeply, he came well nigh being smothered in a slough of unintelligible learning—a fearful peril, from the effects of which he never perfectly recovered. In plain words, like many other profound intermeddlers in this abstruse bewildering science, he so confused his brain with abstract speculations which he could not comprehend and artificial distinctions which he could not realize that he could never think clearly on any subject, however simple, through the whole course of his life afterwards. This, I must confess, was in some measure a misfortune, for he never engaged in argument, of which he was exceeding fond, but what between logical deductions and metaphysical jargon he soon involved himself and his subject in a fog of contradictions and perplexities, and then would get into a mighty passion with his adversary for not being convinced gratis.

It is in knowledge as in swimming; he who ostentatiously sports and flounders on the surface makes more noise and splashing, and attracts more attention, than the industrious pearl diver who plunges in search of treasures to the bottom. The "universal acquirements" of William Kieft were the subject of great marvel and admiration among his countrymen— he figured about at the Hague with as much vainglory as does a profound Bonze at Pekin who has mastered half the letters of the Chinese alphabet; and, in a word, was unanimously pronounced an *universal genius!*—I have known many universal geniuses in my time, though, to speak my mind freely, I never knew one who for the ordinary purposes of life was worth his weight in straw—but for the purposes of government, a little sound judgment and plain common sense is worth all the sparkling genius that ever wrote poetry or invented theories.

Strange as it may sound, therefore, the *universal acquirements* of the illustrious Wilhelmus were very much in his way, and had he been a less learned man, it is possible he would have been a much greater governor. He was exceedingly fond of trying philosophical and political experiments; and having stuffed his head full of scraps and remnants of ancient republics and oligarchies and aristocracies and monarchies and the laws of Solon and Lycurgus and Charondas and the imaginary commonwealth of Plato and the Pandects of Justinian and a thousand other fragments of venerable antiquity, he was forever bent upon introducing some one or other of them into use; so that between one contradictory measure and another, he entangled the government of the little province of Nieuw Nederlandts in more knots during his administration than half a dozen successors could have untied.

No sooner had this bustling little man been blown by a whiff of fortune into the seat of government than he called together his council and delivered a very animated speech on the affairs of the province. As everybody knows what a glorious opportunity a governor, a president, or even an emperor has of drubbing his enemies in his speeches, messages and bulletins, where he has the talk all on his own side, they may be sure the high-mettled William Kieft did not suffer so favorable an occasion to escape him of evincing that gallantry of tongue common to

all able legislators. Before he commenced, it is recorded that
he took out his pocket handkerchief and gave a very sonorous
blast of the nose, according to the usual custom of great orators.
This in general, I believe, is intended as a signal trumpet to
call the attention of the auditors, but with William the Testy
it boasted a more classic cause, for he had read of the singular
expedient of that famous demagogue Caius Gracchus, who,
when he harangued the Roman populace, modulated his tones
by an oratorical flute or pitch pipe.

This preparatory symphony being performed, he commenced
by expressing a humble sense of his own want of talents—his
utter unworthiness of the honor conferred upon him, and his
humiliating incapacity to discharge the important duties of
his new station—in short, he expressed so contemptible an opinion of himself that many simple country members present, ignorant that these were mere words of course, always used on
such occasions, were very uneasy and even felt wroth that he
should accept an office for which he was consciously so inadequate.

He then proceeded in a manner highly classic and profoundly
erudite, and nothing at all to the purpose, being nothing
more than a pompous account of all the governments of ancient
Greece, and the wars of Rome and Carthage, together with the
rise and fall of sundry outlandish empires about which the
assembly knew no more than their great-grandchildren yet un-
born. Thus having, after the manner of your learned orators,
convinced the audience that he was a man of many words and
great erudition, he at length came to the less important part
of his speech, the situation of the province—and here he soon
worked himself into a fearful rage against the Yankees, whom
he compared to the Gauls who desolated Rome and the Goths
and Vandals who overran the fairest plains of Europe—nor
did he forget to mention, in terms of adequate opprobrium,
the insolence with which they had encroached upon the territories of New Netherlands and the unparalleled audacity with
which they had commenced the town of New Plymouth and
planted the onion patches of Weathersfield under the very walls
of Fort Goed Hoop.

Having thus artfully wrought up his tale of terror to a climax,
he assumed a self-satisfied look and declared, with a nod of
knowing import, that he had taken measures to put a final

stop to these encroachments—that he had been obliged to have recourse to a dreadful engine of warfare, lately invented, awful in its effects, but authorized by direful necessity. In a word, he was resolved to conquer the Yankees—by proclamation!

For this purpose he had prepared a tremendous instrument of the kind, ordering, commanding, and enjoining the intruders aforesaid, forthwith to remove, depart, and withdraw from the districts, regions, and territories aforesaid, under pain of suffering all the penalties, forfeitures, and punishments in such cases made and provided, &c. This proclamation, he assured them, would at once exterminate the enemy from the face of the country, and he pledged his valor as a governor that within two months after it was published not one stone should remain on another in any of the towns which they had built.

The council remained for some time silent after he had finished; whether struck dumb with admiration at the brilliancy of his project or put to sleep by the length of his harangue, the history of the times doth not mention. Suffice it to say, they at length gave a universal grunt of acquiescence—the proclamation was immediately despatched with due ceremony, having the great seal of the province, which was about the size of a buckwheat pancake, attached to it by a broad red ribbon. Governor Kieft having thus vented his indignation, felt greatly relieved—adjourned the council *sine die*—put on his cocked hat and corduroy smallclothes, and mounting a tall rawboned charger, trotted out to his country seat, which was situated in a sweet, sequestered swamp, now called Dutch Street, but more commonly known by the name of Dog's Misery.

Here, like the good Numa, he reposed from the toils of legislation, taking lessons in government, not from the nymph Egeria but from the honored wife of his bosom, who was one of that peculiar kind of females sent upon earth a little after the flood as a punishment for the sins of mankind, and commonly known by the appellation of *knowing women*. In fact, my duty as an historian obliges me to make known a circumstance which was a great secret at the time, and consequently was not a subject of scandal at more than half the tea tables in New Amsterdam, but which, like many other great secrets, has leaked out in the lapse of years—and this was, that the great Wilhelmus the Testy, though one of the most potent little men that ever breathed, yet submitted at home to a species of government neither laid down in Aristotle nor Plato; in short, it partook of the nature of a pure unmixed tyranny and is familiarly denominated *petticoat government.*—An absolute sway, which, though exceedingly common in these modern days, was very rare among the ancients, if we may judge from the rout made about the domestic economy of honest Socrates; which is the only ancient case on record.

The great Kieft, however, warded off all the sneers and sarcasms of his particular friends, who are ever ready to joke with a man on sore points of the kind, by alleging that it was a government of his own election, to which he submitted through choice; adding at the same time a profound maxim which he had found in an ancient author, that "he who would aspire to *govern* should first learn to *obey.*"

CHAPTER II

In which are recorded the sage projects of a ruler of universal genius. The art of fighting by proclamation,—and how that the valiant Jacobus Van Curlet came to be foully dishonored at Fort Goed Hoop.

Never was a more comprehensive, a more expeditious, or, what is still better, a more economical measure devised than this of defeating the Yankees by proclamation—an expedient likewise so humane, so gentle and pacific, there were ten chances to one in favor of its succeeding;—but then there was one chance to ten that it would not succeed;—as the ill-natured fates would have it, that single chance carried the day! The proclamation was perfect in all its parts, well constructed, well written, well sealed, and well published—all that was wanting to insure its effect was that the Yankees shoud stand in awe of it; but, provoking to relate, they treated it with the most absolute contempt, applied it to an unseemly purpose, and thus did the first warlike proclamation come to a shameful end—a fate which

I am credibly informed has befallen but too many of its successors.

It was a long time before Wilhelmus Kieft could be persuaded by the united efforts of all his counsellors that his war measures had failed in producing any effect.—On the contrary, he flew in a passion whenever any one dared to question its efficacy; and swore that though it was slow in operating, yet when once it began to work it would soon purge the land of these rapacious intruders. Time, however, that test of all experiments both in philosophy and politics, at length convinced the great Kieft that his proclamation was abortive; and that notwithstanding he had waited nearly four years, in a state of constant irritation, yet he was still further off than ever from the object of his wishes. His implacable adversaries in the east became more and more troublesome in their encroachments, and founded the thriving colony of Hartford close upon the skirts of Fort Goed Hoop. They moreover commenced the fair settlement of New Haven (alias the Red Hills) within the domains of their High Mightinesses—while the onion patches of Pyquag were a continual eyesore to the garrison of Van Curlet. Upon beholding, therefore, the inefficacy of his measure, the sage Kieft, like many a worthy practitioner of physic, laid the blame not to the medicine but to the quantity administered, and resolutely resolved to double the dose.

In the year 1638, therefore, that being the fourth year of his reign, he fulminated against them a second proclamation, of heavier metal than the former; written in thundering long sentences, not one word of which was under five syllables. This, in fact, was a kind of non-intercourse bill, forbidding and prohibiting all commerce and connection between any and every of the said Yankee intruders and the said fortified post of Fort Goed Hoop, and ordering, commanding and advising all his trusty, loyal and well-beloved subjects to furnish them with no supplies of gin, gingerbread or sauerkraut; to buy none of their pacing horses, measly pork, apple brandy, Yankee rum, cider water, apple sweetmeats, Weathersfield onions or wooden bowls, but to starve and exterminate them from the face of the land.

Another pause of a twelvemonth ensued, during which the last proclamation received the same attention and experienced the same fate as the first—at the end of which term, the gallant Jacobus Van Curlet despatched his annual messenger with his customary budget of complaints and entreaties. Whether the regular interval of a year intervening between the arrival of Van Curlet's couriers was occasioned by the systematic regularity of his movements or by the immense distance at which he was stationed from the seat of government is a matter of uncertainty. Some have ascribed it to the slowness of his messengers, who, as I have before noticed, were chosen from the shortest and fattest of his garrison, as least likely to be worn out on the road; and who, being pursy, short-winded little men, generally travelled fifteen miles a day and then laid by a whole week to rest. All these, however, are matters of conjecture; and I rather think it may be ascribed to the immemorial maxim of this worthy country—and which has ever influenced all its public transactions—not to do things in a hurry.

The gallant Jacobus Van Curlet in his despatches respectfully represented that several years had now elapsed since his first application to his late excellency, the renowned Wouter Van Twiller; during which interval his garrison had been reduced nearly one-eighth by the death of two of his most valiant and corpulent soldiers, who had accidentally overeaten themselves on some fat salmon caught in the Varsche river. He further stated that the enemy persisted in their inroads, taking no notice of the fort or its inhabitants; but squatting themselves down, and forming settlements all around it; so that in a little while he should find himself enclosed and blockaded by the enemy and totally at their mercy.

But among the most atrocious of his grievances I find the following still on record, which may serve to show the bloody-minded outrages of these savage intruders. "In the meane time, they of Hartford have not onely usurped and taken in the lands of Connecticott, although unrighteously and against the lawes of nations, but have hindered our nation in sowing theire owne purchased broken up lands, but have also sowed them with corne in the night, which the Netherlanders had broken up and intended to sowe: and have beaten the servants of the high and mighty the honored companie, which were labouring upon theire master's lands, from theire lands, with sticks and plow staves in hostile manner laming, and amongst the rest, struck Ever Duckings* a hole in his head,

---

* This name is no doubt misspelt. In some old Dutch MSS. of the time, we find the name of Evert Duyckingh, who is unquestionably the unfortunate hero above alluded to.

with a stick, soe that the blood ran downe very strongly downe upon his body."

But what is still more atrocious—

"Those of Hartford sold a hogg, that belonged to the honored companie, under pretence that it had eaten of theire grounde grass, when they had not any foot of inheritance. They proffered the hogg for 5*s.* if the commissioners would have given 5*s.* for damage; which the commissioners denied, because noe man's owne hogg (as men use to say) can trespass upon his owne master's grounde."*

The receipt of this melancholy intelligence incensed the whole community—there was something in it that spoke to the dull comprehension and touched the obtuse feelings even of the puissant vulgar, who generally require a kick in the rear to awaken their slumbering dignity. I have known my profound fellow citizens bear without murmur a thousand essential infringements of their rights, merely because they were not immediately obvious to their senses—but the moment the unlucky Pearce was shot upon our coasts, the whole body politic was in a ferment—so the enlightened Nederlanders, though they had treated the encroachments of their eastern neighbors with but little regard and left their quill-valiant governor to bear the whole brunt of war with his single pen—yet now every individual felt his head broken in the broken head of Duckings —and the unhappy fate of their fellow citizen the hog being impressed, carried and sold into captivity awakened a grunt of sympathy from every bosom.

The governor and council, goaded by the clamors of the multitude, now sat themselves earnestly to deliberate upon what was to be done. Proclamations had at length fallen into temporary disrepute; some were for sending the Yankees a tribute, as we make peace offerings to the petty Barbary powers, or as the Indians sacrifice to the devil. Others were for buying them out, but this was opposed as it would be acknowledging their title to the land they had seized. A variety of measures were, as usual in such cases, proposed, discussed and abandoned, and the council had at last to adopt the means which, being the most common and obvious, had been knowingly overlooked— for your amazing acute politicians are for ever looking through

---

* Haz. Col. Stat. Papers.

telescopes which only enable them to see such objects as are far off and unattainable; but which incapacitate them to see such things as are in their reach and obvious to all simple folks who are content to look with the naked eyes heaven has given them. The profound council, as I have said, in their pursuit after Jack-o'-lanterns accidentally stumbled on the very measure they were in need of; which was to raise a body of troops, and despatch them to the relief and reinforcement of the garrison. This measure was carried into such prompt operation that in less than twelve months the whole expedition, consisting of a sergeant and twelve men, was ready to march; and was reviewed for that purpose in the public square now known by the name of the Bowling Green. Just at this juncture the whole community was thrown into consternation by the sudden arrival of the gallant Jacobus Van Curlet, who came straggling into town at the head of his crew of tatterdemalions, and bringing the melancholy tidings of his own defeat and the capture of the redoubtable post of Fort Goed Hoop by the ferocious Yankees.

The fate of this important fortress is an impressive warning to all military commanders. It was neither carried by storm nor famine; no practicable breach was effected by cannon or mines; no magazines were blown up by red-hot shot; nor were the barracks demolished or the garrison destroyed by the bursting of bombshells. In fact, the place was taken by a stratagem no less singular than effectual; and one that can never fail of success whenever an opportunity occurs of putting it in practice. Happy am I to add, for the credit of our illustrious ancestors, that it was a stratagem which, though it impeached the vigilance, yet left the bravery of the intrepid Van Curlet and his garrison perfectly free from reproach.

It appears that the crafty Yankees, having heard of the regular habits of the garrison, watched a favorable opportunity and silently introduced themselves into the fort about the middle of a sultry day when its vigilant defenders having gorged themselves with a hearty dinner and smoked out their pipes, were one and all snoring most obstreperously at their posts, little dreaming of so disastrous an occurrence. The enemy most inhumanly seized Jacobus Van Curlet and his sturdy myrmidons by the nape of the neck, gallanted them to the gate of the fort, and dismissed them severally, with a kick on the crupper, as Charles the twelfth dismissed the heavy-bottomed Russians after the battle of Narva—only taking care to give two kicks to Van Curlet, as a signal mark of distinction.

A strong garrison was immediately established in the fort, consisting of twenty long-sided, hard-fisted Yankees, with Weathersfield onions stuck in their hats by way of cockades and feathers—long rusty fowling pieces for muskets—hasty pudding, dumbfish, pork and molasses for stores; and a huge pumpkin was hoisted on the end of a pole as a standard—liberty caps not having yet come into fashion.

CHAPTER III

Containing the fearful wrath of William the Testy, and the great dolor of the New Amsterdammers, because of the affair of Fort Goed Hoop.—And moreover how William the Testy did strongly fortify the city.— Together with the exploits of Stoffel Brinkerhoff.

Language cannot express the prodigious fury into which the testy Wilhelmus Kieft was thrown by this provoking intelligence. For three good hours the rage of the little man was too great for words, or rather the words were too great for him; and he was nearly choked by some dozen huge, misshapen, nine-cornered Dutch oaths that crowded all at once into his gullet. Having blazed off the first broadside, he kept up a constant firing for three whole days—anathematizing the Yankees, man, woman and child, body and soul, for a set of dieven, schobbejaken, deugenieten, twist-zoekeren, loozen-schalken, blaes-kaken, kakken-bedden, and a thousand other names of which, unfortunately for posterity, history does not make particular mention. Finally, he swore that he would have nothing more to do with such a squatting, bundling, guessing, questioning, swapping, pumpkin-eating, molasses-daubing, shingle-splitting, cider-watering, horse-jockeying, notion-peddling crew—that they might stay at Fort Goed Hoop and rot before he would dirty his hands by attempting to drive them away; in proof of which he ordered the new raised troops to be marched forthwith into winter quarters, although it was not as yet quite midsummer. Governor Kieft faithfully kept his word, and his adversaries as faithfully kept their post; and thus the glorious river Connecticut, and all the gay valleys through which it rolls, together with the salmon, shad and other fish within its waters, fell into the hands of the victorious Yankees, by whom they are held at this very day.

Great despondency seized upon the city of New Amsterdam in consequence of these melancholy events. The name of Yankee became as terrible among our good ancestors as was that of Gaul among the ancient Romans; and all the sage old women of the province used it as a bugbear wherewith to frighten their unruly children into obedience.

The eyes of all the province were now turned upon their governor to know what he would do for the protection of the common weal in these days of darkness and peril. Great apprehensions prevailed among the reflecting part of the community, especially the old women, that these terrible warriors of Connecticut, not content with the conquest of Fort Goed Hoop, would incontinently march on to New Amsterdam and take it by storm—and as these old ladies through means of the governor's spouse, who, as has been already hinted, was "the better horse," had obtained considerable influence in public affairs, keeping the province under a kind of petticoat government, it was determined that measures should be taken for the effective fortification of the city.

Now it happened that at this time there sojourned in New Amsterdam one Anthony Van Corlear,* a jolly fat Dutch trumpeter of a pleasant burly visage, famous for his long wind and his huge whiskers, and who, as the story goes, could twang so potently upon his instrument as to produce an effect upon all within hearing, as though ten thousand bagpipes were singing

---

* David Pietrez *De Veries* in his "Reyze naer Nieuw-Nederlandt onder het year 1640" makes mention of one *Corlear,* a trumpeter in Fort Amsterdam who gave name to Corlear's Hook and who was doubtless this same champion described by Mr. Knickerbocker. EDITOR.

most lustily i' the nose. Him did the illustrious Kieft pick out as the man of all the world most fitted to be the champion of New Amsterdam and to garrison its fort; making little doubt but that his instrument would be as effectual and offensive in war as was that of the Paladin Astolpho or the more classic horn of Alecto. It would have done one's heart good to have seen the governor snapping his fingers and fidgetting with delight while his sturdy trumpeter strutted up and down the ramparts fearlessly twanging his trumpet in the face of the whole world, like a thrice valorous editor daringly insulting all the principalities and powers—on the other side of the Atlantic.

Nor was he content with thus strongly garrisoning the fort, but he likewise added exceedingly to its strength by furnishing it with a formidable battery of quaker guns—rearing a stupendous flagstaff in the center which overtopped the whole city—and moreover by building a great windmill on one of the bastions.* This last, to be sure, was somewhat of a novelty in the art of fortification, but as I have already observed, William Kieft was notorious for innovations and experiments, and traditions do affirm that he was much given to mechanical inventions—constructing patent smokejacks—carts that went before the horses—and especially erecting windmills, for which machines he had acquired a singular predilection in his native town of Saardam.

All these scientific vagaries of the little governor were cried up with ecstacy by his adherents as proof of his universal genius —but there were not wanting ill-natured grumblers who railed at him as employing his mind in frivolous pursuits and devoting that time to smokejacks and windmills which should have been occupied in the more important concerns of the province. Nay, they even went so far as to hint once or twice that his head was turned by his experiments, and that he really thought to manage his government as he did his mills—by mere wind!—such is the illiberality and slander to which enlightened rulers are ever subject.

Notwithstanding all the measures, therefore, of William the Testy to place the city in a posture of defence, the inhabitants continued in great alarm and despondency. But fortune, who seems always careful, in the very nick of time, to throw a bone

---

* De Vries mentions that this windmill stood on the south-east bastion, and it is likewise to be seen, together with the flagstaff, in Justus Danker's View of New Amsterdam prefixed to this history.

for hope to gnaw upon, that the starveling elf may be kept alive, did about this time crown the arms of the province with success in another quarter, and thus cheered the drooping hearts of the forlorn Nederlanders; otherwise there is no knowing to what lengths they might have gone in the excess of their sorrowing—"for grief," says the profound historian of the seven champions of Christendom, "is companion with despair, and despair a procurer of infamous death!"

Among the numerous inroads of the mosstroopers of Connecticut, which for some time past had occasioned such great tribulation, I should particularly have mentioned a settlement made on the eastern part of Long Island at a place which, from the peculiar excellence of its shellfish, was called Oyster Bay. This was attacking the province in a most sensible part and occasioned great agitation at New Amsterdam.

It is an incontrovertible fact, well known to skillful physiologists, that the high road to the affections is through the throat; and this may be accounted for on the same principles which I have already quoted in my strictures on fat aldermen. Nor is the fact unknown to the world at large; and hence do we observe that the surest way to gain the hearts of the million is to feed them well—and that a man is never so disposed to flatter, to please and serve another, as when he is feeding at his expense; which is one reason why your rich men, who give frequent dinners, have such abundance of sincere and faithful friends. It is on this principle that our knowing leaders of parties secure the affections of their partisans by rewarding them bountifully with loaves and fishes; and entrap the suffrages of the greasy mob by treating them with bull-feasts and roasted oxen. I have known many a man in this same city acquire considerable importance in society and usurp a large share of the good will of his enlightened fellow citizens when the only thing that could be said in his eulogium was that "he gave a good dinner and kept excellent wine."

Since, then, the heart and the stomach are so nearly allied, it follows conclusively that what affects the one must sympathetically affect the other. Now it is an equally incontrovertible fact that of all offerings to the stomach there is none more grateful than the testaceous marine animal known commonly by the vulgar name of Oyster. And in such great reverence has it ever been held by my gormandizing fellow citizens that temples have been dedicated to it, time out of mind, in every street, lane and alley throughout this well-fed city. It is not to be expected, therefore, that the seizing of Oyster Bay, a place abounding with their favorite delicacy, would be tolerated by the inhabitants of New Amsterdam. An attack upon their honor they might have pardoned; even the massacre of a few citizens might have been passed over in silence; but an outrage that affected the larders of the great city of New Amsterdam and threatened the stomachs of its corpulent burgomasters was too serious to pass unrevenged. The whole council was unanimous in opinion that the intruders should be immediately driven by force of arms from Oyster Bay and its vicinity, and a detachment was accordingly despatched for the purpose under the command of one Stoffel Brinkerhoff, or Brinkerhoofd, (*i.e.* Stoffel the headbreaker), so called because he was a man of mighty deeds, famous throughout the whole extent of Nieuw Nederlandts for his skill at quarterstaff; and for size, he would have been a match for Colbrand, the Danish champion slain by Guy of Warwick.

Stoffel Brinkerhoff was a man of few words but prompt actions —one of your straight-going officers who march directly forward and do their orders without making any parade about it. He used no extraordinary speed in his movements, but trudged steadily on, through Nineveh and Babylon and Jericho and Patchog and the mighty town of Quag and various other renowned cities of yore which, by some unaccountable witchcraft of the Yankees, have been strangely transplanted to Long Island, until he arrived in the neighborhood of Oyster Bay.

Here was he encountered by a tumultuous host of valiant warriors headed by Preserved Fish and Habbakuk Nutter and Return Strong and Zerubbabel Fisk and Jonathan Doolittle and Determined Cock!—at the sound of whose names the courageous Stoffel verily believed that the whole parliament of Praise God Barebones had been let loose to discomfit him. Finding, however, that this formidable body was composed merely of the "select men" of the settlement, armed with no other weapon but their tongues, and that they had issued forth with no other intent than to meet him on the field of argument—he succeeded in putting them to the rout with little difficulty, and completely broke up their settlement. Without waiting to write an account of his victory on the spot, and thus letting the enemy slip through his fingers while he was securing his own laurels, as a more experienced general would have done, the brave Stoffel thought of nothing but completing his enterprise and utterly driving the Yankees from the island. This hardy enterprise he performed in much the same manner as he had been accustomed to drive his oxen; for as the Yankees fled before him, he pulled up his breeches and trudged steadily after them, and would infallibly have driven them into the sea, had they not begged for quarter and agreed to pay tribute.

The news of this achievement was a seasonable restorative to the spirits of the citizens of New Amsterdam. To gratify them still more, the governor resolved to astonish them with one of those gorgeous spectacles known in the days of classic antiquity, a full account of which had been flogged into his memory when a schoolboy at the Hague. A grand triumph, therefore, was decreed to Stoffel Brinkerhoff, who made his triumphant entrance into town riding on a Naraganset pacer; five pumpkins which, like Roman eagles, had served the enemy for standards were carried before him—fifty cartloads of oysters, five hundred bushels of Weathersfield onions, a hundred quintals of codfish, two hogsheads of molasses, and various other treasures were exhibited as the spoils and tribute of the Yankees; while three notorious counterfeiters of Manhattan notes* were led captive to grace the hero's triumph. The procession was enlivened by martial music from the trumpet of Antony Van Corlear the champion, accompanied by a select band of boys and negroes performing on the national instruments of rattle bones and clam shells. The citizens devoured the spoils in sheer gladness of heart—every man did honor to the conqueror by getting devoutly drunk on New England rum—and the learned Wilhelmus Kieft calling to mind, in a momentary fit of enthusiasm and generosity, that it was customary among the ancients to honor their victorious generals with public statues, passed a gracious decree by which every tavern keeper was permitted to paint the head of the intrepid Stoffel on his sign!

---

* This is one of those trivial anachronisms that now and then occur in the course of this otherwise authentic history. How could Manhattan notes be counterfeited, when as yet Banks were unknown in this country—and our simple progenitors had not even dreamt of those inexhaustible mines of *paper opulence?—Print. Dev.*

Philosophical reflections on the folly of being happy in times of prosperity.—Sundry troubles on the southern frontiers.—How William the Testy had well nigh ruined the province through a cabalistic word.—As also the secret expedition of Jan Jansen Alpendam, and his astonishing reward.

If we could but get a peep at the tally of dame Fortune, where, like a notable landlady, she regularly chalks up the debtor and creditor accounts of mankind, we should find that upon the whole good and evil are pretty nearly balanced in this world; and that though we may for a long while revel in the very lap of prosperity, the time will at length come when we must ruefully pay off the reckoning. Fortune, in fact, is a pestilent shrew, and withal a most inexorable creditor; for though she may indulge her favorites in long credits and overwhelm them with her favors, yet sooner or later she brings up her arrears with the rigor of an experienced publican and washes out her scores with their tears. "Since," says good old Boetius in his Consolations of Philosophy, "Since no man can retain her at his pleasure, and since her flight is so deeply lamented, what are her favors but sure prognostications of approaching trouble and calamity?"

There is nothing that more moves my contempt at the stupidity and want of reflection of my fellow men than to behold them rejoicing, and indulging in security and self-confidence, in times of prosperity. To a wise man who is blessed with the light of reason, those are the very moments of anxiety and apprehension; well knowing that according to the system of things happiness is at best but transient—and that the higher he is elevated by the capricious breath of fortune, the lower must be his proportionate depression. Whereas he who is overwhelmed by calamity has the less chance of encountering fresh disasters,

183

as a man at the bottom of a ladder runs very little risk of breaking his neck by tumbling to the top.

This is the very essence of true wisdom, which consists in
knowing when we ought to be miserable, and was discovered
much about the same time with that invaluable secret that
"every thing is vanity and vexation of spirit"; in consequence
of which maxim your wise men have ever been the unhap-
piest of the human race; esteeming it as an infallible mark of
genius to be distressed without reason—since any man may be
miserable in time of misfortune, but it is the philosopher alone
who can discover cause for grief in the very hour of prosperity.

According to the principle I have just advanced, we find that
the colony of New Netherlands, which under the reign of the
renowned Van Twiller had flourished in such alarming and
fatal serenity, is now paying for its former welfare and discharging the enormous debt of comfort which it contracted. Foes
harass it from different quarters; the city of New Amsterdam,
while yet in its infancy, is kept in constant alarm; and its valiant
commander, William the Testy, answers the vulgar but ex-
pressive idea of "a man in a peck of troubles."

While busily engaged repelling his bitter enemies the Yankees
on one side, we find him suddenly molested in another quarter
and by other assailants. A vagrant colony of Swedes under the
conduct of Peter Minnewits, and professing allegiance to that
redoubtable virago, Christina, queen of Sweden, had settled
themselves and erected a fort on south (or Delaware) river—
within the boundaries claimed by the government of the New
Netherlands. History is mute as to the particulars of their first
landing and their real pretensions to the soil, and this is the
more to be lamented as this same colony of Swedes will hereafter be found most materially to affect not only the interests
of the Nederlanders but of the world at large!

In whatever manner, therefore, this vagabond colony of
Swedes first took possession of the country, it is certain that in
1638 they established a fort, and Minnewits, according to the
offhand usage of his contemporaries, declared himself governor
of all the adjacent country under the name of the province of
NEW SWEDEN. No sooner did this reach the ears of the choleric
Wilhelmus than like a true spirited chieftain he immediately
broke into a violent rage, and calling together his council,
belabored the Swedes most lustily in the longest speech that had

ever been heard in the colony since the memorable dispute of Ten Breeches and Tough Breeches. Having thus given vent to the first ebullitions of his indignation, he had resort to his favorite measure of proclamation and despatched one, piping hot, in the first year of his reign, informing Peter Minnewits that the whole territory bordering on the south river had, time out of mind, been in possession of the Dutch colonists, having been "beset with forts and sealed with their blood."

The latter sanguinary sentence would convey an idea of direful war and bloodshed were we not relieved by the information that it merely related to a fray in which some half a dozen Dutchmen had been killed by the Indians in their benevolent attempts to establish a colony and promote civilization. By this it will be seen that William Kieft, though a very small man, delighted in big expressions, and was much given to a praiseworthy figure in rhetoric, generally cultivated by your little great men, called hyperbole: a figure which has been found of infinite service among many of his class, and which has helped to swell the grandeur of many a mighty, self-important, but windy chief magistrate. Nor can I resist in this place from observing how much my beloved country is indebted to this same figure of hyperbole for supporting certain of her greatest characters—statesmen, orators, civilians and divines; who, by dint of big words, inflated periods and windy doctrines are kept afloat on the surface of society, as ignorant swimmers are buoyed up by blown bladders.

The proclamation against Minnewits concluded by ordering the self-dubbed governor and his gang of Swedish adventurers immediately to leave the country under penalty of the high displeasure and inevitable vengeance of the puissant government of the Nieuw Nederlandts. This "strong measure," however, does not seem to have had a whit more effect than its predecessors which had been thundered against the Yankees—the Swedes resolutely held on to the territory they had taken possession of —whereupon matters for the present remained *in statu quo*.

That Wilhelmus Kieft should put up with this insolent obstinacy in the Swedes would appear incompatible with his valorous temperament; but we find that about this time the little man had his hands full, and what with one annoyance and another was kept continually on the bounce.

There is a certain description of active legislators who by

shrewd management contrive always to have a hundred irons on the anvil, every one of which must be immediately attended to; who consequently are ever full of temporary shifts and expedients, patching up the public welfare and cobbling the national affairs, so as to make nine holes where they mend one —stopping chinks and flaws with whatever comes first to hand, like the Yankees I have mentioned stuffing old clothes in broken windows. Of this class of statesmen was William the Testy—and had he only been blessed with powers equal to his zeal, or his zeal been disciplined by a little discretion, there is very little doubt but he would have made the greatest governor of his size on record—the renowned governor of the island of Barataria alone excepted.

The great defect of Wilhelmus Kieft's policy was that though no man could be more ready to stand forth in an hour of emergency, yet he was so intent upon guarding the national pocket that he suffered the enemy to break its head—in other words, whatever precaution for public safety he adopted, he was so intent upon rendering it cheap that he invariably rendered it ineffectual. All this was a remote consequence of his profound education at the Hague—where, having acquired a smattering of knowledge, he was ever after a great conner of indexes, continually dipping into books without ever studying to the bottom of any subject; so that he had the scum of all kinds of authors fermenting in his pericranium. In some of these title page researches he unluckily stumbled over a grand political *cabalistic word* which with his customary facility he immediately incorporated into his great scheme of government, to the irretrievable injury and delusion of the honest province of Nieuw Nederlandts and the eternal misleading of all experimental rulers.

In vain have I pored over the theurgia of the Chaldeans, the cabala of the Jews, the necromancy of the Arabians, the magic of the Persians, the hocus pocus of the English, the witchcraft of the Yankees, or the pow-wowing of the Indians to discover where the little man first laid eyes on this terrible word. Neither the Sephir Jetzirah, that famous cabalistic volume ascribed to the patriarch Abraham; nor the pages of the Zohar, containing the mysteries of the cabala recorded by the learned Rabbi Simeon Jochaides, yield any light to my inquiries. Nor am I in the least benefited by my painful researches in the Shem-hamphorah of Benjamin, the wandering Jew, though it enabled Davidus

Elm to make a ten days' journey in twenty-four hours. Neither can I perceive the slightest affinity in the Tetragrammaton, or sacred name of four letters, the profoundest word of the Hebrew cabala; a mystery sublime, ineffable and incommunicable—and the letters of which, Jod-He-Vau-He, having been stolen by the pagans, constituted their great name Jao, or Jove. In short, in all my cabalistic, theurgic, necromantic, magical and astrological researches, from the Tetractys of Pythagoras to the recondite works of Breslaw and Mother Bunch, I have not discovered the least vestige of an origin of this word, nor have I discovered any word of sufficient potency to counteract it.

Not to keep my reader in any suspense, the word which had so wonderfully arrested the attention of William the Testy, and which in German characters had a particularly black and ominous aspect, on being fairly translated into the English is no other than ECONOMY—a talismanic term which by constant use and frequent mention has ceased to be formidable in our eyes, but which has as terrible potency as any in the arcana of necromancy.

When pronounced in a national assembly it has an immediate effect in closing the hearts, beclouding the intellects, drawing the purse strings and buttoning the breeches pockets of all philosophic legislators. Nor are its effects on the eyes less wonderful. It produces a contraction of the retina, an obscurity of the crystalline lens, a viscidity of the vitreous and an inspissation of the aqueous humors, an induration of the tunica sclerotica and a convexity of the cornea; insomuch that the organ of vision loses its strength and perspicuity and the unfortunate patient becomes *myopes,* or in plain English, purblind; perceiving only the amount of immediate expense without being able to look further and regard it in connection with the ultimate object to be effected.—"So that," to quote the words of the eloquent Burke, "a briar at his nose is of greater magnitude than an oak at five hundred yards distance." Such are its instantaneous operations, and the results are still more astonishing. By its magic influence seventy-fours shrink into frigates, frigates into sloops, and sloops into gunboats. As the defenseless ships of Eneas, at the command of the protecting Venus, changed into sea nymphs and protected themselves by diving, so the mighty navy of America, by the cabalistic word of *economy,* dwindles into small craft and shelters itself in a millpond!

This all-potent word, which served as his touchstone in politics, at once explains the whole system of proclamations, protests, empty threats, windmills, trumpeters and paper war carried on by Wilhelmus the Testy—and we may trace its operations in an armament which he fitted out in 1642 in a moment of great wrath, consisting of two sloops and thirty men under the command of Mynher Jan Jansen Alpendam as admiral of the fleet and commander in chief of the forces. This formidable expedition, which can only be paralleled by some of the daring cruises of our infant navy about the bay and up the sound, was intended to drive the Marylanders from the Schuylkill, of which they had recently taken possession—and which was claimed as part of the province of New Nederlandts—for it appears that at this time our infant colony was in that enviable state so much coveted by ambitious nations, that is to say, the government had a vast extent of territory, part of which it enjoyed and the greater part of which it had continually to quarrel about.

Admiral Jan Jansen Alpendam was a man of great mettle and prowess, and no way dismayed at the character of the enemy, who were represented as a gigantic, gunpowder race of men who lived on hoe cakes and bacon, drank mint juleps and apple toddy, and were exceedingly expert at boxing, biting, gouging, tar and feathering, and a variety of other athletic accomplishments which they had borrowed from their cousins german and prototypes the Virginians, to whom they have ever borne considerable resemblance.—Notwithstanding all these alarming representations, the admiral entered the Schuylkill most undauntedly with his fleet, and arrived without disaster or opposition at the place of destination.

Here he attacked the enemy in a vigorous speech in Low Dutch which the wary Kieft had previously put in his pocket; wherein he courteously commenced by calling them a pack of lazy, louting, dram-drinking, cock-fighting, horse-racing, slave-driving, tavern-haunting, sabbath-breaking, mulatto-breeding upstarts—and concluded by ordering them to evacuate the country immediately—to which they most laconically replied in plain English, "they'd see him d——d first."

Now this was a reply for which neither Jan Jansen Alpendam nor Wilhelmus Kieft had made any calculation—and finding himself totally unprepared to answer so terrible a rebuff with suitable hostility, he concluded that his wisest course was to return home and report progress. He accordingly sailed back to New Amsterdam, where he was received with great honors and considered as a pattern for all commanders, having achieved a most hazardous enterprise at a trifling expense of treasure and without losing a single man to the state!—He was unanimously called the deliverer of his country (an appellation liberally bestowed on all great men); his two sloops, having done their duty, were laid up (or dry docked) in a cove now called the Albany Basin, where they quietly rotted in the mud; and to immortalize his name they erected by subscription a magnificent shingle monument on the top of Flatten Barrack* Hill, which lasted three whole years, when it fell to pieces and was burnt for firewood.

CHAPTER V

How William the Testy enriched the province by a multitude of laws, and came to be the patron of lawyers and bumbailiffs. And how the people became exceedingly enlightened and unhappy under his instructions.

Among the many wrecks and fragments of exalted wisdom which have floated down the stream of time from venerable antiquity, and have been carefully picked up by those humble but industrious wights who ply along the shores of literature, we find the following sage ordinance of Charondas, the Locrian legislator.—Anxious to preserve the ancient laws of the state from the additions and improvements of profound "country members" or officious candidates for popularity, he ordained, that whoever proposed a new law should do it with a halter about his neck; so that in case his proposition was rejected, they just hung him up—and there the matter ended.

This salutary institution had such an effect that for more than two hundred years there was only one trifling alteration in the criminal code—and the whole race of lawyers starved to

* A corruption of Varleth's Bergh—or Varleth's Hill, so called from one Varleth who lived upon that hill in the early days of the settlement.

death for want of employment. The consequence of this was
that the Locrians, being unprotected by an overwhelming load
of excellent laws and undefended by a standing army of pettifoggers and sheriff's officers, lived very lovingly together and
were such a happy people that they scarce make any figure
throughout the whole Grecian history—for it is well known
that none but your unlucky, quarrelsome, rantipole nations
make any noise in the world.

Well would it have been for William the Testy had he haply
in the course of his "universal acquirements" stumbled upon
this precaution of the good Charondas. On the contrary, he
conceived that the true policy of a legislator was to multiply
laws and thus secure the property, the persons and the morals
of the people by surrounding them in a manner with men traps
and spring guns and besetting even the sweet sequestered walks
of private life with quickset hedges, so that a man could scarcely
turn without the risk of encountering some of these pestiferous
protectors. Thus was he continually coining petty laws for every
petty offence that occurred, until in time they became too
numerous to be remembered, and remained, like those of certain modern legislators, mere dead letters—revived occasionally
for the purpose of individual oppression or to entrap ignorant
offenders.

Petty courts consequently began to appear, where the law was
administered with nearly as much wisdom and impartiality as
in those august tribunals, the aldermen's and justices' courts of
the present day. The plaintiff was generally favored, as being
a customer and bringing business to the shop; the offences of
the rich were discreetly winked at—for fear of hurting the feelings of their friends;—but it could never be laid to the charge
of the vigilant burgomasters that they suffered vice to skulk
unpunished under the disgraceful rags of poverty.

About this time may we date the first introduction of capital
punishments—a goodly gallows being erected on the waterside,
about where Whitehall stairs are at present, a little to the east
of the battery. Hard by also was erected another gibbet of a
very strange, uncouth and unmatchable description, but on
which the ingenious William Kieft valued himself not a little,
being a punishment entirely of his own invention.*

* Both the gibbets may be seen in the sketch of Justus Danker prefixed
to the work.

It was for loftiness of altitude not a whit inferior to that of Haman, so renowned in Bible history; but the marvel of the contrivance was that the culprit, instead of being suspended by the neck according to venerable custom, was hoisted by the waistband and was kept for an hour together dangling and sprawling between heaven and earth—to the infinite entertainment and doubtless great edification of the multitude of respectable citizens who usually attend upon exhibitions of the kind.

It is incredible how the little governor chuckled at beholding caitiff vagrants and sturdy beggars thus swinging by the crupper and cutting antic gambols in the air. He had a thousand pleasantries and mirthful conceits to utter upon these occasions. He called them his dandle lions—his wild fowl—his high flyers—his spread eagles—his goshawks—his scarecrows—and finally his *gallows birds,* which ingenious appellation, though originally confined to worthies who had taken the air in this strange manner, has since grown to be a cant name given to all candidates for legal elevation. This punishment, moreover, if we may credit the assertions of certain grave etymologists, gave the first hint for a kind of harnessing or strapping by which our forefathers braced up their multifarious breeches, and which has of late years been revived and continues to be worn at the present day.

Such were the admirable improvements of William Kieft in criminal law—nor was his civil code less a matter of wonderment, and much does it grieve me that the limits of my work will not suffer me to expatiate on both with the prolixity they deserve. Let it suffice then to say that in a little while the blessings of innumerable laws became notoriously apparent. It was soon found necessary to have a certain class of men to expound and confound them——divers pettifoggers accordingly made their appearance, under whose protecting care the community was soon set together by the ears.

I would not here be thought to insinuate anything derogatory to the profession of the law or to its dignified members. Well am I aware that we have in this ancient city innumerable worthy gentlemen who have embraced that honorable order, not for the sordid love of filthy lucre nor the selfish cravings of renown, but through no other motives but a fervent zeal for the correct administration of justice, and a generous and disinterested devotion to the interests of their fellow citizens!—Sooner would I throw this trusty pen into the flames and cork up my ink bottle for ever than infringe even for a nail's breadth upon the dignity of this truly benevolent class of citizens—on the contrary, I allude solely to that crew of caitiff scouts who in these latter days of evil have become so numerous—who infest the skirts of the profession, as did the recreant Cornish knights the honorable order of chivalry—who, under its auspices, commit their depredations on society—who thrive by quibbles, quirks and chicanery, and like vermin swarm most where there is most corruption.

Nothing so soon awakens the malevolent passions as the facility of gratification. The courts of law would never be so constantly crowded with petty, vexatious and disgraceful suits, were it not for the herds of pettifogging lawyers that infest them. These tamper with the passions of the lower and more ignorant classes; who, as if poverty were not a sufficient misery in itself, are always ready to heighten it by the bitterness of litigation. They are in law what quacks are in medicine—exciting the malady for the purpose of profiting by the cure, and retarding the cure for the purpose of augmenting the fees. Where one destroys the constitution, the other impoverishes the purse; and it may likewise be observed that a patient who has once been under the hands of a quack is ever after dabbling in drugs and poisoning himself with infallible remedies; and an ignorant man who has once meddled with the law under the auspices of one of these empirics is for ever after embroiling himself with his neighbors and impoverishing himself with successful lawsuits.—My readers will excuse this digression into which I have been unwarily betrayed; but I could not avoid giving a cool, unprejudiced account of an abomination too prevalent in this excellent city, and with the effects of which I am unluckily acquainted to my cost; having been nearly ruined by a lawsuit which was unjustly decided against me—and my ruin having been completed by another which was decided in my favor.

It has been remarked by the observant writer of the Stuyvesant manuscript that under the administration of Wilhelmus Kieft the disposition of the inhabitants of New Amsterdam experienced an essential change, so that they became very meddlesome and factious. The constant exacerbations of temper into which the little governor was thrown by the maraudings on his

frontiers, and his unfortunate propensity to experiment and innovation, occasioned him to keep his council in a continual
worry—and the council being to the people at large what yeast
or leaven is to a batch, they threw the whole community into
a ferment—and the people at large being to the city what the
mind is to the body, the unhappy commotions they underwent
operated most disastrously upon New Amsterdam—insomuch
that in certain of their paroxysms of consternation and perplexity they begat several of the most crooked, distorted and abominable streets, lanes and alleys with which this metropolis
is disfigured.

But the worst of the matter was that just about this time the
mob, since called the sovereign people, like Balaam's ass began
to grow more enlightened than its rider and exhibited a strange
desire of governing itself. This was another effect of the "universal acquirements" of William the Testy. In some of his
pestilent researches among the rubbish of antiquity, he was
struck with admiration at the institution of public tables among
the Lacedæmonians, where they discussed topics of a general
and interesting nature—at the schools of the philosophers, where
they engaged in profound disputes upon politics and morals—
where graybeards were taught the rudiments of wisdom, and
youths learned to become little men before they were boys.
"There is nothing," said the ingenious Kieft, shutting up the
book, "There is nothing more essential to the well management
of a country than education among the people; the basis of a
good government should be laid in the public mind."—Now this
was true enough, but it was ever the wayward fate of William
the Testy that when he thought right he was sure to go to work
wrong. In the present instance he could scarcely eat or sleep
until he had set on foot brawling debating societies among the
simple citizens of New Amsterdam. This was the one thing
wanting to complete his confusion. The honest Dutch burghers,
though in truth but little given to argument or wordy altercation, yet by dint of meeting often together, fuddling themselves
with strong drink, beclouding their brains with tobacco smoke,
and listening to the harangues of some half a dozen oracles,
soon became exceedingly wise and, as is always the case where
the mob is politically enlightened, exceedingly discontented.
They found out, with wonderful quickness of discernment, the
fearful error in which they had indulged in fancying themselves

the happiest people in creation—and were fortunately convinced that, all circumstances to the contrary notwithstanding, they were a very unhappy, deluded and, consequently, ruined people!

In a short time the quidnuncs of New Amsterdam formed themselves into sage juntos of political croakers who daily met together to groan over political affairs and make themselves miserable; thronging to these unhappy assemblages with the same eagerness that zealots have in all ages abandoned the milder and more peaceful paths of religion to crowd to the howling convocations of fanaticism. We are naturally prone to discontent and avaricious after imaginary causes of lamentation —like lubberly monks, we belabor our own shoulders and seem to take a vast satisfaction in the music of our own groans. Nor is this said for the sake of paradox; daily experience shows the truth of these observations. It is next to a farce to offer consolation or to think of elevating the spirits of a man groaning under ideal calamities; but nothing is more easy than to render him wretched, though on the pinnacle of felicity; as it is an Herculean task to hoist a man to the top of a steeple, though the merest child can topple him off thence.

In the sage assemblages I have noticed, the philosophic reader will at once perceive the faint germs of those sapient convocatons called popular meetings, prevalent at our day. Thither resorted all those idlers and "squires of low degree" who, like rags, hang loose upon the back of society and are ready to be blown away by every wind of doctrine. Cobblers abandoned their stalls and hastened thither to give lessons on political economy—blacksmiths left their handicraft and suffered their own fires to go out while they blew the bellows and stirred up the fire of faction; and even tailors, though but the shreds and patches, the ninth parts of humanity, neglected their own measures to attend to the measures of government.—Nothing was wanting but half a dozen newspapers and patriotic editors to have completed this public illumination and to have thrown the whole province in an uproar!

I should not forget to mention that these popular meetings were always held at a noted tavern; for houses of that description have always been found the most congenial nurseries of politics; abounding with those genial streams which give strength and sustenance to faction.—We are told that the ancient Germans had an admirable mode of treating any question of importance; they first deliberated upon it when drunk, and afterwards reconsidered it when sober. The shrewder mobs of America, who dislike having two minds upon a subject, both determine and act upon it drunk; by which means a world of cold and tedious speculations is dispensed with—and as it is universally allowed that when a man is drunk he sees *double,* it follows most conclusively that he sees twice as well as his sober neighbors.

CHAPTER VI

Of the great pipe plot—and of the dolorous
perplexities into which William the Testy
was thrown, by reason of his having enlight-
ened the multitude.

Wilhelmus Kieft, as has already been made manifest, was a great legislator upon a small scale. He was of an active, or rather a busy mind; that is to say, his was one of those small but brisk minds that make up by bustle and constant motion for the want of great scope and power. He had, when quite a youngling, been impressed with the advice of Solomon, "go to the ant, thou sluggard; consider her ways and be wise," in conformity to which he had ever been of a restless, ant-like turn, worrying hither and thither, busying himself about little matters with an air of great importance and anxiety—laying up wisdom by the morsel, and often toiling and puffing at a grain of mustard seed under the full conviction that he was moving a mountain.

Thus we are told that once upon a time, in one of his fits of mental bustle which he termed deliberation, he framed an unlucky law to prohibit the universal practice of smoking. This he proved by mathematical demonstration to be not merely a heavy tax on the public pocket but an incredible consumer of time, a great encourager of idleness, and, of course, a deadly bane to the prosperity and morals of the people. Ill-fated Kieft!

had he lived in this enlightened and libel-loving age and attempted to subvert the inestimable liberty of the press, he could not have struck more closely on the sensibilities of the million.

The populace were in as violent a turmoil as the constitutional gravity of their deportment would permit—a mob of factious citizens had even the hardihood to assemble before the governor's house, where, setting themselves resolutely down like a besieging army before a fortress, they one and all fell to smoking with a determined perseverance that seemed as though it were their intention to smoke him into terms. The testy William issued out of his mansion like unto a wrathful spider and demanded to know the cause of this seditious assemblage and this lawless fumigation, to which these sturdy rioters made no other reply than to loll back phlegmatically in their seats and puff away with redoubled fury; whereby they raised such a murky cloud that the governor was fain to take refuge in the interior of his castle .

The governor immediately perceived the object of this unusual tumult, and that it would be impossible to suppress a practice which by long indulgence had become a second nature. And here I would observe, partly to explain why I have so often made mention of this practice in my history, that it was inseparably connected with all the affairs both public and private of our revered ancestors. The pipe, in fact, was never from the mouth of the true born Nederlander. It was his companion in solitude, the relaxation of his gayer hours, his counsellor, his consoler, his joy, his pride; in a word, he seemed to think and breathe through his pipe.

When William the Testy bethought himself of all these matters, which he certainly did, although a little too late, he came to a compromise with the besieging multitude. The result was that though he continued to permit the custom of smoking, yet did he abolish the fair long pipes which were used in the days of Wouter Van Twiller, denoting ease, tranquillity and sobriety of deportment; and in place thereof did introduce little, captious, short pipes, two inches in length; which, he observed, could be stuck in one corner of the mouth, or twisted in the hat band, and would not be in the way of business. By this the multitude seemed somewhat appeased and dispersed to their habitations. Thus ended this alarming insurrection which was long known by the name of the *pipe plot,* and which, it has been somewhat quaintly observed, did end, like most other plots, seditions and conspiracies, in mere smoke.

But mark, Oh reader! the deplorable consequences that did afterwards result. The smoke of these villainous little pipes, continually ascending in a cloud about the nose, penetrated into and befogged the cerebellum, dried up all the kindly moisture of the brain, and rendered the people that used them as vaporish and testy as their renowned little governor—nay, what is more, from a goodly, burly race of folk, they became, like our worthy Dutch farmers who smoke short pipes, a lantern-jawed, smoke-dried, leather-hided race of men.

Nor was this all, for from hence may we date the rise of parties in this province. Certain of the more wealthy and important burghers, adhering to the ancient fashion, formed a kind of aristocracy which went by the appellation of the *Long Pipes;* while the lower orders, submitting to the innovation, which they found to be more convenient in their handicraft employments and to leave them more liberty of action, were branded with the plebeian name of *Short Pipes.* A third party likewise sprang up, differing from both the other, headed by the descendants of the famous Robert Chewit, the companion of the great Hudson. These entirely discarded the use of pipes and took to chewing tobacco, and hence they were called *Quids.* It is worthy of notice that this last appellation has since come to be invariably applied to those mongrel or third parties that will sometimes spring up between two great contending parties, as a mule is produced between a horse and an ass.

And here I would remark the great benefit of these party distinctions by which the people at large are saved the vast trouble of thinking. Hesiod divides mankind into three classes —those who think for themselves, those who let others think for them, and those who will neither do one nor the other. The second class, however, comprises the great mass of society, and hence is the origin of *party,* by which is meant a large body of people, some few of whom think and all the rest talk. The former, who are called the leaders, marshal out and discipline the latter, teaching them what they must approve—what they must hoot at—what they must say—whom they must support— but, above all, whom they must hate—for no man can be a right good partizan unless he be a determined and thoroughgoing hater.

But when the sovereign people are thus properly broken to the harness, yoked, curbed and reined, it is delectable to see with what docility and harmony they jog onward through mud and mire, at the will of their drivers, dragging the dirt carts of faction at their heels. How many a patriotic member of congress have I seen who would never have known how to make up his mind on any question, and might have run a great risk of voting right by mere accident, had he not had others to think for him and a file leader to vote after.

Thus then the enlightened inhabitants of the Manhattoes, being divided into parties, were enabled to organize dissension and to oppose and hate one another more accurately. And now the great business of politics went bravely on; the parties assembling in separate beer houses and smoking at each other with implacable animosity, to the great support of the state and emolument of the tavern keepers. Some, indeed, who were more zealous than the rest went further and began to bespatter one another with numerous very hard names and scandalous little words to be found in the Dutch language; every partisan believing religiously that he was serving his country when he traduced the character or impoverished the pocket of a political adversary. But however they might differ between themselves, all parties agreed on one point, to cavil at and condemn every measure of government whether right or wrong; for as the governor was by his station independent of their power and was not elected by their choice, and as he had not decided in favor of either faction, neither of them was interested in his success nor in the prosperity of the country while under his administration.

"Unhappy William Kieft!" exclaims the sage writer of the Stuyvesant manuscript—"doomed to contend with enemies too knowing to be entrapped and to reign over a people too wise to be governed!" All his expeditions against his enemies were baffled and set at naught, and all his measures for the public safety were cavilled at by the people. Did he propose levying an efficient body of troops for internal defence—the mob, that is to say those vagabond members of the community who have nothing to lose, immediately took the alarm, vociferated that their interests were in danger—that a standing army was a legion of moths, preying on the pockets of society; a rod of iron in the hands of government; and that a government with a military force at its command would inevitably swell into a despotism. Did he, as was but too commonly the case, defer preparation until the moment of emergency and then hastily collect a handful of undisciplined vagrants—the measure was hooted at as feeble and inadequate, as trifling with the public dignity and safety, and as lavishing the public funds on impotent enterprises.—Did he resort to the economic measure of proclamation—he was laughed at by the Yankees; did he back it by non-intercourse— it was evaded and counteracted by his own subjects. Whichever way he turned himself he was beleaguered and distracted by petitions of "numerous and respectable meetings," consisting of some half a dozen brawling pothouse politicians—all of which he read, and what is worse, all of which he attended to. The consequence was that by incessantly changing his measures he gave none of them a fair trial; and by listening to the clamors of the mob and endeavoring to do everything, he in sober truth did nothing.

I would not have it supposed, however, that he took all these memorials and interferences good-naturedly, for such an idea would do injustice to his valiant spirit; on the contrary, he never received a piece of advice in the whole course of his life without first getting into a passion with the giver. But I have ever observed that your passionate little men, like small boats with large sails, are the easiest upset or blown out of their course; and this is demonstrated by Governor Kieft, who, though in temperament as hot as an old radish, and with a mind, the territory of which was subjected to perpetual whirlwinds and tornadoes, yet never failed to be carried away by the last piece of advice that was blown into his ear. Lucky was it for him that his power was not dependent upon the greasy multitude, and that as yet the populace did not possess the important privilege of nominating their chief magistrate. They, however, like a true mob did their best to help along public affairs; pestering their governor incessantly by goading him on with harangues and petitions, and then thwarting his fiery spirit with reproaches and memorials, like a knot of Sunday jockeys managing an unlucky devil of a hack horse—so that Wilhelmus Kieft may be said to have been kept either on a worry or a hand-gallop throughout the whole of his administration.

Containing divers fearful accounts of border wars, and the flagrant outrages of the mosstroopers of Connecticut—with the rise of the great Amphyctionic Council of the east, and the decline of William the Testy.

It was asserted by the wise men of ancient times, who were intimately acquainted with these matters, that at the gate of Jupiter's palace lay two huge tuns, the one filled with blessings, the other with misfortunes—and it verily seems as if the latter had been completely overturned and left to deluge the unlucky province of Nieuw Nederlandts. Among the many internal and external causes of irritation, the incessant irruptions of the Yankees upon his frontiers were continually adding fuel to the inflammable temper of William the Testy. Numerous accounts of these molestations may still be found among the records of the times; for the commanders on the frontiers were especially careful to evince their vigilance and zeal by striving who should send home the most frequent and voluminous budgets of complaints, as your faithful servant is eternally running with complaints to the parlor of all the petty squabbles and misdemeanors of the kitchen. All these valiant tale-bearings were listened to with great wrath by the passionate Kieft and his subjects, who were to the full as eager to hear and credulous to believe these frontier fables as are my fellow citizens to swallow those amusing stories with which our papers are daily filled, about British aggressions at sea, French sequestrations on shore, Spanish infringements in the promised land of Louisiana, and, above all, internal plots and conspiracies.

We are told by the good Plutarch in his life of Nicias that the terrible defeat of the Athenians in Sicily was first mentioned in the shop of a gossipping barber at the Piraeus. Whereupon, with the customary officiousness of his tribe, he ran into Athens to have the first telling of the story, and threw the whole forum

into consternation. Not being able, however, to substantiate his
tale, the unlucky shaver was put upon the wheel and whirled
about, as a reward for his trouble, until he was exculpated by
the arrival of other evidence.

Such was the manner in which busy alarmists and manufacturers of fearful news were treated in Athens; whereas in our
more enlightened country we support whole herds of editors
for no other purpose than to gratify a public appetite for direful
news, and any man who can foist up a full-sounding, hobgoblin
story of a plot or conspiracy may command his own price for it.
I have known two or three of these tales of terror to be bought
up by government for the sovereign people to amuse themselves
withal—which goes further to prove what I have before asserted,
that your enlightened people love to be miserable.

Far be it from me to insinuate, however, that our worthy
ancestors indulged in groundless alarms; on the contrary, they
were daily suffering a repetition of cruel wrongs,* not one of
which but was a sufficient reason, according to the maxims of
national dignity and honor, for throwing the whole universe
into hostility and confusion.

Oh ye powers! into what indignation did every one of these
outrages throw the philosophic William! letter after letter,
protest after protest, proclamation after proclamation, bad
Latin, worse English, and hideous Low Dutch were exhausted
in vain upon the inexorable Yankees, and the four-and-twenty
letters of the alphabet which, excepting his champion, the sturdy

---

* From among a multitude of bitter grievances still on record, I select a
few of the most atrocious, and leave my readers to judge if our ancestors
were not justifiable in getting into a very valiant passion on the occasion.

24 June, 1641. Some of Hartford have taken a hogg out of the vlact or
common and shut it up out of meer hate or other prejudice, causing it to
starve for hunger in the stye!

26 July. The foremencioned English did againe drive the Companies' hoggs
out of the vlact of Sicojoke into Hartford; contending daily with reproaches,
blows, beating the people with all disgrace that they could imagine.

May 20, 1642. The English of Hartford have violently cut loose a horse
of the honored Companies', that stood bound upon the common or vlact.

May 9, 1643. The Companies' horses pastured upon the Companies' ground
were driven away by them of Connecticott or Hartford, and the herdsmen
lustily beaten with hatchets and sticks.

16. Again they sold a young hogg belonging to the Companie which piggs
had pastured on the Companies' land.

                                                Haz. Col. State Pap.

trumpeter Van Corlear, composed the only standing army he
had at his command, were never off duty throughout the whole
of his administration.—Nor did Antony the trumpeter remain a
whit behind his patron, the gallant Kieft, in his fiery zeal; but
like a faithful champion and preserver of the public safety, on
the arrival of every fresh article of news he was sure to sound
his trumpet from the ramparts, with most disastrous notes,
throwing the people into violent alarms and disturbing their
rest at all times and seasons—which caused him to be held in
very great regard, the public pampering and rewarding him as
we do brawling editors for reasons that have just been mentioned.

I am well aware of the perils that environ me in this part of
my history. While raking with curious hands but pious heart
among the mouldering remains of former days, anxious to draw
therefrom the honey of wisdom, I may fare somewhat like that
valiant worthy Samson, who, in meddling with the carcass of
a dead lion, drew a swarm of bees about his ears. Thus while
narrating the many misdeeds of the Yanokie or Yankee tribe
it is ten chances to one but I offend the morbid sensibilities of
certain of their unreasonable descendants, who may fly out and
raise such a buzzing about this unlucky head of mine that
I shall need the tough hide of an Achilles or an Orlando Furioso
to protect me from their stings.

Should such be the case, I should deeply and sincerely lament
—not my misfortune in giving offense—but the wrong-headed
perverseness of an ill-natured generation in taking offense at any
thing I say. That their ancestors did use my ancestors ill is true,
and I am very sorry for it. I would with all my heart the fact
were otherwise; but as I am recording the sacred events of
history, I'd not bate one nail's breadth of the honest truth,
though I were sure the whole edition of my work should be
bought up and burnt by the common hangman of Connecticut.
And in sooth, now that these testy gentlemen have drawn me
out, I will make bold to go further and observe that this is one
of the grand purposes for which we impartial historians are
sent into the world—to redress wrongs and render justice on the
heads of the guilty. So that though a powerful nation may wrong
its neighbors with temporary impunity, yet sooner or later an
historian springs up who wreaks ample chastisement on it in
return.

Thus these mosstroopers of the east little thought, I'll warrant

it, while they were harassing the inoffensive province of Nieuw
Nederlandts and driving its unhappy governor to his wit's end,
that an historian should ever arise and give them their own
with interest. Since, then, I am but performing my bounden
duty as an historian in avenging the wrongs of our revered
ancestors, I shall make no further apology; and indeed, when
it is considered that I have all these ancient borderers of the
east in my power and at the mercy of my pen, I trust that it
will be admitted I conduct myself with great humanity and
moderation.

To resume then the course of my history—Appearances to the
eastward began now to assume a more formidable aspect than
ever—for I would have you note that hitherto the province had
been chiefly molested by its immediate neighbors, the people
of Connecticut, particularly of Hartford; which, if we may judge
from ancient chronicles, was the stronghold of these sturdy
mosstroopers, from whence they sallied forth on their daring
incursions, carrying terror and devastation into the barns, the
hen roosts and pigsties of our revered ancestors.

Albeit about the year 1643 the people of the east country,
inhabiting the colonies of Massachusetts, Connecticut, New
Plymouth and New Haven, gathered together into a mighty
conclave, and after buzzing and debating for many days, like a
political hive of bees in swarming time, at length settled themselves into a formidable confederation under the title of the
United Colonies of New England. By this union they pledged
themselves to stand by one another in all perils and assaults,
and to co-operate in all measures, offensive and defensive, against
the surrounding savages, among which were doubtlessly included
our honored ancestors of the Manhattoes; and to give more
strength and system to this confederation, a general assembly
or grand council was to be annually held, composed of representatives from each of the provinces.

On receiving accounts of this puissant combination, the fiery
Wilhelmus was struck with vast consternation, and for the first
time in his whole life forgot to bounce at hearing an unwelcome
piece of intelligence—which a venerable historian of the times
observes was especially noticed among the sage politicians of
New Amsterdam. The truth was, on turning over in his mind
all that he had read at the Hague about leagues and combinations, he found that this was an exact imitation of the famous Am-

phyctionic council by which the states of Greece were enabled to attain to such power and supremacy, and the very idea made his heart to quake for the safety of his empire at the Manhattoes.

He strenuously insisted that the whole object of this confederation was to drive the Newerlanders out of their fair domains; and always flew into a great rage if any one presumed to doubt the probability of his conjecture. Nor was he wholly unwarranted in such a suspicion; for at the very first annual meeting of the grand council, held at Boston (which Governor Kieft denominated the Delphos of this truly classic league), strong representations were made against the Nederlanders, forasmuch as that in their dealings with the Indians they carried on a traffic in "guns, powther and shott—a trade damnable and injurious to the colonists."* Not but what certain of the Connecticut traders did likewise dabble a little in this "damnable traffic"—but then they always sold the Indians such scurvy guns that they burst at the first discharge—and consequently hurt no one but these pagan savages.

The rise of this potent confederacy was a death-blow to the glory of William the Testy, for from that day forward, it was remarked by many, he never held up his head, but appeared quite crestfallen. His subsequent reign, therefore, affords but scanty food for the historic pen—we find the grand council continually augmenting in power and threatening to overwhelm the mighty but defenseless province of Nieuw Nederlandts; while Wilhelmus Kieft kept constantly firing off his proclamations and protests like a shrewd sea captain firing off so many carronades and swivels in order to break and disperse a waterspout—but alas! they had no more effect than if they had been so many blank cartridges.

The last document on record of this learned, philosophic, but unfortunate little man is a long letter to the council of the Amphyctions, wherein in the bitterness of his heart he rails at the people of New Haven, or Red Hills, for their uncourteous contempt of his protest levelled at them for squatting within the province of their High Mightinesses. From this letter, which is a model of epistolary writing, abounding with pithy apophthegms and classic figures, my limits will barely allow me to extract the following recondite passage:†—"Certainly

---

* Haz. Col. S. Papers.
† Vide Haz. Col. State Papers.

when we heare the Inhabitants of New-Hartford complayninge of us, we seem to heare Esop's wolf complayninge of the lamb, or the admonition of the younge man who cryed out to his mother, chideing with her neighboures, 'Oh Mother, revile her, lest she first take up that practice against you.' But being taught by precedent passages, we received such an answer to our protest from the inhabitants of New Haven as we expected: *the Eagle always despiseth the Beetle fly;* yet nothwithstanding, we doe undauntedly continue on our purpose of pursuing our own right, by just arms and righteous means, and doe hope without scruple to execute the express commands of our superiours." To show that this last sentence was not a mere empty menace, he concluded his letter by intrepidly protesting against the whole council as a horde of *squatters* and interlopers inasmuch as they held their meeting at New Haven, or the Red Hills, which he claimed as being within the province of the New Netherlands.

Thus end the authenticated chronicles of the reign of William the Testy—for henceforth, in the troubles, the perplexities and the confusion of the times, he seems to have been totally overlooked and to have slipped forever through the fingers of scrupulous history. Indeed, for some cause or other which I cannot divine, there appears to have been a combination among historians to sink his very name into oblivion, in consequence of which they have one and all forborne even to speak of his exploits. This shows how important it is for great men to cultivate the favor of the learned if they are ambitious of honor and renown. "Insult not the dervise," said a wise caliph to his son, "lest thou offend thine historian," and many a mighty man of the olden time, had he observed so obvious a maxim, might have escaped divers cruel wipes of the pen which have been drawn across his character.

It has been a matter of deep concern to me that such darkness and obscurity should hang over the latter days of the illustrious Kieft—for he was a mighty and great little man, worthy of being utterly renowned, seeing that he was the first potentate that introduced into this land the art of fighting by proclamation and defending a country by trumpeters and windmills—an economic and humane mode of warfare, since revived with great applause, and which promises, if it can ever be carried into full effect, to save great trouble and treasure and spare

infinitely more bloodshed than either the discovery of gunpowder or the invention of torpedoes.

It is true that certain of the early provincial poets, of whom
there were great numbers in the Nieuw Nederlandts, taking
advantage of the mysterious exit of William the Testy, have
fabled that like Romulus he was translated to the skies and
forms a very fiery little star somewhere on the left claw of the
crab; while others, equally fanciful, declare that he had experienced a fate similar to that of the good King Arthur; who, we
are assured by ancient bards, was carried away to the delicious
abodes of fairy land, where he still exists in pristine worth and
vigor, and will one day or another return to rescue poor old
England from the hands of paltry, flippant, pettifogging cabinets,
and to restore the gallantry, the honor and the immaculate probity which prevailed in the glorious days of the Round Table.*

All these, however, are but pleasing fantasies, the cobweb
visions of those dreaming varlets, the poets, to which I would
not have my judicious reader attach any credibility. Neither
am I disposed to yield any credit to the assertion of an ancient
and rather apocryphal historian who alleges that the ingenious
Wilhelmus was annihilated by the blowing down of one of his
windmills—nor to that of a writer of later times who affirms
that he fell a victim to a philosophical experiment which he
had for many years been vainly striving to accomplish; having
the misfortune to break his neck from the garret window of
the Stadt House in an ineffectual attempt to catch swallows by
sprinkling fresh salt upon their tails.

The most probable account, and to which I am inclined to give
my implicit faith, is contained in a very obscure tradition which
declares that what with the constant troubles on his frontiers—
the incessant schemings and projects going on in his own
pericranium—the memorials, petitions, remonstrances and sage

---

* The old Welsh bards believed that king Arthur was not dead, but carried
awaie by the faries into some pleasent place, where he shold remaine for a
time, and then returne againe and reigne in as great authority as ever.—
HOLLINGSHED.

The Britons suppose that he shall come yet and conquere all Britaigne,
for certes this is the prophicye of Merlyn—He say'd that his deth shall be
doubteous; and said soth, for men thereof yet have doubte and shullen for
ever more—for men wyt not whether that he lyveth or is dede.—DE LEEW.
CHRON.

pieces of advice from divers respectable meetings of the sovereign people—together with the refractory disposition of his
council, who were sure to differ from him on every point and
uniformly to be in the wrong—all these, I say, did eternally
operate to keep his mind in a kind of furnace heat, until he at
length became as completely burnt out as a Dutch family pipe
which has passed through three generations of hard smokers.
In this manner did the choleric but magnanimous William the
Testy undergo a kind of animal combustion, consuming away
like a farthing rushlight—so that when grim death finally
snuffed him out, there was scarce left enough of him to bury!

BOOK V

Containing the first part of the reign of Peter Stuyvesant and his troubles with the Amphyctionic Council.

CHAPTER I

In which the death of a great man is shown to be no very inconsolable matter of sorrow —and how Peter Stuyvesant acquired a great name from the uncommon strength of his head.

To a profound philosopher like myself who am apt to see clear through a subject, where the penetration of ordinary people extends but half way, there is no fact more simple and manifest than that the death of a great man is a matter of very little importance. Much as we may think of ourselves, and much as we may excite the empty plaudits of the million, it is certain that the greatest among us do actually fill but an exceeding small space in the world; and it is equally certain that even that small space is quickly supplied when we leave it vacant. "Of what consequence is it," said the elegant Pliny, "that individuals appear or make their exit? the world is a theater whose scenes and actors are continually changing." Never did philosopher speak more correctly, and I only wonder that so wise a remark could have existed so many ages and mankind not have laid it more to heart. Sage follows on in the footsteps of sage; one hero just steps out of his triumphal car to make way for the hero who comes after him; and of the proudest monarch it is merely said that—"he slept with his fathers, and his successor reigned in his stead."

The world, to tell the private truth, cares but little for their loss, and if left to itself would soon forget to grieve; and though a nation has often been figuratively drowned in tears on the death of a great man, yet it is ten chances to one if an individual tear has been shed on the occasion, excepting from the forlorn pen of some hungry author. It is the historian, the biographer and the poet who have the whole burden of grief to sustain; who—kind souls!—like undertakers in England, act the part of chief mourners—who inflate a nation with sighs it never heaved and deluge it with tears it never dreamt of shedding. Thus, while the patriotic author is weeping and howling in prose, in blank verse and in rhyme, and collecting the drops of public sorrow into his volume as into a lachrymal vase, it is more than probable his fellow citizens are eating and drinking, fiddling and dancing, as utterly ignorant of the bitter lamentations made in their name as are those men of straw, John Doe and Richard Roe, of the plaintiffs for whom they are generously pleased on divers occasions to become sureties.

The most glorious and praiseworthy hero that ever desolated nations might have mouldered into oblivion among the rubbish of his own monument did not some historian take him into favor and benevolently transmit his name to posterity—and much as the valiant William Kieft worried and bustled and turmoiled while he had the destinies of a whole colony in his hand, I question seriously whether he will not be obliged to this authentic history for all his future celebrity.

His exit occasioned no convulsion in the city of New Amsterdam or its vicinity: the earth trembled not, neither did any stars shoot from their spheres—the heavens were not shrouded in black, as poets would fain persuade us they have been on the unfortunate death of a hero—the rocks (hard-hearted varlets!) melted not into tears, nor did the trees hang their heads in silent sorrow, and as to the sun, he laid abed the next night just as long, and showed as jolly a face when he arose, as he ever did on the same day of the month in any year either before or since. The good people of New Amsterdam one and all declared that he had been a very busy, active, bustling little governor; that he was "the father of his country"—that he was "the noblest work of God"—that "he was a man, take him for all in all, they ne'er should look upon his like again"—together with sundry other civil and affectionate speeches that are regularly said on the death of all great men; after which they smoked their pipes, thought no more about him, and Peter Stuyvesant succeeded to his station.

Peter Stuyvesant was the last, and, like the renowned Wouter Van Twiller, he was also the best, of our ancient Dutch gov-

ernors: Wouter having surpassed all who preceded him, and
Pieter or Piet, as he was sociably called by the old Dutch burghers who were ever prone to familiarize names, having never
been equalled by any successor. He was in fact the very man
fitted by nature to retrieve the desperate fortunes of her beloved
province, had not the fates, those most potent, immaculate and
unrelenting of all ancient and immortal spinsters, destined them
to inextricable confusion.

To say merely that he was a hero would be doing him great
injustice—he was in truth a combination of heroes—for he was
of a sturdy, rawboned make like Ajax Telamon, so famous for
his prowess in belaboring the little Trojans, with a pair of
round shoulders that Hercules would have given his hide for
(meaning his lion's hide) when he undertook to ease old Atlas
of his load. He was moreover, as Plutarch describes Coriolanus,
not only terrible for the force of his arm, but likewise of his
voice, which sounded as though it came out of a barrel; and,
like the self-same warrior, he possessed a sovereign contempt
for the sovereign people, and an iron aspect which was enough
of itself to make the very bowels of his adversaries quake with
terror and dismay. All this martial excellency of appearance
was inexpressibly heightened by an accidental advantage with
which I am surprised that neither Homer nor Virgil have graced
any of their heroes, for it is worth all the scars and wounds in
the Iliad and Eneid, or Lucan's Pharsalia into the bargain.
This was nothing less than a redoubtable wooden leg, which
was the only prize he had gained in bravely fighting the battles
of his country, but of which he was so proud that he was often
heard to declare he valued it more than all his other limbs put
together; indeed so highly did he esteem it that he had it
gallantly enchased and relieved with silver devices, which caused
it to be related in divers histories and legends that he wore a
silver leg.*

Like that choleric warrior Achilles, he was somewhat subject
to extempore bursts of passion, which were ofttimes rather un-
pleasant to his favorites and attendants, whose perceptions he
was apt to quicken, after the manner of his illustrious imitator,
Peter the Great, by anointing their shoulders with his walking
staff.

* See the histories of Masters Josselyn and Blome.

But the resemblance for which I most value him was that which he bore in many particulars to the renowned Charlemagne. Though I cannot find that he had read Plato or Aristotle or Hobbes or Bacon or Algernon Sydney or Tom Paine, yet did he sometimes manifest a shrewdness and sagacity in his measures that one would hardly expect from a man who did not know Greek and had never studied the ancients. True it is, and I confess it with sorrow, that he had an unreasonable aversion to experiments, and was fond of governing his province after the simplest manner—but then he contrived to keep it in better order than did the erudite Kieft, though he had all the philosophers ancient and modern to assist and perplex him. I must likewise own that he made but very few laws, but then again he took care that those few were rigidly and impartially enforced —and I do not know but justice on the whole was as well administered as if there had been volumes of sage acts and statutes yearly made, and daily neglected and forgotten.

He was, in fact, the very reverse of his predecessors, being neither tranquil and inert like Walter the Doubter, nor restless and fidgeting like William the Testy; but a man, or rather a governor, of such uncommon activity and decision of mind that he never sought or accepted the advice of others; depending confidently upon his single head, as did the heroes of yore upon their single arms, to work his way through all difficulties and dangers. To tell the simple truth, he wanted no other requisite for a perfect statesman than to think always right, for no one can deny that he always acted as he thought; and if he wanted in correctness, he made up for it in perseverance—an excellent quality since it is surely more dignified for a ruler to be persevering and consistent in error than wavering and contradictory in endeavoring to do what is right. This much is certain, and it is a maxim worthy the attention of all legislators both great and small who stand shaking in the wind without knowing which way to steer—a ruler who acts according to his own will is sure of pleasing himself, while he who seeks to satisfy the wishes and whims of others runs a great risk of pleasing nobody. The clock that stands still and points steadfastly in one direction is certain of being right twice in the four-and-twenty hours —while others may keep going continually and continually be going wrong.

Nor did this magnanimous virtue escape the discernment

of the good people of Nieuw Nederlandts; on the contrary, so high an opinion had they of the independent mind and vigorous intellects of their new governor that they universally called him *Hard-Koppig Piet,* or PETER THE HEADSTRONG—a great compliment to his understanding!

If from all that I have said thou dost not gather, worthy reader, that Peter Stuyvesant was a tough, sturdy, valiant, weather-beaten, mettlesome, obstinate, leathern-sided, lion-hearted, generous-spirited old governor, either I have written to but little purpose or thou art very dull at drawing conclusions.

This most excellent governor, whose character I have thus attempted feebly to delineate, commenced his administration on the 29th day of May, 1647; a remarkably stormy day, distinguished in all the almanacks of the time which have come down to us by the name of *Windy Friday.* As he was very jealous of his personal and official dignity, he was inaugurated into office with great ceremony; the goodly oaken chair of the renowned Wouter Van Twiller being carefully preserved for such occasions, in like manner as the chair and stone were reverentially preserved at Schone in Scotland for the coronation of the Caledonian monarchs.

I must not omit to mention that the tempestuous state of the elements, together with its being that unlucky day of the week termed "hanging day," did not fail to excite much grave speculation and divers very reasonable apprehensions among the more ancient and enlightened inhabitants; and several of the sager sex, who were reputed to be not a little skilled in the mysteries of astrology and fortune telling, did declare outright that they were omens of a disastrous administration—an event that came to be lamentably verified, and which proves beyond dispute the wisdom of attending to those preternatural intimations furnished by dreams and visions, the flying of birds, falling of stones and cackling of geese on which the sages and rulers of ancient times placed such reliance—or to those shootings of stars, eclipses of the moon, howlings of dogs and flarings of candles carefully noted and interpreted by the oracular sybils of our day; who, in my humble opinion, are the legitimate inheritors and preservers of the ancient science of divination. This much is certain, that Governor Stuyvesant succeeded to the chair of state at a turbulent period; when foes thronged and threatened from without; when anarchy and stiff-necked opposition reigned rampant within; when the authority of their High Mightinesses the Lords States General, though founded on the broad Dutch bottom of unoffending imbecility, though supported by economy and defended by speeches, protests, proclamations, yet tottered to its very center; and when the great city of New Amsterdam, though fortified by flagstaffs, trumpeters and windmills, seemed, like some fair lady of easy virtue, to lay open to attack and ready to yield to the first invader.

CHAPTER II

Showing how Peter the Headstrong bestirred himself among the rats and cobwebs on entering into office—And the perilous mistake he was guilty of in his dealings with the Amphyctions.

The very first movements of the great Peter, on taking the reins of government, displayed the magnanimity of his mind, though they occasioned not a little marvel and uneasiness among the people of the Manhattoes. Finding himself constantly interrupted by the opposition and annoyed by the sage advice of his privy council, the members of which had acquired the unreasonable habit of thinking and speaking for themselves during the preceding reign, he determined at once to put a stop to such grievous abominations. Scarcely, therefore, had he entered upon his authority than he turned out of office all those meddlesome spirits that composed the factious cabinet of William the Testy, in place of whom he chose unto himself counsellors from those fat, somniferous, respectable families that had flourished and slumbered under the easy reign of Walter the Doubter. All these he caused to be furnished with abundance of fair long pipes and to be regaled with frequent corporation dinners, admonishing them to smoke and eat and sleep for the good of the nation, while he took all the burden of government upon his own shoulders—an arrangement to which they all gave hearty acquiescence.

Nor did he stop here, but made a hideous rout among the inventions and expedients of his learned predecessor—demolishing his flagstaffs and windmills which, like mighty giants, guarded the ramparts of New Amsterdam—pitching to the duyvel whole batteries of quaker guns—rooting up his patent gallows where caitiff vagabonds were suspended by the waistband—and, in a word, turning topsy-turvy the whole philosophic, economic and windmill system of the immortal sage of Saardam.

The honest folk of New Amsterdam began to quake now for the fate of their matchless champion, Antony the trumpeter, who had acquired prodigious favor in the eyes of the women by means of his whiskers and his trumpet. Him did Peter the Headstrong cause to be brought into his presence, and eyeing him for a moment from head to foot, with a countenance that would have appalled any thing else than a sounder of brass—"Prythee, who and what art thou?" said he.—"Sire," replied the other, in nowise dismayed,—"for my name, it is Antony Van Corlear—for my parentage, I am the son of my mother—for my profession, I am champion and garrison of this great city of New Amsterdam."—"I doubt me much," said Peter Stuyvesant, "that thou art some scurvy costardmonger knave—how didst thou acquire this paramount honor and dignity?"—"Marry, sir," replied the other, "like many a great man before me, simply *by sounding my own trumpet.*"—"Ay, is it so?" quoth the governor, "why then let us have a relish of thy art." Whereupon he put his instrument to his lips and sounded a charge with such a tremendous outset, such a delectable quaver and such a triumphant cadence that it was enough to make your heart leap out of your mouth only to be within a mile of it. Like as a war-worn charger, while sporting in peaceful plains, if by chance he hear the strains of martial music, pricks up his ears and snorts and paws and kindles at the noise, so did the heroic soul of the mighty Peter joy to hear the clangor of the trumpet; for of him might truly be said what was recorded of the renowned St. George of England, "there was nothing in all the world that more rejoiced his heart than to hear the pleasant sound of war and see the soldiers brandish forth their steeled weapons." Casting his eyes more kindly, therefore, upon the sturdy Van Corlear, and finding him to be a jolly, fat, little man, shrewd in his discourse yet of great discretion and immeasurable wind, he straightway conceived a vast kindness for him, and discharging him from the troublesome duty of garrisoning, defending and alarming the city, ever after retained him about his person, as his chief favorite, confidential envoy and trusty squire. Instead of disturbing the city with disastrous notes, he was instructed to play so as to delight the governor while at his repasts, as did the minstrels of yore in the days of glorious chivalry—and on all public occasions to rejoice the ears of the people with warlike melody—thereby keeping alive a noble and martial spirit.

Many other alterations and reformations, both for the better and for the worse, did the governor make, of which my time will not serve me to record the particulars; suffice it to say, he soon contrived to make the province feel that he was its master, and treated the sovereign people with such tyrannical rigor that they were all fain to hold their tongues, stay at home and attend to their business; insomuch that party feuds and distinctions were almost forgotten, and many thriving keepers of taverns and dramshops were utterly ruined for want of business.

Indeed, the critical state of public affairs at this time demanded the utmost vigilance and promptitude. The formidable council of the Amphyctions, which had caused so much tribulation to the unfortunate Kieft, still continued augmenting its forces and threatened to link within its union all the mighty principalities and powers of the east. In the very year following the inauguration of Governor Stuyvesant, a grand deputation departed from the city of Providence (famous for its dusty streets and beauteous women) in behalf of the puissant plantation of Rhode Island, praying to be admitted into the league.

The following mention is made of this application in certain records of that assemblage of worthies, which are still extant.*

"Mr. Will Cottington and captain Partridg of Rhoode Iland presented this insewing request to the commissioners in wrighting—

"Our request and motion is in behalfe of Rhoode Iland, that wee the Ilanders of Rhoode Iland may be rescauied into com-

---

* Haz. Col. Stat. Pap.

bination with all the united colonyes of New England in a
firme and perpetuall league of friendship and amity of ofence
and defence, mutuall advice and succor upon all just occasions
for our mutuall safety and wellfaire, &c.

> Will Cottington,
> Alicxsander Partridg."

There is certainly something in the very physiognomy of this
document that might well inspire apprehension. The name of
Alexander, however misspelt, has been warlike in every age, and
though its fierceness is in some measure softened by being
coupled with the gentle cognomen of Partridge, still, like the
color of scarlet, it bears an exceeding great resemblance to the
sound of a trumpet. From the style of the letter, moreover, and
the soldierlike ignorance of orthography displayed by the noble
captain Alicxsander Partridg in spelling his own name, we may
picture to ourselves this mighty man of Rhodes, like a second
Ajax, strong in arms, potent in the field, and as great a scholar
as though he had been educated among that learned people of
Thrace who, Aristotle assures us, could not count beyond the
number four.

But whatever might be the threatening aspect of this famous
confederation, Peter Stuyvesant was not a man to be kept in a
state of incertitude and vague apprehension; he liked nothing
so much as to meet danger face to face and take it by the beard.
Determined, therefore, to put an end to all these petty maraudings on the borders, he wrote two or three categorical letters to
the grand council; which, though neither couched in bad Latin
nor yet graced by rhetorical tropes about wolves and lambs and
beetle flies, yet had more effect than all the elaborate epistles,
protests and proclamations of his learned predecessor put together. In consequence of his urgent propositions, the great
confederacy of the east agreed to enter into a final adjustment of
grievances and settlement of boundaries, to the end that a perpetual and happy peace might take place between the two
powers. For this purpose Governor Stuyvesant deputed two ambassadors to negotiate with commissioners from the grand
council of the league, and a treaty was solemnly concluded at
Hartford. On receiving intelligence of this event, the whole
community was in an uproar of exultation. The trumpet of
the sturdy Van Corlear sounded all day with joyful clangor

from the ramparts of Fort Amsterdam, and at night the city
was magnificently illuminated with two hundred and fifty tallow
candles; besides a barrel of tar, which was burnt before the
governor's house, on the cheering aspect of public affairs.

And now my worthy reader is, doubtless, like the great and
good Peter, congratulating himself with the idea that his feelings will no longer be molested by afflicting details of stolen
horses, broken heads, impounded hogs and all the other catalogue of heart-rending cruelties that disgraced these border wars.
But if he should indulge in such expectations, it is proof that he
is but little versed in the paradoxical ways of cabinets; to convince him of which, I solicit his serious attention to my next
chapter wherein I will show that Peter Stuyvesant has already
committed a great error in politics; and by effecting a peace, has
materially jeopardized the tranquillity of the province.

CHAPTER III

*Containing divers speculations on war and
negotiations—showing that a treaty of peace
is a great national evil.*

It was the opinion of that poetical philosopher, Lucretius, that
war was the original state of man, whom he described as being
primitively a savage beast of prey engaged in a constant state
of hostility with his own species, and that this ferocious spirit
was tamed and ameliorated by society. The same opinion has
been advocated by the learned Hobbes,* nor have there been
wanting many other philosophers to admit and defend it.

For my part, though prodigiously fond of these valuable
speculations so complimentary to human nature, yet in this
instance I am inclined to take the proposition by halves, believing with Horace† that though war may have been originally the

---

* Hobbes' Leviathan. Part i. chap. 13.
† Quum prorepserunt primis animalia terris,
  Mutum ac turpe pecus, glandem atque cubilia propter,
  Unguibus et pugnis, dein fustibus, atque ita porro
  Pugnabant armis, quae post fabricaverat usus.

                                              Hor. Sat. L. i. S. 3.

favorite amusement and industrious employment of our progenitors, yet, like many other excellent habits, so far from being ameliorated, it has been cultivated and confirmed by refinement and civilization, and increases in exact proportion as we approach towards that state of perfection which is the *ne plus ultra* of modern philosophy.

The first conflict between man and man was the mere exertion of physical force, unaided by auxiliary weapons—his arm was his buckler, his fist was his mace, and a broken head the catastrophe of his encounters. The battle of unassisted strength was succeeded by the more rugged one of stones and clubs, and war assumed a sanguinary aspect. As man advanced in refinement, as his faculties expanded and his sensibilities became more exquisite, he grew rapidly more ingenious and experienced in the art of murdering his fellow beings. He invented a thousand devices to defend and to assault—the helmet, the cuirass and the buckler, the sword, the dart and the javelin, prepared him to elude the wound as well as to launch the blow. Still urging on, in the brilliant and philanthropic career of invention, he enlarges and heightens his powers of defense and injury—The Aries, the Scorpio, the Balista and the Catapulta give a horror and sublimity to war, and magnify its glory by increasing its desolation. Still insatiable, though armed with machinery that seemed to reach the limits of destructive invention and to yield a power of injury commensurate even with the desires of revenge—still deeper researches must be made in the diabolical arcana. With furious zeal he dives into the bowels of the earth; he toils midst poisonous minerals and deadly salts—the sublime discovery of gunpowder blazes upon the world—and finally the dreadful art of fighting by proclamation seems to endow the demon of war with ubiquity and omnipotence!

This, indeed, is grand!—this, indeed, marks the powers of mind and bespeaks that divine endowment of reason which distinguishes us from the animals, our inferiors. The unenlightened brutes content themselves with the native force which providence has assigned them.—The angry bull butts with his horns, as did his progenitors before him—the lion, the leopard and the tiger seek only with their talons and their fangs to gratify their sanguinary fury; and even the subtle serpent darts the same venom and uses the same wiles as did his sire before the flood. Man alone, blessed with the inventive mind, goes on from discovery to discovery—enlarges and multiplies his powers of destruction; arrogates the tremendous weapons of Deity itself, and tasks creation to assist him in murdering his brother worm!

In proportion as the art of war has increased in improvement has the art of preserving peace advanced in equal ratio; and as we have discovered in this age of wonders and inventions that proclamation is the most formidable engine in war, so have we discovered the no less ingenious mode of maintaining peace by perpetual negotiations.

A treaty, or, to speak more correctly, a negotiation, therefore, according to the acceptation of experienced statesmen learned in these matters, is no longer an attempt to accommodate differences, to ascertain rights and to establish an equitable exchange of kind offices; but a contest of skill between two powers, which shall overreach and take in the other. It is a cunning endeavor to obtain by peaceful manoeuver and the chicanery of cabinets those advantages which a nation would otherwise have wrested by force of arms—in the same manner that a conscientious highway man reforms and becomes an excellent and praiseworthy citizen, contenting himself with cheating his neighbor out of that property he would formerly have seized with open violence.

In fact the only time when two nations can be said to be in a state of perfect amity is when a negotiation is open and a treaty pending. Then, as there are no stipulations entered into, no bonds to restrain the will, no specific limits to awaken that captious jealousy of right implanted in our nature, as each party has some advantage to hope and expect from the other, then it is that the two nations are so gracious and friendly to each other; their ministers professing the highest mutual regard, exchanging billets-doux, making fine speeches and indulging in all those little diplomatic flirtations, coquetries and fondlings that do so marvelously tickle the good humor of the respective nations. Thus it may paradoxically be said that there is never so good an understanding between two nations as when there is a little misunderstanding—and that so long as they are on no terms, they are on the best terms in the world!

I do not by any means pretend to claim the merit of having made the above political discovery. It has in fact long been secretly acted upon by certain enlightened cabinets, and is, together with divers other notable theories, privately copied out of the commonplace book of an illustrious gentleman who has been member of congress and enjoyed the unlimited confidence of heads of departments. To this principle may be ascribed the wonderful ingenuity that has been shown of late years in protracting and interrupting negotiations.—Hence the cunning measure of appointing as ambassador some political pettifogger skilled in delays, sophisms and misapprehensions, and dexterous in the art of baffling argument—or some blundering statesman whose errors and misconstructions may be a plea for refusing to ratify his engagements. And hence too that most notable expedient, so popular with our government, of sending out a brace of ambassadors; who having each an individual will to consult, character to establish and interest to promote, you may as well look for unanimity and concord between two lovers with one mistress, two dogs with one bone, or two naked rogues with one pair of breeches. This disagreement therefore is continually breeding delays and impediments, in consequence of which the negotiation goes on swimmingly—inasmuch as there is no prospect of its ever coming to a close. Nothing is lost by these delays and obstacles but time, and in a negotiation according to the theory I have exposed all time lost is in reality so much time gained—with what delightful paradoxes does modern political economy abound!

Now all that I have here advanced is so notoriousy true, that I almost blush to take up the time of my readers with treating of matters which must many a time have stared them in the face. But the proposition to which I would most earnestly call their attention is this, that though a negotiation be the most harmonizing of all national transactions, yet a treaty of peace is a great political evil, and one of the most fruitful sources of war.

I have rarely seen an instance of any special contract between individuals that did not produce jealousies, bickerings and often downright ruptures between them; nor did I ever know of a treaty between two nations that did not occasion continual misunderstandings. How many worthy country neighbors have I known who, after living in peace and good fellowship for years, have been thrown into a state of distrust, cavilling and animosity by some ill-starred agreement about fences, runs of water and stray cattle. And how many well-meaning nations, who would otherwise have remained in the most amicable disposition towards each other, have been brought to swords' points about the infringement or misconstruction of some treaty which in an evil hour they had concluded by way of making their amity more sure.

Treaties at best are but complied with so long as interest requires their fulfilment; consequently they are virtually binding on the weaker party only, or, in plain truth, they are not binding at all. No nation will wantonly go to war with another if it has nothing to gain thereby, and therefore needs no treaty to restrain it from violence; and if it have anything to gain, I much question, from what I have witnessed of the righteous conduct of nations, whether any treaty could be made so strong that it could not thrust the sword through—nay, I would hold ten to one, the treaty itself would be the very source to which resort would be had to find a pretext for hostilities.

Thus, therefore, I conclude—that though it is the best of all policies for a nation to keep up a constant negotiation with its neighbors, yet it is the summit of folly for it ever to be beguiled into a treaty; for then comes on the non-fulfilment and infraction, then remonstrance, then altercation, then retaliation, then recrimination and finally open war. In a word, negotiation is like courtship, a time of sweet words, gallant speeches, soft looks and endearing caresses—but the marriage ceremony is the signal for hostilities.

CHAPTER IV

How Peter Stuyvesant was greatly belied by his adversaries the mosstroopers—and his conduct thereupon.

If my painstaking reader be not somewhat perplexed in the course of the ratiocination of my last chapter, he will doubtless at one glance perceive that the great Peter in concluding a treaty with his eastern neighbors was guilty of a lamentable error and heterodoxy in politics. To this unlucky agreement may justly be ascribed a world of little infringements, altercations, negotiations and bickerings which afterwards took place between the irreproachable Stuyvesant and the evil-disposed council of Amphyctions. All these did not a little disturb the constitutional serenity of the good burghers of Manna-hata; but in sooth they were so very pitiful in their nature and effects that a grave historian, who grudges the time spent in anything less than recording the fall of empires and the revolution of worlds, would think them unworthy to be inscribed on his sacred page.

The reader is therefore to take it for granted, though I scorn to waste in the detail that time which my furrowed brow and trembling hand inform me is invaluable, that all the while the great Peter was occupied in those tremendous and bloody contests that I shall shortly rehearse, there was a continued series of little, dirty, sniveling skirmishes, scourings, broils and maraudings made on the eastern frontiers by the mosstroopers of Connecticut. But like that mirror of chivalry, the sage and valorous Don Quixote, I leave these petty contests for some future Sancho Panza of an historian, while I reserve my prowess and my pen for achievements of higher dignity.

Now did the great Peter conclude that his labors had come to a close in the east, and that he had nothing to do but apply himself to the internal prosperity of his beloved Manhattoes. Though a man of great modesty, he could not help boasting that he had at length shut the temple of Janus, and that, were all rulers like a certain person who should be nameless, it would never be opened again. But the exultation of the worthy governor was put to a speedy check, for scarce was the treaty concluded, and hardly was the ink dried on the paper, before the crafty and discourteous council of the league sought a new pretence for reilluming the flames of discord.

It seems to be the nature of confederacies, republics, and such like powers that want the true masculine character, to indulge exceedingly in certain feminine panics and suspicions. Like some good lady of delicate and sickly virtue who is in constant dread of having her vestal purity contaminated or seduced, and who, if a man do but take her by the hand or look her in the face, is ready to cry out, rape! and ruin!—so these squeamish governments are perpetually on the alarm for the virtue of the country: every manly measure is a violation of the constitution—every monarchy or other masculine government around them is laying snares for their seduction; and they are forever detecting infernal plots by which they were to be betrayed, dishonored and "brought upon the town."

If any proof were wanting of the truth of these opinions, I would instance the conduct of a certain republic of our day; who, good dame, has already withstood so many plots and conspiracies against her virtue, and has so often come near being made "no better than she should be." I would notice her constant jealousies of poor old England, who, by her own account, has been incessantly trying to sap her honor; though, from my soul, I never could believe the honest old gentleman meant her any rudeness. Whereas, on the contrary, I think I have several times caught her squeezing hands and indulging in certain amorous oglings with that sad fellow Bonaparte—who all the world knows to be a great despoiler of national virtue, to have ruined all the empires in his neighborhood, and to have debauched every republic that came in his way—but so it is these rakes seem always to gain singular favor with the ladies.

But I crave pardon of my reader for thus wandering, and will endeavor in some measure to apply the foregoing remarks; for in the year 1651 we are told that the great confederacy of the east accused the immaculate Peter—the soul of honor and heart of steel—that by divers gifts and promises he had been secretly endeavoring to instigate the Narrohigansett (or Narraganset), Mohaque and Pequot Indians to surprise and massacre the Yankee settlements. "For," as the council slanderously observed, "the Indians round about for divers hundred miles cercute seeme to have drunke deep of an intoxicating cupp, att or from the Manhatoes against the English, whoe have sought their good, both in bodily and spirituall respects."

History does not make mention how the great council of the Amphyctions came by this precious plot; whether it were honestly bought at a fair market price or discovered by sheer good fortune—It is certain, however, that they examined divers Indians who all swore to the fact as sturdily as though they had been so many Christian troopers: and to be more sure of their veracity, the sage council previously made every mother's son of them devoutly drunk, remembering an old and trite proverb which it is not necessary for me to repeat.

Though descended from a family which suffered much injury from the losel Yankees of those times—my great-grandfather having had a yoke of oxen and his best pacer stolen, and having received a pair of black eyes and a bloody nose in one of these border wars; and my grandfather, when a very little boy tending pigs, having been kidnapped and severely flogged by a long-sided Connecticut schoolmaster—Yet I should have passed over all these wrongs with forgiveness and oblivion—I could even have suffered them to have broken Evert Ducking's head, to have kicked the doughty Jacobus Van Curlet and his ragged regiment out of doors, carried every hog into captivity, and depopulated every hen roost on the face of the earth with perfect impunity—But this wanton attack upon one of the most gallant and irreproachable heroes of modern times is too much even for me to digest, and has overset, with a singe puff, the patience of the historian and the forbearance of the Dutchman.

Oh reader, it was false!—I swear to thee, it was false!—if thou hast any respect for my word—if the undeviating character for veracity which I have endeavored to maintain throughout this work has its due weight with thee, thou wilt not give thy faith to this tale of slander; for I pledge my honor and my immortal fame to thee that the gallant Peter Stuyvesant was not only innocent of this foul conspiracy, but would have suffered his right arm or even his wooden leg to consume with slow and everlasting flames rather than attempt to destroy his enemies in any other way than open generous warfare—Beshrew those caitiff scouts that conspired to sully his honest name by such an imputation!

Peter Stuyvesant, though he perhaps had never heard of a knight errant, yet had he as true a heart of chivalry as ever beat at the round table of King Arthur. There was a spirit of native gallantry, a noble and generous hardihood diffused through his rugged manners, which altogether gave unquestionable tokens of an heroic mind. He was, in truth, a hero of chivalry struck off by the hand of nature at a single heat, and though she had taken no further care to polish and refine her workmanship, he stood forth a miracle of her skill.

But not to be figurative (a fault in historic writing which I particularly eschew), the great Peter possessed in an eminent degree the seven renowned and noble virtues of knighthood, which, as he had never consulted authors in the disciplining and cultivating of his mind, I verily believe must have been implanted in a corner of his heart by dame Nature herself—

where they flourished among his hardy qualities like so many
sweet wild flowers shooting forth and thriving with redundant
luxuriance among stubborn rocks. Such was the mind of Peter
the Headstrong, and if my admiration for it has on this occasion transported my style beyond the sober gravity which becomes the laborious scribe of historic events, I can plead as
an apology that, though a little grey-headed Dutchman, arrived
almost at the bottom of the down-hill of life, I still retain some
portion of that celestial fire which sparkles in the eye of youth
when contemplating the virtues and achievements of ancient
worthies. Blessed, thrice and nine times blessed, be the good
St. Nicholas—that I have escaped the influence of that chilling
apathy which too often freezes the sympathies of age; which,
like a churlish spirit, sits at the portals of the heart repulsing
every genial sentiment and paralyzing every spontaneous glow
of enthusiasm.

No sooner, then, did this scoundrel imputation on his honor
reach the ear of Peter Stuyvesant than he proceeded in a manner
which would have redounded to his credit even though he had
studied for years in the library of Don Quixote himself. He immediately despatched his valiant trumpeter and squire, Antony Van Corlear, with orders to ride night and day as herald
to the Amphyctionic council, reproaching them in terms of
noble indignation for giving ear to the slanders of heathen
infidels against the character of a Christian, a gentleman and
a soldier—and declaring that as to the treacherous and bloody
plot alleged against him, whoever affirmed it to be true lied in
his teeth!—to prove which, he defied the president of the council and all of his compeers, or if they pleased, their puissant
champion, Captain Alicxsander Partridg, that mighty man of
Rhodes, to meet him in single combat, where he would trust
the vindication of his innocence to the prowess of his arm.

This challenge being delivered with due ceremony, Antony
Van Corlear sounded a trumpet of defiance before the whole
council, ending with a most horrific and nasal twang full in the
face of Captain Partridg, who almost jumped out of his skin
in an ecstasy of astonishment at the noise. This done, he
mounted a tall Flanders mare which he always rode, and trotted
merrily towards the Manhattoes—passing through Hartford and
Pyquag and Middletown and all the other border towns—twanging his trumpet like a very devil, so that the sweet valleys and

banks of the Connecticut resounded with the warlike melody —and stopping occasionally to eat pumpkin pies, dance at country frolics and bundle with the beauteous lasses of those parts—whom he rejoiced exceedingly with his soul-stirring instrument.

But the grand council, being composed of considerate men, had no idea of running a tilting with such a fiery hero as the hardy Peter—on the contrary, they sent him an answer couched in the meekest, the most mild and provoking terms, in which they assured him that his guilt was proved to their perfect satisfaction by the testimony of divers sober and respectable Indians, and concluding with this truly amiable paragraph—"For youre confidant denialls of the Barbarous plott charged will waigh little in balance against such evidence, soe that we must still require and seeke due satisfaction and cecuritie, so we rest,

Sir,
Youres in wayes of Righteousness, &c."

I am aware that the above transaction has been differently recorded by certain historians of the east and elsewhere; who seem to have inherited the bitter enmity of their ancestors to the brave Peter—and much good may their inheritance do them! These declare that Peter Stuyvesant requested to have the charges against him inquired into by commissioners to be appointed for the purpose; and yet that when such commissioners were appointed, he refused to submit to their examination. In this artful account there is but the semblance of truth—he did indeed most gallantly offer, when that he found a deaf ear was turned to his challenge, to submit his conduct to the rigorous inspection of a court of honor—but then he expected to find it an august tribunal, composed of courteous gentlemen, the governors and nobility of the confederate plantations and of the province of New Netherlands; where he might be tried by his peers in a manner worthy of his rank and dignity—whereas, let me perish if they did not send to the Manhattoes two lean-sided hungry pettifoggers, mounted on Narraganset pacers, with saddlebags under their bottoms and green satchels under their arms, as though they were about to beat the hoof from one county court to another in search of a lawsuit.

The chivalric Peter, as might be expected, took no notice of these cunning varlets; who with professional industry fell to

prying and sifting about in quest of *ex parte* evidence; perplex-
ing divers simple Indians and old women with their cross-
questioning until they contradicted and forswore themselves
most horribly—as is too often done in our courts of justice. Thus
having fulfilled their errand to their own satisfaction, they returned to the grand council with their satchels and saddlebags
stuffed full of villainous rumors, apocryphal stories and outrageous calumnies—for all which the great Peter did not care a
tobacco stopper; but, I warrant me, had they attempted to play
off the same trick upon William the Testy, he would have treated
them both to an aerial gambol on his patent gallows.

The grand council of the east held a very solemn meeting on
the return of their envoys, and after they had pondered a long
time on the situation of affairs, were upon the point of ad-
journing without being able to agree upon anything. At this
critical moment one of those meddlesome, indefatigable spirits
who endeavor to establish a character for patriotism by blowing
the bellows of party until the whole furnace of politics is red-
hot with sparks and cinders—and who have just cunning enough
to know that there is no time so favorable for getting on the
people's backs as when they are in a state of turmoil and attending to everybody's business but their own—this aspiring imp
of faction, who was called a great politician because he had
secured a seat in council by calumniating all his opponents—
he, I say, conceived this a fit opportunity to strike a blow that
should secure his popularity among his constituents, who lived
on the borders of Nieuw Nederlandt, and were the greatest
poachers in Christendom, excepting the Scotch border nobles.
Like a second Peter the hermit, therefore, he stood forth and
preached up a crusade against Peter Stuyvesant and his devoted
city.

He made a speech which lasted six hours, according to the
ancient custom in these parts, in which he represented the
Dutch as a race of impious heretics who neither believed in
witchcraft nor the sovereign virtues of horseshoes—who left their
country for the lucre of gain, not like themselves for the enjoyment of *liberty of conscience*—who, in short, were a race of
mere cannibals and anthropophagi, inasmuch as they never ate
codfish on Saturdays, devoured swine's flesh without molasses,
and held pumpkins in utter contempt.

This speech had the desired effect, for the council, being

awakened by the sergeant at arms, rubbed their eyes and declared that it was just and politic to declare instant war against these unchristian anti-pumpkinites. But it was necessary that the people at large should first be prepared for this measure, and for this purpose the arguments of the orator were preached from the pulpit for several Sundays subsequent and earnestly recommended to the consideration of every good Christian who professed as well as practiced the doctrine of meekness, charity and the forgiveness of injuries. This is the first time we hear of the "Drum Ecclesiastic" beating up for political recruits in our country; and it proved of such signal efficacy that it has since been called into frequent service throughout our union. A cunning politician is often found sculking under the clerical robe, with an outside all religion and an inside all political rancor. Things spiritual and things temporal are strangely jumbled together, like poisons and antidotes on an apothecary's shelf, and instead of a devout sermon, the simple churchgoing folk have often a political pamphlet thrust down their throats, labeled with a pious text from Scripture.

CHAPTER V

How the New Amsterdammers became great in arms, and of the direful catastrophe of a mighty army—together with Peter Stuyvesant's measures to fortify the city—and how he was the original founder of the Battery.

But notwithstanding that the grand council, as I have already shown, were amazingly discreet in their proceedings respecting the New Netherlands, and conducted the whole with almost as much silence and mystery as does the sage British cabinet one of its ill-starred *secret expeditions*—yet did the ever-watchful Peter receive as full and accurate information of every movement as does the court of France of all the notable enterprises I have mentioned.—He accordingly sat himself to work to render the machinations of his bitter adversaries abortive.

I know that many will censure the precipitation of this stout-hearted old governor, in that he hurried into the expenses of fortification without ascertaining whether they were necessary, by prudently waiting until the enemy was at the door. But they should recollect that Peter Stuyvesant had not the benefit of an insight into the modern arcana of politics, and was strangely bigoted to certain obsolete maxims of the old school; among which he firmly believed that to render a country respected abroad it was necessary to make it formidable at home—and that a nation should place its reliance for peace and security more upon its own strength than on the justice or good will of its neighbors.—He proceeded, therefore, with all diligence to put the province and metropolis in a strong posture of defense.

Among the few remnants of ingenious inventions which remained from the days of William the Testy were those impregnable bulwarks of public safety, militia laws; by which the inhabitants were obliged to turn out twice a year, with such military equipments—as it pleased God; and were put under the command of very valiant tailors and man milliners, who though on ordinary occasions the meekest, pippin-hearted little men in the world, were very devils at parades and court-martials, when they had cocked hats on their heads and swords by their sides. Under the instructions of these periodical warriors, the gallant trainbands made marvelous proficiency in the mystery of gunpowder. They were taught to face to the right, to wheel to the left, to snap off empty firelocks without winking, to turn a corner without any great uproar or irregularity, and to march through sun and rain from one end of the town to the other without flinching—until in the end they became so valorous that they fired off blank cartridges without so much as turning away their heads—could hear the largest fieldpiece discharged without stopping their ears or falling into much confusion—and would even go through all the fatigues and perils of a summer day's parade without having their ranks much thinned by desertion!

True it is, the genius of this truly pacific people was so little given to war that during the intervals which occurred between field days they generally contrived to forget all the military tuition they had received; so that when they reappeared on parade they scarcely knew the butt end of the musket from the muzzle, and invariably mistook the right shoulder for the left

—a mistake which, however, was soon obviated by chalking their left arms. But whatever might be their blunders and awkwardness, the sagacious Kieft declared them to be of but little importance—since, as he judiciously observed, one campaign would be of more instruction to them than a hundred parades; for though two-thirds of them might be food for powder, yet such of the other third as did not run away would become most experienced veterans.

The great Stuyvesant had no particular veneration for the ingenious experiments and institutions of his shrewd predecessor, and among other things, held the militia system in very considerable contempt, which he was often heard to call in joke—for he was sometimes fond of a joke—governor Kieft's broken reed. As, however, the present emergency was pressing, he was obliged to avail himself of such means of defense as were next at hand, and accordingly appointed a general inspection and parade of the trainbands. But oh! Mars and Bellona, and all ye other powers of war both great and small, what a turning out was here!—Here came men without officers, and officers without men—long fowling pieces and short blunderbusses—muskets of all sorts and sizes, some without bayonets, others without locks, others without stocks, and many without lock, stock or barrel.—Cartridge boxes, shot belts, powder horns, swords, hatchets, snickersnees, crowbars and broomsticks all mingled higgledy-piggledy—like one of our continental armies at the breaking out of the revolution.

This sudden transformation of a pacific community into a band of warriors is doubtless what is meant, in modern days, by "putting a nation in armor," and "fixing it in an attitude." In which armor and attitude it makes as martial a figure, and is likely to acquit itself with as much prowess, as the renowned Sancho Panza when suddenly equipped to defend his Island of Barataria.

The sturdy Peter eyed this ragged regiment with some such rueful aspect as a man would eye the devil; but knowing, like a wise man, that all he had to do was to make the best out of a bad bargain, he determined to give his heroes a seasoning. Having, therefore, drilled them through the manual exercise over and over again, he ordered the fifes to strike up a quick march, and trudged his sturdy boots backwards and forwards about the streets of New Amsterdam and the fields adjacent until their short legs ached and their fat sides sweated again. But this was not all; the martial spirit of the old governor caught fire from the sprightly music of the fife, and he resolved to try the mettle of his troops and give them a taste of the hardships of iron war. To this end he encamped them, as the shades of evening fell, upon a hill formerly called Bunker's Hill, at some distance from the town, with a full intention of initiating them into the discipline of camps, and of renewing the next day the toils and perils of the field. But so it came to pass, that in the night there fell a great and heavy rain, which descended in torrents upon the camp, and the mighty army strangely melted away before it; so that when Gaffer Phœbus came to shed his morning beams upon the place, saving Peter Stuyvesant and his trumpeter Van Corlear, scarce one was to be found of all the multitude that had encamped there the night before.

This awful dissolution of his army would have appalled a commander of less nerve than Peter Stuyvesant; but he considered it as a matter of but small importance, though he thenceforward regarded the militia system with ten times greater contempt than ever, and took care to provide himself with a good garrison of chosen men, whom he kept in pay, of whom he boasted that they at least possessed the quality, indispensable in soldiers, of being *waterproof*.

The next care of the vigilant Stuyvesant was to strengthen and fortify New Amsterdam. For this purpose he caused to be built a strong picket fence that reached across the island from river to river, being intended to protect the city not merely from the sudden invasions of foreign enemies, but likewise from the incursions of the neighboring savages.*

Some traditions, it is true, have ascribed the building of this wall to a later period, but they are wholly incorrect; for a memorandum in the Stuyvesant manuscript, dated towards the middle of the governor's reign, mentions this wall particularly, as

---

* In an antique view of New Amsterdam, taken some years after the above period, is a representation of this wall, which stretched along the course of Wall Street, so called in commemoration of this great bulwark. One gate, called the Land-Poort, opened upon Broadway, hard by where at present stands the Trinity Church; and another, called the Water-Poort, stood about where the Tontine Coffee House is at present—opening upon Smits Vleye, or as it is commonly called, Smith Fly, then a marshy valley with a creek or inlet extending up what we call Maiden Lane.

a very strong and curious piece of workmanship and the admiration of all the savages in the neighborhood. And it mentions, moreover, the alarming circumstance of a drove of stray cows breaking through the grand wall of a dark night; by which the whole community of New Amsterdam was thrown into a terrible panic.

In addition to this great wall, he cast up several outworks to Fort Amsterdam to protect the seaboard, at the point of the island. These consisted of formidable mud batteries, solidly faced, after the manner of the Dutch ovens common in those days, with clam shells.

These frowning bulwarks, in process of time, came to be pleasantly overrun by a verdant carpet of grass and clover, and their high embankments overshadowed by wide-spreading sycamores, among whose foliage the little birds sported about, rejoicing the ear with their melodious notes. The old burghers would repair of an afternoon to smoke their pipes under the shade of their branches, contemplating the golden sun as he gradually sunk into the west, an emblem of that tranquil end toward which themselves were hastening—while the young men and the damsels of the town would take many a moonlight stroll among these favorite haunts, watching the silver beams of chaste Cynthia tremble along the calm bosom of the bay or light up the white sail of some gliding bark, and interchanging the honest vows of constant affection. Such was the origin of that renowned walk, *the Battery,* which, though ostensibly devoted to the purposes of war, has ever been consecrated to the sweet delights of peace. The favorite walk of declining age—the healthful resort of the feeble invalid—the Sunday refreshment of the dusty tradesman—the scene of many a boyish gambol—the rendezvous of many a tender assignation —the comfort of the citizen—the ornament of New York—and the pride of the lovely island of Manna-hata.

How the people of the east country were suddenly afflicted with a diabolical evil—and their judicious measures for the extirpation thereof.

Having thus provided for the temporary security of New Amsterdam, and guarded it against any sudden surprise, the gallant Peter took a hearty pinch of snuff, and snapping his fingers, set the great council of Amphyctions and their champion, the doughty Alicxander Partridg, at defiance. It is impossible to say, notwithstanding, what might have been the issue of this affair had not the council been all at once involved in sad perplexity, and as much dissension sown among its members as of yore was stirred up in the camp of the brawling warriors of Greece.

The council of the league, as I have shown in my last chapter, had already announced its hostile determinations, and already was the mighty colony of New Haven and the puissant town of Pyquag, otherwise called Weathersfield—famous for its onions and its witches—and the great trading house of Hartford, and all the other redoubtable border towns, in a prodigious turmoil, furbishing up their rusty fowling pieces and shouting aloud for war; by which they anticipated easy conquests and gorgeous spoils from the little fat Dutch villages. But this joyous brawling was soon silenced by the conduct of the colony of Massachusetts. Struck with the gallant spirit of the brave old Peter, and convinced by the chivalric frankness and heroic warmth of his vindication, they refused to believe him guilty of the infamous plot most wrongfully laid at his door. With a generosity for which I would yield them immortal honor, they declared that no determination of the grand council of the league should bind the general court of Massachusetts to join in an offensive war which should appear to such general court to be unjust.*

---

* Haz. Col. S. Pap.

This refusal immediately involved the colony of Massachusetts and the other combined colonies in very serious difficulties and disputes, and would no doubt have produced a dissolution of the confederacy but that the council of Amphyctions, finding that they could not stand alone if mutilated by the loss of so important a member as Massachusetts, were fain to abandon for the present their hostile machinations against the Manhattoes. Such is the marvelous energy and the puissance of those confederacies composed of a number of sturdy, self-willed, discordant parts loosely banded together by a puny general government. As it was, however, the warlike towns of Connecticut had no cause to deplore this disappointment of their martial ardor; for by my faith—though the combined powers of the league might have been too potent in the end for the robustious warriors of the Manhattoes—yet in the interim would the lion-hearted Peter and his myrmidons have choked the stomachful heroes of Pyquag with their own onions, and have given the other little border towns such a scouring that I warrant they would have had no stomach to squat on the land or invade the hen roost of a New Nederlander for a century to come.

Indeed there was more than one cause to divert the attention of the good people of the east from their hostile purposes; for just about this time were they horribly beleaguered and harassed by the inroads of the prince of darkness, divers of whose liege subjects they detected lurking within their camp, all of whom they incontinently roasted as so many spies and dangerous enemies. Not to speak in parables, we are informed that at this juncture the New England provinces were exceedingly troubled by multitudes of losel witches, who wrought strange devices to beguile and distress the multitude; and notwithstanding numerous judicious and bloody laws had been enacted against all "solem conversing or compacting with the divil, by way of conjuracon or the like,"* yet did the dark crime of witchcraft continue to increase to an alarming degree that would almost transcend belief, were not the fact too well authenticated to be even doubted for an instant.

What is particularly worthy of admiration is that this terrible art, which so long has baffled the painful researches and

* New Plymouth record.

abstruse studies of philosophers, astrologers, alchemists, theurgists and other sages, was chiefly confined to the most ignorant,
decrepit and ugly old women in the community, who had
scarcely more brains than the broomsticks they rode upon.
Where they first acquired their infernal education—whether
from the works of the ancient Theurgists—the demonology of
the Egyptians—the belomancy, or divination by arrows of the
Scythians—the spectrology of the Germans—the magic of the
Persians—the enchantment of the Laplanders—or from the archives of the dark and mysterious caverns of the Dom Daniel
—is a question pregnant with many learned and ingenious
doubts—particularly as most of them were totally unversed
in the occult mysteries of the alphabet.

When once an alarm is sounded, the public, who love dearly
to be in a panic, are not long in want of proofs to support it
—raise but the cry of yellow fever, and immediately every
headache and indigestion and overflowing of the bile is pronounced the terrible epidemic.—In like manner in the present
instance, whoever was troubled with a colic or lumbago was
sure to be bewitched, and woe to any unlucky old woman that
lived in his neighborhood. Such a howling abomination could
not be suffered to remain long unnoticed, and it accordingly
soon attracted the fiery indignation of the sober and reflective
part of the community—more especially of those who whilom
had evinced so much active benevolence in the conversion of
quakers and anabaptists. The grand council of the Amphyctions publicly set their faces against so deadly and dangerous
a sin, and a severe scrutiny took place after those nefarious
witches, who were easily detected by devil's pinches, black
cats, broomsticks and the circumstance of their only being
able to weep three tears, and those out of the left eye.

It is incredible the number of offences that were detected,
"for every one of which," says the profound and revered Cotton
Mather in that excellent work, the history of New England—
"we have such a sufficient evidence that no reasonable man in
this whole country ever did question them; *and it will be unreasonable to do it in any other.*"*

Indeed, that authentic and judicious historian, John Josselyn, gent., furnishes us with unquestionable facts on this subject. "There are none," observes he, "that beg in this country,

* Mather's Hist. New Eng. B. 6. ch. 7.

but there be witches too many—bottle-bellied witches and others, that produce many strange apparitions, if you will believe report of a shallop at sea manned with women—and of a ship and great red horse standing by the mainmast; the ship being in a small cove to the eastward vanished of a sudden," &c.

The number of delinquents, however, and their magical devices were not more remarkable than their diabolical obstinacy. Though exhorted in the most solemn, persuasive and affectionate manner to confess themselves guilty and be burnt for the good of religion and the entertainment of the public; yet did they most pertinaciously persist in asserting their innocence. Such incredible obstinacy was in itself deserving of immediate punishment, and was sufficient proof, if proof were necessary, that they were in league with the devil, who is perverseness itself. But their judges were just and merciful, and were determined to punish none that were not convicted on the best of testimony; not that they needed any evidence to satisfy their own minds, for, like true and experienced judges, their minds were perfectly made up and they were thoroughly satisfied of the guilt of the prisoners before they proceeded to try them; but still something was necessary to convince the community at large—to quiet those prying quidnuncs who should come after them—in short, the world must be satisfied. Oh the world—the world!—all the world knows the world of trouble the world is eternally occasioning!—The worthy judges, therefore, were driven to the necessity of sifting, detecting and making evident as noonday matters which were at the commencement all clearly understood and firmly decided upon in their own pericraniums—so that it may truly be said that the witches were burnt to gratify the populace of the day—but were tried for the satisfaction of the whole world that should come after them!

Finding, therefore, that neither exhortation, sound reason nor friendly entreaty had any avail on these hardened offenders, they resorted to the more urgent arguments of the torture, and having thus absolutely wrung the truth from their stubborn lips—they condemned them to undergo the roasting due unto the heinous crimes they had confessed. Some even carried their perverseness so far as to expire under the torture, protesting their innocence to the last; but these were looked upon as thoroughly and absolutely possessed by the devil, and the pious bystanders only lamented that they had not lived a little longer, to have perished in the flames.

In the city of Ephesus, we are told that the plague was expelled by stoning a ragged old beggar to death, whom Apollonius pointed out as being the evil spirit that caused it, and who actually showed himself to be a demon by changing into a shagged dog. In like manner and by measures equally sagacious, a salutary check was given to this growing evil. The witches were all burnt, banished or panic-struck, and in a little while there was not an ugly old woman to be found throughout New England—which is doubtless one reason why all the young women there are so handsome. Those honest folk who had suffered from their incantations gradually recovered, excepting such as had been afflicted with twitches and aches, which, however, assumed the less alarming aspects of rheumatisms, sciatics and lumbagos—and the good people of New England, abandoning the study of the occult sciences, turned their attention to the more profitable hocus pocus of trade and soon became expert in the legerdemain art of turning a penny. Still, however, a tinge of the old leaven is discernible even unto this day in their characters—witches occasionally start up among them in different disguises, as physicians, civilians and divines. The people at large show a keenness, a cleverness and a profundity of wisdom that savors strongly of witchcraft—and it has been remarked that whenever any stones fall from the moon, the greater part of them is sure to tumble into New England!

CHAPTER VII

Which records the rise and renown of a valiant commander, showing that a man, like a bladder, may be puffed up to greatness and importance by mere wind.

When treating of these tempestuous times, the unknown writer of the Stuyvesant manuscript breaks out into a vehement apostrophe in praise of the good St. Nicholas; to whose protecting care he entirely ascribes the strange dissensions that broke out in the council of the Amphyctions, and the direful witchcraft that prevailed in the east country—whereby the hostile machinations against the Nederlanders were for a time frustrated, and his favorite city of New Amsterdam preserved from imminent peril and deadly warfare. Darkness and lowering superstition hung over the fair valleys of the east; the pleasant banks of the Connecticut no longer echoed with the sounds of rustic gaiety; direful phantoms and portentous apparitions were seen in the air—gliding spectrums haunted every wild brook and dreary glen—strange voices, made by viewless forms, were heard in desert solitudes—and the border towns were so occupied in detecting and punishing the knowing old women that had produced these alarming appearances that for a while the province of Nieuw Nederlandt and its inhabitants were totally forgotten.

The great Peter, therefore, finding that nothing was to be immediately apprehended from his eastern neighbors, turned himself about, with a praiseworthy vigilance that ever distinguished him, to put a stop to the insults of the Swedes. These freebooters, my attentive reader will recollect, had begun to be very troublesome towards the latter part of the reign of William the Testy, having set the proclamations of that doughty little governor at naught and put the intrepid Jan Jansen Alpendam to a perfect nonplus!

Peter Stuyvesant, however, as has already been shown, was a governor of different habits and turn of mind—without more ado he immediately issued orders for raising a corps of troops to be stationed on the southern frontier, under the command of Brigadier General Jacobus Von Poffenburgh. This illustrious warrior had risen to great importance during the reign of Wilhelmus Kieft, and if histories speak true, was second in command to the hapless Van Curlet when he and his ragged regiment were inhumanly kicked out of Fort Good Hope by the Yankees. In consequence of having been in such a "memorable affair," and of having received more wounds on a certain honorable part that shall be nameless than any of his comrades, he was ever after considered as a hero who had "seen some service." Certain it is, he enjoyed the unlimited confidence and friendship of William the Testy, who would sit for hours and listen with wonder to his gunpowder narratives of surprising victories —he had never gained; and dreadful battles—from which he had run away; and the governor was once heard to declare that had he lived in ancient times he might unquestionably have claimed the armor of Achilles—being not merely, like Ajax, a mighty blustering man of battle, but in the cabinet a second Ulysses; that is to say, very valiant of speech and long winded—all which, as nobody in New Amsterdam knew aught of the ancient heroes in question, passed totally uncontradicted.

It was tropically observed by honest old Socrates that heaven had infused into some men at their birth a portion of intellectual gold; into others of intellectual silver; while others were bounteously furnished out with abundance of brass and iron— now of this last class was undoubtedly the great General Von Poffenburgh, and from the display he continually made thereof, I am inclined to think that dame Nature, who will sometimes be partial, had blessed him with enough of those valuable materials to have fitted up a dozen ordinary braziers. But what is most to be admired is that he contrived to pass off all his brass and copper upon Wilhelmus Kieft, who was no great judge of base coin, as pure and genuine gold. The consequence was that upon the resignation of Jacobus Van Curlet, who, after the loss of Fort Good Hope, retired like a veteran general to live under the shade of his laurels, the mighty "copper captain" was promoted to his station. This he filled with great importance, always styling himself "commander in chief of the armies of the New Netherlands"; though, to tell the truth, the armies, or rather army, consisted of a handful of hen-stealing, bottle-bruising ragamuffins.

Such was the character of the warrior appointed by Peter Stuyvesant to defend his southern frontier, nor may it be uninteresting to my reader to have a glimpse of his person. He was not very tall, but, notwithstanding, a huge full-bodied man whose bulk did not so much arise from his being fat, as windy; being so completely inflated with his own importance that he resembled one of those bags of wind which Aeolus, in an incredible fit of generosity, gave to that wandering warrior Ulysses.

His dress comported with his character, for he had almost as much brass and copper without as nature had stored away within—His coat was crossed and slashed, and carbonadoed with stripes of copper lace, and swathed round the body with a crimson sash of the size and texture of a fishing net—doubtless to keep his valiant heart from bursting through his ribs. His head and whiskers were profusely powdered, from the midst of which his full-blooded face glowed like a fiery furnace; and his magnanimous soul seemed ready to bounce out at a pair of large glassy blinking eyes which projected like those of a lobster.

I swear to thee, worthy reader, if report belie not this warrior, I would give all the money in my pocket to have seen him accoutred cap-a-pie in martial array—booted to the middle—sashed to the chin—collared to the ears—whiskered to the teeth—crowned with an overshadowing cocked hat—and girded with a leathern belt ten inches broad, from which trailed a falchion of a length that I dare not mention. Thus equipped, he strutted about, as bitter-looking a man of war as the far-famed More of More Hall when he sallied forth, armed at all points, to slay the Dragon of Wantley.*

Notwithstanding all the great endowments and transcendent qualities of this renowned general, I must confess he was not exactly the kind of man that the gallant Peter would have chosen to command his troops—but the truth is that in those days the province did not abound, as at present, in great military characters; who, like so many Cincinnatuses, people every little village—marshalling out cabbages instead of soldiers, and signalizing themselves in the corn field instead of the field of battle—who have surrendered the toils of war for the more useful but inglorious arts of peace; and so blended the laurel with the olive that you may have a general for a landlord, a colonel for a stage driver, and your horse shod by a valiant "captain of volunteers."—Neither had Peter Stuyvesant an opportunity of choosing, like modern rulers, from a loyal band of editors of newspapers—no mention being made in the histories of the times of any such class of mercenaries being retained in pay by government, either as trumpeters, champions or bodyguards. The redoubtable General Von Poffenburgh, therefore, was appointed to the command of the new-levied troops, chiefly because there

---

* "Had you but seen him in this dress,
   How fierce he look'd and how big;
You would have thought him for to be
   Some Egyptian Porcupig.

He frighted all, cats, dogs and all,
   Each cow, each horse, and each hog;
For fear they did flee, for they took him to be
   Some strange outlandish hedge-hog.'"

                                   Ballad of Drag. of Want.

were no competitors for the station, and partly because it would
have been a breach of military etiquette to have appointed a
younger officer over his head—an injustice which the great Peter
would have rather died than have committed.

No sooner did this thrice-valiant copper captain receive marching orders than he conducted his army undauntedly to the
southern frontier; through wild lands and savage deserts; over
insurmountable mountains, across impassable floods and through
impenetrable forests; subduing a vast tract of uninhabited
country and encountering more perils, according to his own
account, than did ever the great Xenophon in his far-famed
retreat with his ten thousand Grecians. All this accomplished,
he established on the South (or Delaware) River a redoubtable
redoubt named FORT CASIMIR, in honor of a favorite pair of
brimstone-colored trunk-breeches of the governor. As this fort
will be found to give rise to very important and interesting
events, it may be worth while to notice that it was afterwards
called Nieuw Amstel, and was the original germ of the present
flourishing town of NEW CASTLE, an appellation erroneously
substituted for *No Castle,* there neither being nor ever having
been a castle or anything of the kind upon the premises.

The Swedes did not suffer tamely this menacing movement of
the Nederlanders; on the contrary, Jan Printz, at that time governor of New Sweden, issued a protest against what he termed an
encroachment upon his jurisdiction.—But the valiant Von Poffenburgh had become too well versed in the nature of proclamations and protests while he served under William the Testy to
be in any wise daunted by such paper warfare. His fortress being
finished, it would have done any man's heart good to behold
into what a magnitude he immediately swelled. He would stride
in and out a dozen times a day, surveying it in front and in
rear, on this side and on that. Then would he dress himself in
full regimentals and strut backwards and forwards for hours
together on the top of his little rampart—like a vainglorious
cock pigeon vaporing on the top of his coop. In a word, unless
my readers have noticed with curious eye the petty commander
of one of our little, snivelling, military posts swelling with all
the vanity of new regimentals and the pomposity derived from
commanding a handful of tatterdemalions, I despair of giving
them any adequate idea of the prodigious dignity of General
Von Poffenburgh.

It is recorded in the delectable romance of Pierce Forest that a young knight being dubbed by King Alexander did incontinently gallop into an adjoining forest and belabored the trees with such might and main that the whole court was convinced that he was the most potent and courageous gentleman on the face of the earth. In like manner, the great Von Poffenburgh would ease off that valorous spleen which like wind is so apt to grow unruly in the stomachs of new-made soldiers, impelling them to box-lobby brawls and broken-headed quarrels.—For at such times, when he found his martial spirit waxing hot within him, he would prudently sally forth into the fields, and lugging out his trusty sabre, would lay about him most lustily, decapitating cabbages by platoons; hewing down whole phalanxes of sunflowers, which he termed gigantic Swedes; and if peradventure he espied a colony of honest big-bellied pumpkins quietly basking themselves in the sun, "Ah, caitiff Yankees," would he roar, "have I caught ye at last!"—So saying, with one sweep of his sword he would cleave the unhappy vegetables from their chins to their waistbands: by which warlike havoc his choler being in some sort allayed, he would return to his garrison with a full conviction that he was a very miracle of military prowess.

The next ambition of general Von Poffenburgh was to be thought a strict disciplinarian. Well knowing that discipline is the soul of all military enterprise, he enforced it with the most rigorous precision; obliging every man to turn out his toes and hold up his head on parade, and prescribing the breadth of their ruffles to all such as had any shirts to their backs.

Having one day, in the course of his devout researches in the Bible (for the pious Eneas himself could not exceed him in outward religion) encountered the history of Absalom and his melancholy end, the general in an evil hour issued orders for cropping the hair of both officers and men throughout the garrison. Now it came to pass that among his officers was one Kildermeester; a sturdy veteran who had cherished through the course of a long life a rugged mop of hair, not a little resembling the shag of a Newfoundland dog, terminating with an immoderate queue like the handle of a frying pan, and queued so tightly to his head that his eyes and mouth generally stood ajar and his eyebrows were drawn up to the top of his forehead. It may naturally be supposed that the possessor of so goodly an appendage would resist with abhorrence an order condemning it to the shears. Sampson himself could not have held his locks more sacred, and on hearing the general orders, he discharged a tempest of veteran, soldier-like oaths and dunder and blixums —swore he would break any man's head who attempted to meddle with his tail—queued it stiffer than ever, and whisked it about the garrison as fiercely as the tail of a crocodile.

The eelskin queue of old Kildermeester became instantly an affair of the utmost importance. The commander in chief was too enlightened an officer not to perceive that the discipline of the garrison, the subordination and good order of the *armies* of the Nieuw Nederlandts, the consequent safety of the whole province, and ultimately the dignity and prosperity of their High Mightinesses the Lords States General, but above all, the dignity of the great General Von Poffenburgh, all imperiously demanded the docking of that stubborn queue. He therefore determined that old Kildermeester should be publicly shorn of his glories in presence of the whole garrison—the old man as resolutely stood on the defensive—whereupon the general, as became a great man, was highly exasperated, and the offender was arrested and tried by a court-martial for mutiny, desertion and all the other list of offences noticed in the articles of war, ending with a "videlicet, in wearing an eel skin queue, three feet long, contrary to orders." Then came on arraignments and trials and pleadings, and the whole country was in a ferment about this unfortunate queue. As it is well known that the commander of a distant frontier post has the power of acting pretty much after his own will, there is little doubt but that the veteran would have been hanged or shot at least, had he not luckily fallen ill of a fever, through mere chagrin and mortification—and most flagitiously deserted from all earthly command, with his beloved locks unviolated. His obstinacy remained unshaken to the very last moment, when he directed that he should be carried to his grave with his eelskin queue sticking out of a hole in his coffin.

This magnanimous affair obtained the general great credit as an excellent disciplinarian, but it is hinted that he was ever after subject to bad dreams and fearful visitations in the night —when the grisly spectrum of old Kildermeester would stand sentinel by his bed-side, erect as a pump, his enormous queue strutting out like the handle.

BOOK VI
Containing the second part
of the reign of
Peter the Headstrong—
and his gallant
achievements on the Delaware.

*In which is exhibited a warlike portrait of
the great Peter—and how General Von Poffenburgh distinguished himself at Fort Casimir.*

Hitherto, most venerable and courteous reader, have I shown
thee the administration of the valorous Stuyvesant under the
mild moonshine of peace, or rather the grim tranquillity of
awful expectation; but now the war-drum rumbles from afar,
the brazen trumpet brays its thrilling note, and the rude clash
of hostile arms speaks fearful prophecies of coming troubles.
and voluptuous ease; where in the dulcet "piging time of peace"
The gallant warrior starts from soft repose, from golden visions
he sought sweet solace after all his toils. No more in beauty's
siren lap reclined, he weaves fair garlands for his lady's brows;
no more entwines with flowers his shining sword, nor through
the livelong lazy summer's day chants forth his lovesick soul in
madrigals. To manhood roused, he spurns the amorous flute;
doffs from his brawny back the robe of peace and clothes his
pampered limbs in panoply of steel. O'er his dark brow, where
late the myrtle waved, where wanton roses breathed enervate
love, he rears the beaming casque and nodding plume; grasps
the bright shield and shakes the ponderous lance; or mounts
with eager pride his fiery steed, and burns for deeds of glorious
chivalry!

But soft, worthy reader! I would not have you imagine that
any *preux chevalier* thus hideously begirt with iron existed in
the city of New Amsterdam.—This is but a lofty and gigantic
mode in which heroic writers always talk of war, thereby to
give it a noble and imposing aspect; equipping our warriors

with bucklers, helms and lances and such-like outlandish and obsolete weapons, the like of which perchance they had never seen or heard of; in the same manner that a cunning statuary arrays a modern general or an admiral in the accoutrements of a Cæsar or an Alexander. The simple truth then of all this oratorical flourish is this—that the valiant Peter Stuyvesant all of a sudden found it necessary to scour his trusty blade, which too long had rusted in its scabbard, and prepare himself to undergo those hardy toils of war in which his mighty soul so much delighted.

Methinks I at this moment behold him in my imagination— or rather, I behold his goodly portrait, which still hangs up in the family mansion of the Stuyvesants—arrayed in all the terrors of a true Dutch general.—His regimental coat of German blue, gorgeously decorated with a goodly show of large brass buttons, reaching from his waistband to his chin.—The voluminous skirts turned up at the corners and separating gallantly behind so as to display the seat of a sumptuous pair of brimstone-colored trunk breeches—a graceful style still prevalent among the warriors of our day, and which is in conformity to the custom of ancient heroes, who scorned to defend themselves in rear.—His face rendered exceeding terrible and warlike by a pair of black mustachios; his hair strutting out on each side in stiffly poma- tumed earlocks and descending in a rat-tail queue below his waist; a shining stock of black leather supporting his chin, and a little but fierce cocked hat, stuck with a gallant and fiery air over his left eye. Such was the chivalric port of Peter the Head- strong; and when he made a sudden halt, planted himsef firmly on his solid supporter, with his wooden leg inlaid with silver a little in advance in order to strengthen his position, his right hand grasping a gold-headed cane, his left resting upon the pummel of his sword; his head dressing spiritedly to the right, with a most appalling and hard-favored frown upon his brow— he presented altogether one of the most commanding, bitter- looking and soldierlike figures that ever strutted upon canvas.— Proceed we now to inquire the cause of this warlike preparation.

The encroaching disposition of the Swedes on the south or Delaware river has been duly recorded in the chronicles of the reign of William the Testy. These encroachments having been endured with that heroic magnanimity which is the cornerstone or, according to Aristotle, the left hand neighbor of true courage, had been repeated and wickedly aggravated.

The Swedes, who were of that class of cunning pretenders to Christianity who read the Bible upside down whenever it interferes with their interests, inverted the golden maxim, and when their neighbor suffered them to smite him on the one cheek, they generally smote him on the other also, whether turned to them or not. Their repeated aggressions had been among the numerous sources of vexation that conspired to keep the irritable sensibilities of Wilhelmus Kieft in a constant fever, and it was only owing to the unfortunate circumstance that he had always a hundred things to do at once that he did not take such unrelenting vengeance as their offences merited. But they had now a chieftain of a different character to deal with; and they were soon guilty of a piece of treachery that threw his honest blood in a ferment and precluded all further sufferance.

Printz, the governor of the province of New Sweden, being either deceased or removed, for of this fact some uncertainty exists, was succeeded by Jan Risingh, a gigantic Swede, and who, had he not been rather knock-kneed and splay-footed, might have served for the model of a Samson or a Hercules. He was no less rapacious than mighty, and withal as crafty as he was rapacious; so that, in fact, there is very little doubt, had he lived some four or five centuries before he would have been one of those wicked giants who took such a cruel pleasure in pocketing distressed damsels, when gadding about the world, and locking them up in enchanted castles without a toilet, a change of linen, or any other convenience.—In consequence of which enormities they fell under the high displeasure of chivalry, and all true, loyal and gallant knights were instructed to attack and slay outright any miscreant they might happen to find above six feet high; which is doubtless one reason that the race of large men is nearly extinct and the generations of latter ages so exceeding small.

No sooner did Governor Risingh enter upon his office than he immediately cast his eyes upon the important post of Fort Casimir and formed the righteous resolution of taking it into his possession. The only thing that remained to consider was the mode of carrying his resolution into effect; and here I must do him the justice to say that he exhibited a humanity rarely to be met with among leaders, and which I have never seen equalled in modern times, excepting among the English in their glorious affair at Copenhagen. Willing to spare the effusion of blood and the miseries of open warfare, he benevolently

shunned everything like avowed hostility or regular siege, and
resorted to the less glorious but more merciful expedient of
treachery.

Under pretence therefore of paying a neighborly visit to General Von Poffenburgh at his new post of Fort Casimir, he made
requisite preparation, sailed in great state up the Delaware,
displayed his flag with the most ceremonious punctilio, and
honored the fortress with a royal salute previous to dropping
anchor. The unusual noise awakened a veteran Dutch sentinel
who was napping faithfully at his post and who, having suffered
his match to go out, contrived to return the compliment by discharging his rusty musket with the spark of a pipe which he
borrowed from one of his comrades. The salute indeed would
have been answered by the guns of the fort, had they not unfortunately been out of order and the magazine deficient in
ammunition—accidents to which forts have in all ages been
liable, and which were the more excusable in the present instance, as Fort Casimir had only been erected about two years
and General Von Poffenburgh, its mighty commander, had been
fully occupied with matters of much greater importance.

Risingh, highly satisfied with this courteous reply to his
salute, treated the fort to a second, for he well knew its commander was marvelously delighted with these little ceremonials,
which he considered as so many acts of homage paid unto his
greatness. He then landed in great state, attended by a suite of
thirty men—a prodigious and vainglorious retinue for a petty
governor of a petty settlement in those days of primitive simplicity; and to the full as great an army as generally swells the
pomp and marches in the rear of our frontier commanders at
the present day.

The number in fact might have awakened suspicion, had not
the mind of the great Von Poffenburgh been so completely engrossed with an all-pervading idea of himself that he had not
room to admit a thought besides. In fact, he considered the
concourse of Risingh's followers as a compliment to himself—so
apt are great men to stand between themselves and the sun and
completely eclipse the truth by their own shadow.

It may readily be imagined how much General Von Poffenburgh was flattered by a visit from so august a personage; his
only embarrassment was how he should receive him in such a
manner as to appear to the greatest advantage and make the

most advantageous impression. The main guard was ordered immediately to turn out, and the arms and regimentals (of which the garrison possessed full half a dozen suits) were equally distributed among the soldiers. One tall lank fellow appeared in a coat intended for a small man, the skirts of which reached a little below his waist, the buttons were between his shoulders, and the sleeves half way to his wrists, so that his hands looked like a couple of huge spades—and the coat, not being large enough to meet in front, was linked together by loops made of a pair of red worsted garters. Another had an old cocked hat stuck on the back of his head and decorated with a bunch of cocks' tails—a third had a pair of rusty gaiters hanging about his heels—while a fourth, who was a short duck-legged little Trojan, was equipped in a huge pair of the general's cast off breeches which he held up with one hand while he grasped his firelock with the other. The rest were accoutred in similar style, excepting three graceless ragamuffins who had no shirts and but a pair and a half of breeches between them, wherefore they were sent to the black hole to keep them out of view. There is nothing in which the talents of a prudent commander are more completely testified than in thus setting matters off to the greatest advantage; and it is for this reason that our frontier posts at the present day (that of Niagara for example) display their best suit of regimentals on the back of the sentinel who stands in sight of travelers.

His men being thus gallantly arrayed—those who lacked muskets shouldering spades and pickaxes, and every man being ordered to tuck in his shirt tail and pull up his brogues, General Von Poffenburgh first took a sturdy draught of foaming ale, which like the magnanimous More of Morehall* was his invariable practice on all great occasions—which done, he put himself at their head, ordered the pine planks which served as a drawbridge to be laid down, and issued forth from his castle like a mighty giant just refreshed with wine. But when the two heroes met, then began a scene of warlike parade and chivalric courtesy that beggars all description. Risingh, who, as I before hinted, was a shrewd, cunning politician and had grown gray

---

     * "——————— as soon as he rose,
         To make him strong and mighty,
         He drank by the tale six pots of ale,
         And a quart of aqua vitae."

much before his time in consequence of his craftiness, saw at one glance the ruling passion of the great Von Poffenburgh and humored him in all his valorous fantasies.

Their detachments were accordingly drawn up in front of each other—They carried arms and they presented arms, they gave the standing salute and the passing salute—They rolled their drums, they flourished their fifes, and they waved their colors— They faced to the left, and they faced to the right, and they faced to the right about—They wheeled forward, and they wheeled backward, and they wheeled into *echellon*—They marched and they countermarched, by grand divisions, by single divisions, and by sub-divisions—by platoons, by sections, and by files—in quick time, in slow time, and in no time at all; for, having gone through all the evolutions of two great armies, including the eighteen manœuvres of Dundas, having exhausted all that they could recollect or imagine of military tactics, including sundry strange and irregular evolutions the like of which were never seen before or since, excepting among certain of our newly raised militia, the two great commanders and their respective troops came at length to a dead halt, completely exhausted by the toils of war—Never did two valiant trainband captains or two buskined theatric heroes in the renowned tragedies of Pizarro, Tom Thumb, or any other heroical and fighting tragedy marshal their gallows-looking, duck-legged, heavy-heeled myrmidons with more glory and self-admiration.

These military compliments being finished, General Von Poffenburgh escorted his illustrious visitor with great ceremony into the fort; attended him throughout the fortifications; showed him the horn works, crown works, half moons and various other outworks, or rather the places where they ought to be erected and where they might be erected if he pleased; plainly demonstrating that it was a place of "great capability," and though at present but a little redoubt, yet that it evidently was a formidable fortress in embryo. This survey over, he next had the whole garrison put under arms, exercised and reviewed, and concluded by ordering the three bridewell birds to be hauled out of the black hole, brought up to the halberts, and soundly flogged for the amusement of his visitor and to convince him that he was a great disciplinarian.

There is no error more dangerous than for a commander to

make known the strength or, as in the present case, the weakness of his garrison; this will be exemplified before I have arrived to an end of my present story, which thus carries its moral, like a roasted goose his pudding, in the very middle. The cunning Risingh, while he pretended to be struck dumb outright with the puissance of the great Von Poffenburgh, took silent note of the incompetency of his garrison, of which he gave a hint to his trusty followers, who tipped each other the wink and laughed most obstreperously—in their sleeves.

The inspection, review and flogging being concluded, the party adjourned to the table; for among his other great qualities, the general was remarkably addicted to huge entertainments, or rather carousals, and in one afternoon's campaign would leave more *dead men* on the field than he ever did in the whole course of his military career. Many bulletins of these bloodless victories do still remain on record; and the whole province was once thrown in amaze by the return of one of his campaigns; wherein it was stated that though like Captain Bobadil he had only twenty men to back him, yet in the short space of six months he had conquered and utterly annihilated sixty oxen, ninety hogs, one hundred sheep, ten thousand cabbages, one thousand bushels of potatoes, one hundred and fifty kilderkins of small beer, two thousand seven hundred and thirty-five pipes, seventy-eight pounds of sugarplums and forty bars of iron, besides sundry small meats, game, poultry, and garden stuff—An achievement unparalleled since the days of Pantagruel and his all-devouring army, and which showed that it was only necessary to let bellipotent Von Poffenburgh and his garrison loose in an enemy's country, and in a little while they would breed a famine and starve all the inhabitants.

No sooner, therefore, had the general received the first intimation of the visit of Governor Risingh, than he ordered a great dinner to be prepared; and privately sent out a detachment of his most experienced veterans to rob all the hen-roosts in the neighborhood and lay the pigsties under contribution—a service to which they had been long inured and which they discharged with such incredible zeal and promptitude that the garrison table groaned under the weight of their spoils.

I wish with all my heart my readers could see the valiant Von Poffenburgh, as he presided at the head of the banquet; it was a sight worth beholding—there he sat, in his greatest glory, surrounded by his soldiers, like that famous win-bibber, Alexander, whose thirsty virtues he did most ably imitate—telling astounding stories of his hair-breadth adventures and heroic exploits, at which, though all his auditors knew them to be most incontinent and outrageous gasconadoes, yet did they cast up their eyes in admiration and utter many interjections of astonishment. Nor could the general pronounce anything that bore the remotest semblance to a joke but the stout Risingh would strike his brawny fist upon the table till every glass rattled again, throwing himself back in his chair and uttering gigantic peals of laughter, swearing most horribly it was the best joke he ever heard in his life.—Thus all was rout and revelry and hideous carousal within Fort Casimir, and so lustily did Von Poffenburgh ply the bottle that in less than four short hours he made himself and his whole garrison, who all sedulously emulated the deeds of their chieftain, dead drunk in singing songs, quaffing bumpers and drinking patriotic toasts, none of which but was as long as a Welsh pedigree or a plea in chancery.

No sooner did things come to this pass than the crafty Risingh and his Swedes, who had cunningly kept themselves sober, rose on their entertainers, tied them neck and heels, and took formal possession of the fort and all its dependencies in the name of Queen Christina of Sweden; administering at the same time an oath of allegiance to all the Dutch soldiers who could be made sober enough to swallow it. Risingh then put the fortifications in order, appointed his discreet and vigilant friend Suen Scutz, a tall, wind-dried, water-drinking Swede, to the command, and departed, bearing with him this truly amiable garrison and their puissant commander; who, when brought to himself by a sound drubbing, bore no little resemblance to a "deboshed fish," or bloated sea monster caught upon dry land.

The transportation of the garrison was done to prevent the transmission of intelligence to New Amsterdam; for much as the cunning Risingh exulted in his stratagem, he dreaded the vengeance of the sturdy Peter Stuyvesant; whose name spread as much terror in the neighborhood as did whilom that of the unconquerable Scanderbeg among his scurvy enemies the Turks.

Showing how profound secrets are often brought to light; with the proceedings of Peter the Headstrong when he heard of the misfortune of General Von Poffenburgh.

Whoever first described common fame, or rumor, as belonging to the sager sex was a very owl for shrewdness. She has in truth certain feminine qualities to an astonishing degree; particularly that benevolent anxiety to take care of the affairs of others which keeps her continually hunting after secrets and gadding about proclaiming them. Whatever is done openly and in the face of the world she takes but transient notice of, but whenever a transaction is done in a corner and attempted to be shrouded in mystery, then her goddessship is at her wit's end to find it out, and takes a most mischievous and lady-like pleasure in publishing it to the world. It is this truly feminine propensity that induces her continually to be prying into cabinets of princes, listening at the keyholes of senate chambers and peering through chinks and crannies when our worthy Congress are sitting with closed doors deliberating between a dozen excellent modes of ruining the nation. It is this which makes her so obnoxious to all wary statesmen and intriguing commanders —such a stumbling-block to private negotiations and secret expeditions; which she often betrays by means and instruments which never would have been thought of by any but a female head.

Thus it was in the case of the affair of Fort Casimir. No doubt the cunning Risingh imagined that by securing the garrison he should for a long time prevent the history of its fate from reaching the ears of the gallant Stuyvesant; but his exploit was blown to the world when he least expected it, and by one of the last beings he would ever have suspected of enlisting as trumpeter to the wide-mouthed deity.

This was one Dirk Schuiler (or Skulker), a kind of hanger-on to the garrison who seemed to belong to nobody and in a manner to be self-outlawed. He was one of those vagabond cosmopolites who shark about the world as if they had no right or business in it, and who infest the skirts of society like poachers and interlopers. Every garrison and country village has one or more scapegoats of this kind, whose life is a kind of enigma, whose existence is without motive, who comes from the Lord knows where, who lives the Lord knows how, and seems to be made for no other earthly purpose but to keep up the ancient and honorable order of idleness.—This vagrant philosopher was supposed to have some Indian blood in his veins, which was manifested by a certain Indian complection and cast of countenance, but more especially by his propensities and habits. He was a tall, lank fellow, swift of foot and long-winded. He was generally equipped in a half Indian dress with belt, leggings and moccasons. His hair hung in straight gallows locks about his ears, and added not a little to his sharking demeanor. It is an old remark that persons of Indian mixture are half civilized, half savage and half devil—a third half being expressly provided for their particular convenience. It is for similar reasons, and probably with equal truth, that the backwoodmen of Kentucky are styled half man, half horse and half alligator by the settlers on the Mississippi, and held accordingly in great respect and abhorrence.

The above character may have presented itself to the garrison as applicable to Dirk Schuiler, whom they familiarly dubbed Gallows Dirk. Certain it is, he acknowledged allegiance to no one—was an utter enemy to work, holding it in no manner of estimation—but lounged about the fort, depending upon chance for a subsistence, getting drunk whenever he could get liquor and stealing whatever he could lay his hands on. Every day or two he was sure to get a sound rib-roasting for some of his misdemeanors, which, however, as it broke no bones, he made very light of and scrupled not to repeat the offence whenever another opportunity presented. Sometimes in consequence of some flagrant villainy he would abscond from the garrison and be absent for a month at a time; skulking about the woods and swamps, with a long fowling piece on his shoulder, laying in ambush for game—or squatting himself down on the edge of a pond catching fish for hours together, and bearing no little resemblance to that notable bird ycleped the Mud-poke. When he thought his crimes had been forgotten or forgiven, he would sneak back to the fort with a bundle of skins or a bunch of poultry, which perchance he had stolen, and would exchange them for liquor, with which having well soaked his carcass, he would lay in the sun and enjoy all the luxurious indolence of that swinish philosopher Diogenes. He was the terror of all the farmyards in the country, into which he made fearful inroads; and sometimes he would make his sudden appearance at the garrison at daybreak with the whole neighborhood at his heels, like a scoundrel thief of a fox detected in his maraudings and hunted to his hole. Such was this Dirk Schuiler; and from the total indifference he showed to the world or its concerns, and from his truly Indian stoicism and taciturnity, no one would ever have dreamt that he would have been the publisher of the treachery of Risingh.

When the carousal was going on which proved so fatal to the brave Von Poffenburgh and his watchful garrison, Dirk skulked about from room to room, being a kind of privileged vagrant or useless hound whom nobody noticed. But though a fellow of few words, yet, like your taciturn people, his eyes and ears were always open, and in the course of his prowlings he overheard the whole plot of the Swedes. Dirk immediately settled in his own mind how he should turn the matter to his own advantage. He played the perfect jack-of-both-sides—that is to say, he made a prize of everything that came in his reach, robbed both parties, stuck the copper-bound cocked hat of the puissant Von Poffenburgh on his head, whipped a huge pair of Risingh's jackboots under his arms, and took to his heels just before the catastrophe and confusion at the garrison.

Finding himself completely dislodged from his haunt in this quarter, he directed his flight towards his native place, New Amsterdam, from whence he had formerly been obliged to abscond precipitately in consequence of misfortune in business— that is to say, having been detected in the act of sheep stealing. After wandering many days in the woods, toiling through swamps, fording brooks, swimming various rivers and encountering a world of hardships that would have killed any other being but an Indian, a backwoodman or the devil, he at length arrived, half famished and lank as a starved weasel, at Communipaw, where he stole a canoe and paddled over to New Amsterdam. Immediately on landing, he repaired to Governor Stuyvesant and in more words than he had ever spoken before in the whole course of his life gave an account of the disastrous affair.

On receiving these direful tidings, the valiant Peter started
from his seat, as did the stout King Arthur when at "merry
Carleile" the news was brought him of the uncourteous misdeeds of the "grim barone"—without uttering a word he dashed
the pipe he was smoking against the back of the chimney—
thrust a prodigious quid of negro head tobacco into his left
cheek—pulled up his galligaskins and strode up and down the
room humming, as was customary with him when in a passion,
a hideous northwest ditty. But, as I have before shown, he was
not a man to vent his spleen in idle vaporing. His first measure,
after the paroxysm of wrath had subsided, was to stump up-
stairs to a huge wooden chest which served as his armory, from
whence he drew forth that identical suit of regimentals described in the preceding chapter. In these portentous habiliments
he arrayed himself, like Achilles in the armor of Vulcan, maintaining all the while a most appalling silence, knitting his brows
and drawing his breath through his clinched teeth. Being hastily
equipped, he strode down into the parlor, jerked down his
trusty sword from over the fireplace where it was usually suspended; but before he girded it on his thigh he drew it from its
scabbard, and as his eye coursed along the rusty blade, a grim
smile stole over his iron visage—It was the first smile that had
visited his countenance for five long weeks; but everyone who
beheld it prophesied that there would soon be warm work in
the province!

Thus armed at all points, with grisly war depicted in each
feature, his very cocked hat assuming an air of uncommon defiance, he instantly put himself on the alert and dispatched
Antony Van Corlear hither and thither, this way and that way,
through all the muddy streets and crooked lanes of the city,
summoning by sound of trumpet his trusty peers to assemble
in instant council.—This done, by way of expediting matters,
according to the custom of people in a hurry, he kept in continual bustle, shifting from chair to chair, popping his head out
of every window and stumping up and down stairs with his wood-
en leg in such brisk and incessant motion that, as we are informed by an authentic historian of the times, the continual
clatter bore no small resemblance to the music of a cooper
hooping a flour barrel.

A summons so peremptory, and from a man of the governor's
mettle, was not to be trifled with; the sages forthwith repaired
to the council chamber, where the gallant Stuyvesant entered

in martial style and took his chair like another Charlemagne among his Paladins. The counselors seated themselves with the utmost tranquillity, and lighting their long pipes, gazed with unruffled composure on his excellency and his regimentals; being, as all counselors should be, not easily flustered or taken by surprise. The governor, looking around for a moment with a lofty and soldierlike air, and resting one hand on the pummel of his sword and flinging the other forth in a free and spirited manner, addressed them in a short but soul-stirring harangue.

I am extremely sorry that I have not the advantages of Livy, Thucydides, Plutarch and others of my predecessors who were furnished, as I am told, with the speeches of all their great emperors, generals and orators taken down in shorthand by the most accurate stenographers of the time; whereby they were enabled wonderfully to enrich their histories and delight their readers with sublime strains of eloquence. Not having such important auxiliaries, I cannot possibly pronounce what was the tenor of Governor Stuyvesant's speech—whether he with maiden coyness hinted to his hearers that "there was a speck of war in the horizon"—that it would be necessary to resort to the "unprofitable trial of which could do each other the most harm"— or any other delicate construction of language whereby the odious subject of war is handled so fastidiously by modern statesmen; as a gentleman volunteer handles his filthy saltpeter weapons with gloves lest he should soil his dainty fingers.

I am bold, however, to say, from the tenor of Peter Stuyvesant's character, that he did not wrap his rugged subject in silks and ermines and other sickly trickeries of phrase; but spoke forth like a man of nerve and vigor who scorned to shrink in words from those dangers which he stood ready to encounter in very deed. This much is certain, that he concluded by announcing his determination of leading on his troops in person and routing these costardmonger Swedes from their usurped quarters at Fort Casimir. To this hardy resolution, such of his council as were awake gave their usual signal of concurrence, and as to the rest who had fallen asleep about the middle of the harangue (their "usual custom in the afternoon")—they made not the least objection.

And now was seen in the fair city of New Amsterdam a prodigious bustle and preparation for iron war. Recruiting parties marched hither and thither, calling lustily upon all the scrubs, the runagates and tatterdemalions of the Manhattoes and its vicinity who had any ambition to six-pence a day, and immortal fame into the bargain, to enlist in the cause of glory. For I would have you note that your warlike heroes who trudge in the rear of conquerors are generally of that illustrious class of gentlemen who are equal candidates for the army or the bride-well—the halberts or the whipping post—for whom dame fortune has cast an even die whether they shall make their exit by the sword or the halter—and whose deaths shall, at all events, be a lofty example to their countrymen.

But notwithstanding all this martial rout and invitation, the ranks of honor were but scantily supplied; so averse were the peaceful burghers of New Amsterdam from enlisting in foreign broils or stirring beyond that home which rounded all their earthly ideas. Upon beholding this, the great Peter, whose noble heart was all on fire with war and sweet revenge, determined to wait no longer for the tardy assistance of these oily citizens but to muster up his merry men of the Hudson; who, brought up among woods and wilds and savage beasts like our yeomen of Kentucky, delighted in nothing so much as desperate adventures and perilous expeditions through the wilderness. Thus resolving, he ordered his trusty squire Antony Van Corlear to have his state galley prepared and duly victualled; which being performed, he attended public service at the great Church of St. Nicholas, like a true and pious governor, and then leaving peremptory orders with his council to have the chivalry of the Manhattoes marshalled out and appointed against his return, departed upon his recruiting voyage up the waters of the Hudson.

CHAPTER III

Containing Peter Stuyvesant's voyage up the Hudson, and the wonders and delights of that renowned river.

Now did the soft breezes of the south steal sweetly over the beauteous face of nature, tempering the panting heats of summer into genial and prolific warmth; when that miracle of hardihood and chivalric virtue, the dauntless Peter Stuyvesant, spread his canvas to the wind and departed from the fair island of Mannahata. The galley in which he embarked was sumptuously adorned with pendants and streamers of gorgeous dyes which fluttered gaily in the wind or drooped their ends in the bosom of the stream. The bow and poop of this majestic vessel were gallantly bedight, after the rarest Dutch fashion, with figures of little pursy Cupids with periwigs on their heads and bearing in their hands garlands of flowers, the like of which are not to be found in any book of botany; being the matchless flowers which flourished in the golden age and exist no longer, unless it be in the imaginations of ingenious carvers of wood and discolorers of canvas.

Thus rarely decorated in style befitting the state of the puissant potentate of the Manhattoes did the galley of Peter Stuyvesant launch forth upon the bosom of the lordly Hudson, which as it rolled its broad waves to the ocean seemed to pause for a while and swell with pride, as if conscious of the illustrious burthen it sustained.

But trust me, gentlefolk, far other was the scene presented to the contemplation of the crew from that which may be witnessed at this degenerate day. Wildness and savage majesty reigned on the borders of this mighty river—the hand of cultivation had not as yet laid low the dark forests and tamed the features of the landscape—nor had the frequent sail of commerce yet broken in upon the profound and awful solitude of ages. Here and there might be seen a rude wigwam perched among the cliffs of the mountains, with its curling column of smoke mounting in the transparent atmosphere—but so loftily situated that the whoopings of the savage children gamboling on the margin of the dizzy heights fell almost as faintly on the ear as do the notes of the lark when lost in the azure vault of heaven. Now and then from the beetling brow of some rocky precipice the wild deer would look timidly down upon the splendid pageant as it passed below; and then, tossing his branching antlers in the air, would bound away into the thickets of the forest.

Through such scenes did the stately vessel of Peter Stuyvesant pass. Now did they skirt the bases of the rocky heights of Jersey which spring up like everlasting walls reaching from the waves unto the heavens; and were fashioned, if tradition may be believed, in times long past by the mighty spirit Manetho to protect his favorite abodes from the unhallowed eyes of mortals. Now did they career it gaily across the vast expanse of Tappan Bay, whose wide extended shores present a vast variety of delectable scenery—here the bold promontory, crowned with embowering trees, advancing into the bay—there the long woodland slope, sweeping up from the shore in rich luxuriance and terminating in the upland precipice—while at a distance a long waving line of rocky heights threw their gigantic shades across the water. Now would they pass where some modest little interval, opening among these stupendous scenes yet retreating as it were for protection into the embraces of the neighboring mountains, displayed a rural paradise fraught with sweet and pastoral beauties: the velvet tufted lawn—the bushy copse—the tinkling rivulet stealing through the fresh and vivid verdure, on whose banks was situated some little Indian village or peradventure the rude cabin of some solitary hunter.

The different periods of the revolving day seemed each with cunning magic to diffuse a different charm over the scene. Now would the jovial sun break gloriously from the east, blazing from the summits of the eastern hills and sparkling the landscape with a thousand dewy gems; while along the borders of the river were seen heavy masses of mist which, like midnight caitiffs disturbed at his approach, made a sluggish retreat, rolling in sullen reluctance up the mountains. At such times all was brightness and life and gaiety—the atmosphere seemed of an indescribable pureness and transparency—the birds broke forth in wanton madrigals, and the freshening breezes wafted the vessel merrily on her course. But when the sun sunk amid a flood of glory in the west, mantling the heavens and the earth with a thousand gorgeous dyes—then all was calm and silent and magnificent. The late swelling sail hung lifelessly against the mast—the simple seaman with folded arms leaned against the shrouds, lost in that involuntary musing which the sober grandeur of nature commands in the rudest of her children. The vast bosom of the Hudson was like an unruffled mirror reflecting the golden splendor of the heavens, excepting that now and then a bark canoe would steal across its surface, filled with painted savages whose gay feathers glared brightly as perchance a lingering ray of the setting sun gleamed upon them from the western mountains.

But when the hour of twilight spread its magic mists around, then did the face of nature assume a thousand fugitive charms which to the worthy heart that seeks enjoyment in the glorious works of its maker are inexpressibly captivating. The mellow dubious light that prevailed just served to tinge with illusive colors the softened features of the scenery. The deceived but delighted eye sought vainly to discern in the broad masses of shade the separating line between the land and water; or to distinguish the fading objects that seemed sinking into chaos. Now did the busy fancy supply the feebleness of vision, producing with industrious craft a fairy creation of her own. Under her plastic wand the barren rocks frowned upon the watery waste in the semblance of lofty towers and high embattled castles—trees assumed the direful forms of mighty giants, and the inaccessible summits of the mountains seemed peopled with a thousand shadowy beings.

Now broke forth from the shores the notes of an innumerable variety of insects who filled the air with a strange but not inharmonious concert—while ever and anon was heard the melancholy plaint of the Whippoorwill who, perched on some lone tree, wearied the ear of night with his incessant moanings. The mind, soothed into a hallowed melancholy by the solemn mystery of the scene, listened with pensive stillness to catch and distinguish each sound that vaguely echoed from the shore—now and then startled perchance by the whoop of some straggling savage or the dreary howl of some caitiff wolf stealing forth upon his nightly prowlings.

Thus happily did they pursue their course until they entered upon those awful defiles denominated THE HIGHLANDS, where it would seem that the gigantic Titans had erst waged their impious war with heaven, piling up cliffs on cliffs and hurling vast masses of rock in wild confusion. But in sooth very different is the history of these cloud-capped mountains.—These in ancient days, before the Hudson poured his waters from the lakes, formed one vast prison within whose rocky bosom the omnipotent Manetho confined the rebellious spirits who repined at his control. Here, bound in adamantine chains or jammed in rifted pines or crushed by ponderous rocks, they groaned for many an age.—At length the conquering Hudson, in his irresistible career towards the ocean, burst open their prison-house, rolling his tide triumphantly through its stupendous ruins.

Still, however, do many of them lurk about their old abodes; and these it is, according to venerable legends, that cause the echoes which resound throughout these awful solitudes; which are nothing but their angry clamors when any noise disturbs the profoundness of their repose.—For when the elements are agitated by tempest, when the winds are up and the thunder rolls, then horrible is the yelling and howling of these troubled spirits, making the mountains to rebellow with their hideous uproar; for at such times it is said that they think the great Manetho is returning once more to plunge them in gloomy caverns and renew their intolerable captivity.

But all these fair and glorious scenes were lost upon the gallant Stuyvesant; naught occupied his mind but thoughts of iron war and proud anticipations of hardy deeds of arms. Neither did his honest crew trouble their vacant heads with any romantic speculations of the kind. The pilot at the helm quietly smoked his pipe, thinking of nothing either past, present or to come—those of his comrades who were not industriously snoring under the hatches were listening with open mouths to Antony Van Corlear; who, seated on the windlass, was relating to them the marvelous history of those myriads of fireflies that sparkled like gems and spangles upon the dusky robe of night. These, according to tradition, were originally a race of pestilent sempiternous beldames who peopled these parts long before the memory of man; being of that abominated race emphatically called *brimstones;* and who for their innumerable sins against the children of men, and to furnish an awful warning to the beauteous sex, were doomed to infest the earth in the shape of these threatening and terrible little bugs; enduring the internal torments of that fire which they formerly carried in their hearts and breathed forth in their words; but now are sentenced to bear about forever—in their tails!

And now am I going to tell a fact which I doubt much my readers will hesitate to believe; but if they do, they are welcome not to believe a word in this whole history, for nothing which it contains is more true. It must be known then that the nose of Antony the trumpeter was of a very lusty size, strutting boldly from his countenance like a mountain of Golconda; being sumptuously bedecked with rubies and other precious stones—the true regalia of a king of good fellows which jolly Bacchus grants to all who bouse it heartily at the flagon. Now thus it happened that bright and early in the morning, the good Antony, having washed his burly visage, was leaning over the quarter railing of the galley, contemplating it in the glassy wave below—just at this moment the illustrious sun, breaking in all his splendor from behind one of the high bluffs of the Highlands, did dart one of his most potent beams full upon the refulgent nose of the sounder of brass—the reflection of which shot straightway down, hissing-hot, into the water and killed a mighty sturgeon that was sporting beside the vessel! This huge monster, being with infinite labor hoisted on board, furnished a luxurious repast to all the crew, being accounted of excellent flavor excepting about the wound where it smacked a little of brimstone—and this, on my veracity, was the first time that ever sturgeon was eaten in these parts by Christian people.*

When this astonishing miracle came to be made known to Peter Stuyvesant, and that he tasted of the unknown fish, he, as may well be supposed, marvelled exceedingly; and as a monument thereof, he gave the name of *Anthony's Nose* to a stout promontory in the neighborhood—and it has continued to be called Anthony's Nose ever since that time.

But hold—Whither am I wandering?—By the mass, if I attempt to accompany the good Peter Stuyvesant on this voyage I shall never make an end; for never was there a voyage so fraught with marvelous incidents, nor a river so abounding with transcendent beauties worthy of being severally recorded. Even now I have it on the point of my pen to relate how his crew were most horribly frightened, on going on shore above the highlands, by a gang of merry roistering devils frisking and curvetting on a huge flat rock which projected into the river—and which is called the *Duyvel's Dans-Kamer* to this very day—But no! Diedrich Knickerbocker—it becomes thee not to idle thus in thy historic wayfaring.

Recollect that while dwelling with the fond garrulity of age over these fairy scenes, endeared to thee by the recollections of thy youth, and the charms of a thousand legendary tales which beguiled the simple ear of thy childhood; recollect that thou art trifling with those fleeting moments which should be devoted to loftier themes.—Is not time—relentless time!—shaking with

---

* The learned Hans Megapolensis, treating of the country about Albany in a letter which was written some time after the settlement thereof, says, "There is in the river great plenty of sturgeon, which we Christians do not make use of; but the Indians eat them greedilie."

palsied hand his almost exhausted hourglass before thee?—
hasten then to pursue thy weary task lest the last sands be run
ere thou hast finished thy history of the Manhattoes.

Let us then commit the dauntless Peter, his brave galley and
his loyal crew to the protection of the blessed St. Nicholas; who
I have no doubt will prosper him in his voyage while we await
his return at the great city of New Amsterdam.

CHAPTER IV

*Describing the powerful army that assembled
at the city of New Amsterdam—together
with the interview between Peter the Headstrong and General Von Poffenburgh, and
Peter's sentiments touching unfortunate
great men.*

While thus the enterprising Peter was coasting with flowing
sail up the shores of the lordly Hudson and arousing all the
phlegmatic little Dutch settlements upon its borders, a great
and puissant concourse of warriors was assembling at the city
of New Amsterdam. And here that invaluable fragment of
antiquity, the Stuyvesant manuscript, is more than commonly
particular; by which means I am enabled to record the illustrious
host that encamped itself in the public square in front of the
fort, at present denominated the Bowling Green.

In the center, then, was pitched the tent of the men of battle
of the Manhattoes, who being the inmates of the metropolis,
composed the life guards of the governor. These were commanded by the valiant Stoffel Brinkerhoff who whilom had
acquired such immortal fame at Oyster Bay—they displayed as
a standard a beaver *rampant* on a field of orange; being the
arms of the province and denoting the persevering industry
and the amphibious origin of the Nederlanders.*

---

* This was likewise the great seal of the New Netherlands, as may still be
seen in ancient records.

On their right hand might be seen the vassals of that renowned Mynheer, Michael Paw,* who lorded it over the fair regions of ancient Pavonia and the lands away south, even unto the Navesink mountains,† and was moreover patroon of Gibbet Island. His standard was borne by his trusty squire, Cornelius Van Vorst; consisting of a huge oyster *recumbent* upon a sea-green field; being the armorial bearings of his favorite metropolis, Communipaw. He brought to the camp a stout force of warriors, heavily armed, being each clad in ten pair of linsey-woolsey breeches, and overshadowed by broad-brimmed beavers with short pipes twisted in their hatbands. These were the men who vegetated in the mud along the shores of Pavonia; being of the race of genuine copperheads, and were fabled to have sprung from oysters.

At a little distance was encamped the tribe of warriors who came from the neighborhood of Hell Gate. These were commanded by the Suy Dams and the Van Dams, incontinent hard swearers, as their names betoken—they were terrible looking fellows, clad in broad-skirted gaberdines of that curious colored cloth called thunder and lightning—and bore as a standard three Devil's darning needles, *volant,* in a flame-colored field.

Hard by was the tent of the men of battle from the marshy borders of the Wael-bogtig‡ and the country thereabouts—these were of a sour aspect, by reason that they lived on crabs, which abound in these parts. They were the first institutors of that honorable order of knighthood called *Fly market shirks,* and if tradition speak true, did likewise introduce the far-famed step in dancing called "double trouble." They were commanded by the fearless Jacobus Varra Vanger, and had, moreover, a jolly

---

* Besides what is related in the Stuyvesant MS. I have found mention made of this illustrious Patroon in another manuscript, which says: "De Heer (or the Squire) Michael Paw, a Dutch subject, about 10th Aug. 1630, by deed purchased Staten Island. N. B. The same Michael Paw had what the Dutch call a colonie at Pavonia, on the Jersey shore opposite New York, and his overseer in 1636 was named Corns. Van Vorst—a person of the same name in 1769 owned Pawles Hook and a large farm at Pavonia and is a lineal descendant from Van Vorst."

† So called from the Navesink tribe of Indians that inhabited these parts—at present they are erroneously denominated the Neversink or Neversunk mountains.

‡ I. E. The *Winding Bay,* named from the winding of its shores. This has since been corrupted by the vulgar into the *Wallabout,* and is the basin which shelters our infant navy.

band of Breukelen* ferrymen, who performed a brave concerto on conch shells.

But I refrain from pursuing this minute description, which goes on to describe the warriors of Bloemen Dael and Wee-hawk and Hoboken and sundry other places, well known in history and song—for now does the sound of martial music alarm the people of New Amsterdam, sounding afar from beyond the walls of the city. But this alarm was in a little while relieved, for lo, from the midst of a vast cloud of dust they recognised the brimstone-colored breeches and splendid silver leg of Peter Stuyvesant glaring in the sunbeams; and beheld him approaching at the head of a formidable army which he had mustered along the banks of the Hudson. And here the excellent but anonymous writer of the Stuyvesant manuscript breaks out into a brave and glorious description of the forces as they defiled through the principal gate of the city that stood by the head of Wall Street.

First of all came the Van Bummels, who inhabit the pleasant borders of the Bronx.—These were short fat men wearing exceeding large trunk breeches, and are renowned for feats of the trencher—they were the first inventors of suppawn, or mush and milk.—Close in their rear marched the Van Vlotens of Kaats Kill, most horrible quaffers of new cyder, and arrant braggarts in their liquor.—After them came the Van Pelts of Groodt Esopus, dexterous horsemen mounted upon goodly switch-tailed steeds of the Esopus breed—these were mighty hunters of minks and musk rats, whence came the word *Peltry*.—Then the Van Nests of Kinderhoeck, valiant robbers of birds' nests, as their name denotes; to these, if report may be believed, are we indebted for the invention of slapjacks, or buckwheat cakes. —Then the Van Higginbottoms of Wapping's Creek; these came armed with ferules and birchen rods, being a race of school-masters who first discovered the marvelous sympathy between the seat of honor and the seat of intellect—and that the shortest way to get knowledge into the head was to hammer it into the bottom.—Then the Van Grolls of Anthony's Nose, who carried their liquor in fair round little pottles, by reason they could not bouse it out of their canteens, having such rare long noses. —Then the Gardeniers of Hudson and thereabouts, distinguished

---

* Now spelt Brooklyn.

by many triumphant feats such as robbing watermelon patches, smoking rabbits out of their holes and the like; and by being great lovers of roasted pigs' tails; these were the ancestors of the renowned congressman of that name.—Then the Van Hoesens of Sing Sing, great choristers and players upon the jews harp; these marched two and two, singing the great song of St. Nicholas.—Then the Couenhovens of Sleepy Hollow; these gave birth to a jolly race of publicans who first discovered the magic artifice of conjuring a quart of wine into a pint bottle.—Then the Van Kortlandts, who lived on the wild banks of the Croton and were great killers of wild ducks, being much spoken of for their skill in shooting with the long bow.—Then the Van Bunschotens of Nyack and Kakiat, who were the first that did ever kick with the left foot; they were gallant bushwhackers and hunters of racoons by moonlight.—Then the Van Winkles of Haerlem, potent suckers of eggs, and noted for running of horses and running up of scores at taverns; they were the first that ever winked with both eyes at once.—Lastly came the KNICKERBOCKERS of the great town of Scaghtikoke, where the folk lay stones upon the houses in windy weather lest they should be blown away. These derive their name, as some say, from *Knicker,* to shake, and *Beker,* a goblet, indicating thereby that they were sturdy toss pots of yore; but, in truth, it was derived from *Knicker,* to nod, and *Boeken,* books; plainly meaning that they were great nodders or dozers over books—from them did descend the writer of this history.

Such was the legion of sturdy bush-beaters that poured in at the grand gate of New Amsterdam; the Stuyvesant manuscript indeed speaks of many more whose names I omit to mention, seeing that it behooves me to hasten to matters of greater moment. Nothing could surpass the joy and martial pride of the lion-hearted Peter as he reviewed this mighty host of warriors, and he determined no longer to defer the gratification of his much wished for revenge upon the scoundrel Swedes at Fort Casimir.

But before I hasten to record those unmatchable events, which will be found in the sequel of this faithful history, let me pause to notice the fate of Jacobus Von Poffenburgh, the discomfited commander in chief of the armies of the New Netherlands. Such is the inherent uncharitableness of human nature that scarcely did the news become public of his deplorable discomfiture at Fort Casimir than a thousand scurvy rumors were set

afloat in New Amsterdam, wherein it was insinuated that he had
in reality a treacherous understanding with the Swedish commander; that he had long been in the practice of privately
communicating with the Swedes; together with divers hints
about "secret service money."—To all which deadly charges I do
not give a jot more credit than I think they deserve.

Certain it is that the general vindicated his character by the
most vehement oaths and protestations, and put every man out
of the ranks of honor who dared to doubt his integrity. Moreover, on returning to New Amsterdam, he paraded up and down
the streets with a crew of hard swearers at his heels—sturdy
bottle companions whom he gorged and fattened and who were
ready to bolster him through all the courts of justice—heroes
of his own kidney, fierce-whiskered, broadshouldered, colbrand-
looking swaggerers—not one of whom but looked as though he
could eat up an ox and pick his teeth with the horns. These
lifeguard men quarrelled all his quarrels, were ready to fight
all his battles, and scowled at every man that turned up his
nose at the general, as though they would devour him alive.
Their conversation was interspersed with oaths like minute
guns, and every bombastic rhodomontado was rounded off by a
thundering execration, like a patriotic toast honored with a
discharge of artillery.

All these valorous vaporings had a considerable effect in
convincing certain profound sages, many of whom began to
think the general a hero of unutterable loftiness and magnanimity of soul, particularly as he was continually protesting *on
the honor of a soldier*—a marvelously high-sounding assevera-
tion. Nay, one of the members of the council went so far as to
propose they should immortalize him by an imperishable statue
of plaster of Paris.

But the vigilant Peter the Headstrong was not thus to be
deceived.—Sending privately for the commander in chief of all
the armies, and having heard all his story, garnished with the
customary pious oaths, protestations and ejaculations—"Harkee,
comrade," cried he, "though by your own account you are the
most brave, upright and honorable man in the whole province,
yet do you lie under the misfortune of being damnably traduced
and immeasurably despised. Now though it is certainly hard to
punish a man for his misfortunes, and though it is very possible
you are totally innocent of the crimes laid to your charge, yet

as heaven at present, doubtless for some wise purpose, sees fit to withhold all proofs of your innocence, far be it from me to counteract its sovereign will. Beside, I cannot consent to venture my armies with a commander whom they despise, or to trust the welfare of my people to a champion whom they distrust. Retire therefore, my friend, from the irksome toils and cares of public life, with this comforting reflection—that if you be guilty, you are but enjoying your just reward—and if innocent, you are not the first great and good man who has most wrongfully been slandered and maltreated in this wicked world—doubtless to be better treated in a better world where there shall be neither error, calumny nor persecution.—In the meantime let me never see your face again, for I have a horrible antipathy to the countenances of unfortunate great men like yourself."

CHAPTER V

In which the Author discourses very ingeniously of himself.—After which is to be found much interesting history about Peter the Headstrong and his followers.

As my readers and myself are about entering on as many perils as ever a confederacy of meddlesome knights-errant wilfully ran their heads into, it is meet that, like those hardy adventurers, we should join hands, bury all differences and swear to stand by one another, in weal or woe, to the end of the enterprise. My readers must doubtless perceive how completely I have altered my tone and deportment since we first set out together. I warrant they then thought me a crabbed, cynical, impertinent little son of a Dutchman; for I scarcely ever gave them a civil word, nor so much as touched my beaver when I had occasion to address them. But as we jogged along together in the high road of my history, I gradually began to relax, to grow more courteous, and occasionally to enter into familiar discourse, until at length I came to conceive a most social, companionable kind of regard for them. This is just my way—I am always a little cold and reserved at first, particularly to people whom I neither know nor care for, and am only to be completely won by long intimacy.

Besides, why should I have been sociable to the crowd of how-d'ye-do acquaintances that flocked around me at my first appearance? Many were merely attracted by a new face; and having stared me full in the title page, walked off without saying a word; while others lingered yawningly through the preface, and having gratified their short-lived curiosity, soon dropped off one by one. But more especially to try their mettle, I had recourse to an expedient similar to one which we are told was used by that peerless flower of chivalry, King Arthur; who, before he admitted any knight to his intimacy, first required that he should show himself superior to danger or hardships by encountering unheard-of mishaps, slaying some dozen giants, vanquishing wicked enchanters, not to say a word of dwarfs, hippogriffs and fiery dragons. On a similar principle, I cunningly led my readers at the first sally into two or three knotty chapters where they were most woefully belabored and buffeted by a host of pagan philosophers and infidel writers. Though naturally a very grave man, yet could I scarce refrain from smiling outright at seeing the utter confusion and dismay of my valiant cavaliers—some dropped down dead (asleep) on the field; others threw down my book in the middle of the first chapter, took to their heels and never ceased scampering until they had fairly run it out of sight; when they stopped to take breath, to tell their friends what troubles they had undergone and to warn all others from venturing on so thankless an expedition. Every page thinned my ranks more and more; and of the vast multitude that first set out, but a comparatively few made shift to survive, in exceedingly battered condition, through the five introductory chapters.

What then! would you have had me take such sunshine, faint-hearted recreants to my bosom at our first acquaintance? No—no; I reserved my friendship for those who deserved it, for those who undauntedly bore me company in despite of difficulties, dangers and fatigues. And now, as to those who adhere to me at present, I take them affectionately by the hand—Worthy and thrice-beloved readers! brave and well-tried comrades! who have

faithfully followed my footsteps through all my wanderings—
I salute you from my heart—I pledge myself to stand by you to
the last; and to conduct you (so heaven speed this trusty weapon
which I now hold between my fingers) triumphantly to the end
of this our stupendous undertaking.

But hark! while we are thus talking, the city of New Amsterdam is in a bustle. The gallant host of warriors encamped in the
Bowling Green are striking their tents; the brazen trumpet of
Antony Van Corlear makes the welkin to resound with portentous clangor—the drums beat—the standards of the Manhattoes, of Hell Gate and of Michael Paw wave proudly in the
air. And now behold where the mariners are busily employed
hoisting the sails of yon topsail schooner and those two clump-
built Albany sloops which are to waft the army of the Nederlanders to gather immortal honors on the Delaware!

The entire population of the city, man, woman and child,
turned out to behold the chivalry of New Amsterdam as it
paraded the streets previous to embarkation. Many a handkerchief was waved out of the windows; many a fair nose was
blown in melodious sorrow on the mournful occasion. The
grief of the fair dames and beauteous damsels of Grenada could
not have been more vociferous on the banishment of the gallant
tribe of Abencerrages than was that of the kindhearted fair
ones of New Amsterdam on the departure of their intrepid
warriors. Every lovesick maiden fondly crammed the pockets
of her hero with gingerbread and doughnuts—many a copper
ring was exchanged and crooked sixpence broken in pledge of
eternal constancy—and there remain extant to this day some
love verses written on that occasion, sufficiently crabbed and
incomprehensible to confound the whole universe.

But it was a moving sight to see the buxom lasses, how they
hung about the doughty Antony Van Corlear—for he was a
jolly, rosy-faced, lusty bachelor, fond of his joke and withal a
desperate rogue among the women. Fain would they have kept
him to comfort them while the army was away; for besides what
I have said of him, it is no more than justice to add that he was
a kindhearted soul, noted for his benevolent attentions in comforting disconsolate wives during the absence of their husbands
—and this made him to be very much regarded by the honest
burghers of the city. But nothing could keep the valiant Antony
from following the heels of the old governor, whom he loved

as he did his very soul—so embracing all the young vrouws and giving every one of them that had good teeth and rosy lips a dozen hearty smacks—he departed loaded with their kind wishes.

Nor was the departure of the gallant Peter among the least causes of public distress. Though the old governor was by no means indulgent to the follies and waywardness of his subjects, yet somehow or other he had become strangely popular among the people. There is something so captivating in personal bravery that with the common mass of mankind it takes the lead of most other merits. The simple folk of New Amsterdam looked upon Peter Stuyvesant as a prodigy of valor. His wooden leg, that trophy of his martial encounters, was regarded with reverence and admiration. Every old burgher had a budget of miraculous stories to tell about the exploits of Hardkoppig Piet wherewith he regaled his children of a long winter night; and on which he dwelt with as much delight and exaggeration as do our honest country yeomen on the hardy adventures of old General Putnam (or as he is familiarly termed, *Old Put*) during our glorious revolution—Not an individual but verily believed the old governor was a match for Belzebub himself; and there was even a story told, with great mystery and under the rose, of his having shot the devil with a silver bullet one dark stormy night as he was sailing in a canoe through Hell Gate.—But this I do not record as being an absolute fact—perish the man who would let fall a drop to discolor the pure stream of history!

Certain it is, not an old woman in New Amsterdam but considered Peter Stuyvesant as a tower of strength and rested satisfied that the public welfare was secure so long as he was in the city. It is not surprising then that they looked upon his departure as a sore affliction. With heavy hearts they draggled at the heels of his troop as they marched down to the riverside to embark. The governor from the stern of his schooner gave a short but truly patriarchal address to his citizens, wherein he recommended them to comport like loyal and peaceful subjects—to go to church regularly on Sundays and to mind their business all the week besides—That the women should be dutiful and affectionate to their husbands—looking after nobody's concerns but their own: eschewing all gossipings and morning gaddings— and carrying short tongues and long petticoats—That the men should abstain from intermeddling in public concerns, entrusting the cares of government to the officers appointed to support them—staying at home, like good citizens, making money for themselves and getting children for the benefit of their country— That the burgomasters should look well to the public interest —not oppressing the poor nor indulging the rich—not tasking their security to devise new laws, but faithfully enforcing those which were already made—rather bending their attention to prevent evil than to punish it; ever recollecting that civil magistrates should consider themselves more as guardians of public morals than rat catchers employed to entrap public delinquents.—Finally, he exhorted them, one and all, high and low, rich and poor to conduct themselves *as well as they could;* assuring them that if they faithfully and conscientiously complied with this golden rule, there was no danger but that they would all conduct themselves well enough. This done, he gave them a paternal benediction; the sturdy Antony sounded a most loving farewell with his trumpet, the jolly crews put up a lusty shout of triumph, and the invincible armada swept off proudly down the bay.

The good people of New Amsterdam crowded down to the battery—that blest resort from whence so many a tender prayer has been wafted, so many a fair hand waved, so many a tearful look been cast by love-sick damsel after the lessening bark which bore her adventurous swain to distant climes!—Here the populace watched with straining eyes the gallant squadron as it slowly floated down the bay, and when the intervening land at the Narrows shut it from their sight, gradually dispersed with silent tongues and downcast countenances.

A heavy gloom hung over the late bustling city—The honest burghers smoked their pipes in profound thoughtfulness, casting many a wistful look to the weathercock on the church of St. Nicholas; and all the old women, having no longer the presence of Peter Stuyvesant to hearten them, gathered their children home and barricadoed the doors and windows every evening at sundown.

In the meanwhile the armada of the sturdy Peter proceeded prosperously on its voyage, and after encountering about as many storms and waterspouts and whales and other horrors and phenomena as generally befall adventurous landsmen in perilous voyages of the kind; and after undergoing a severe scouring from that deplorable and unpitied malady called seasickness, the whole squadron arrived safely in the Delaware.

Without so much as dropping anchor and giving his wearied ships time to breathe after laboring so long in the ocean, the intrepid Peter pursued his course up the Delaware and made a sudden appearance before Fort Casimir. Having summoned the astonished garrison by a terrific blast from the trumpet of the long-winded Van Corlear, he demanded in a tone of thunder an instant surrender of the fort. To this demand, Suen Scutz, the wind-dried commandant, replied in a shrill whiffling voice which by reason of his extreme spareness sounded like the wind whistling through a broken bellows—"that he had no very strong reason for refusing, except that the demand was particularly disagreeable, as he had been ordered to maintain his post to the last extremity." He requested time, therefore, to consult with Governor Risingh, and proposed a truce for that purpose.

The choleric Peter, indignant at having his rightful fort so treacherously taken from him and thus pertinaciously withheld, refused the proposed armistice, and swore by the pipe of St. Nicholas, which like the sacred fire was never extinguished, that unless the fort were surrendered in ten minutes, he would incontinently storm the works, make all the garrison run the gauntlet and split their scoundrel of a commander like a pickled shad. To give this menace the greater effect, he drew forth his trusty sword and shook it at them with such a fierce and vigorous motion that doubtless if it had not been exceeding rusty it would have lightened terror into the eyes and hearts of the enemy. He then ordered his men to bring a broadside to bear upon the fort, consisting of two swivels, three muskets, a long duck fowling piece and two brace of horse pistols.

In the meantime the sturdy Van Corlear marshalled all his forces and commenced his warlike operations—Distending his cheeks like a very Boreas, he kept up a most horrific twanging of his trumpet—the lusty choristers of Sing Sing broke forth into a hideous song of battle—the warriors of Breukelen and the Wael Bogtig blew a potent and astounding blast on their conch shells, all together forming as outrageous a concerto as though five thousand French orchestras were displaying their skill in a modern overture.

Whether the formidable front of war thus suddenly presented smote the garrison with sore dismay—or whether the concluding terms of the summons, which mentioned that he should surrender "at discretion," were mistaken by Suen Scutz, who though a Swede was a very considerate, easy-tempered man—as a compliment to his discretion, I will not take upon me to say; certain it is he found it impossible to resist so courteous a demand. Accordingly, in the very nick of time, just as the cabin boy had gone after a coal of fire to discharge the swivel, a chamade was beat on the rampart by the only drum in the garrison, to the no small satisfaction of both parties; who, notwithstanding their great stomach for fighting, had full as good an inclination to eat a quiet dinner as to exchange black eyes and bloody noses.

Thus did this impregnable fortress once more return to the domination of their High Mightinesses; Scutz and his garrison of twenty men were allowed to march out with the honors of war, and the victorious Peter, who was as generous as brave, permitted them to keep possession of all their arms and ammunition—the same on inspection being found totally unfit for service, having long rusted in the magazine of the fortress, even before it was rested by the Swedes from the magnanimous but windy Von Poffenburgh. But I must not omit to mention that the governor was so well pleased with the services of his faithful squire Van Corlear in the reduction of this great fortress that he made him on the spot lord of a goodly domain in the vicinity of New Amsterdam—which goes by the name of Corlear's Hook unto this very day.*

The unexampled liberality of the valiant Stuyvesant towards the Swedes occasioned great surprise in the city of New Amsterdam—nay, certain of those factious individuals who had been enlightened by the political meetings that prevailed during the days of William the Testy—but who had not dared to indulge their meddlesome habits under the eye of their present ruler—now emboldened by his absence dared even to give vent to their censures in the streets.—Murmurs were heard in the very council chamber of New Amsterdam; and there is no knowing whether they would not have broken out into downright speeches and invectives had not Peter Stuyvesant privately sent home his walking staff to be laid as a mace on the table of the council chamber in the midst of his counselors; who, like wise men, took the hint and for ever after held their peace.

---

* De Vries makes mention in one of his voyages of *Corlear's Hoeck* and *Corlear's Plantagie,* or *Bouwery.*

CHAPTER VI

*Showing the great advantage that the author
has over his reader in time of battle—together
with divers portentous movements which
betoken that something terrible is about to
happen.*

Like as a mighty alderman, when at a corporation feast the
first spoonful of turtle soup salutes his palate, feels his impatient appetite but tenfold quickened and redoubles his vigorous attacks upon the tureen, while his voracious eyes, projecting
from his head, roll greedily round, devouring everything at
table—so did the mettlesome Peter Stuyvesant feel that intolerable hunger for martial glory which raged within his very
bowels inflamed by the capture of Fort Casimir, and nothing
could allay it but the conquest of all New Sweden. No sooner
therefore had he secured his conquest than he stumped resolutely on, flushed with success, to gather fresh laurels at Fort
Christina.*

This was the grand Swedish post, established on a small
river (or, as it is improperly termed, creek) of the same name;
and here that crafty governor Jan Risingh lay grimly drawn
up like a gray-bearded spider in the citadel of his web.

But before we hurry into the direful scenes that must attend
the meeting of two such potent chieftains, it is advisable that
we pause for a moment and hold a kind of warlike council.
Battles should not be rushed into precipitately by the historian
and his readers, any more than by the general and his soldiers.
The great commanders of antiquity never engaged the enemy
without previously preparing the minds of their followers by
animating harangues; spiriting them up to heroic feelings,
assuring them of the protection of the gods, and inspiring them
with a confidence in the prowess of their leaders. So the his-

---

* This is at present a flourishing town called Christiana, or Christeen,
about thirty-seven miles from Philadelphia on the post road to Baltimore.

torian should awaken the attention and enlist the passions of his readers; and having set them all on fire with the importance of his subject, he should put himself at their head, flourish his pen, and lead them on to the thickest of the fight.

An illustrous example of this rule may be seen in that mirror of historians, the immortal Thucydides. Having arrived at the breaking out of the Peloponnesian war, one of his commentators observes that "he sounds the charge in all the disposition and spirit of Homer. He catalogues the allies on both sides. He awakens our expectations and fast engages our attention. All mankind are concerned in the important point now going to be decided. Endeavors are made to disclose futurity. Heaven itself is interested in the dispute. The earth totters and nature seems to labor with the great event. This is his solemn sublime manner of setting out. Thus he magnifies a war between two, as Rapin styles them, petty states; and thus artfully he supports a little subject by treating it in a great and noble method."*

In like manner, having conducted my readers into the very teeth of peril—having followed the adventurous Peter and his band into foreign regions—surrounded by foes and stunned by the horrid din of arms—at this important moment, while darkness and doubt hang o'er each coming chapter, I hold it meet to harangue them and prepare them for the events that are to follow.

And here I would premise one great advantage which, as the historian, I possess over my reader; and this it is, that though I cannot save the life of my favorite hero, nor absolutely contradict the event of a battle (both which liberties, though often taken by the French writers of the present reign, I hold to be utterly unworthy of a scrupulous historian), yet I can now and then make him bestow on his enemy a sturdy back stroke sufficient to fell a giant, though in honest truth he may never have done anything of the kind—or I can drive his antagonist clear round and round the field, as did Homer make that fine fellow Hector scamper like a poltroon round the walls of Troy; for which, if ever they have encountered one another in the Elysian fields, I'll warrant the prince of poets has had to make the most humble apology.

---

* Smith's Thucyd. Vol. I. p. lxx.

I am aware that many conscientious readers will be ready to cry out "foul play!" whenever I render a little assistance to my hero—but I consider it one of those privileges exercised by historians of all ages—and one which has never been disputed. In fact, an historian is, as it were, bound in honor to stand by his hero—the fame of the latter is entrusted to his hands, and it is his duty to do the best by it he can. Never was there a general, an admiral or any other commander who in giving an account of any battle he had fought did not sorely belabor the enemy; and I have no doubt that had my heroes written the history of their own achievements, they would have dealt much harder blows than any that I shall recount. Standing forth, therefore, as the guardian of their fame, it behooves me to do them the same justice they would have done themselves; and if I happen to be a little hard upon the Swedes, I give free leave to any of their descendants who may write a history of the State of Delaware to take fair retaliation and belabor Peter Stuyvesant as hard as they please.

Therefore stand by for broken heads and bloody noses!—my pen has long itched for a battle—siege after siege have I carried on without blows or bloodshed; but now I have at length got a chance, and I vow to Heaven and St. Nicholas that, let the chronicles of the times say what they please, neither Sallust, Livy, Tacitus, Polybius, nor any other battle-monger of them all did ever record a fiercer fight than that in which my valiant chieftains are now about to engage.

And you, oh most excellent readers, whom for your faithful adherence I could cherish in the warmest corner of my heart— be not uneasy—trust the fate of our favorite Stuyvesant to me —for by the rood, come what may, I'll stick by Hard-koppig Piet to the last; I'll make him drive about these losels vile as did the renowned Launcelot of the Lake a herd of recreant Cornish knights—and if he does fall, let me never draw my pen to fight another battle in behalf of a brave man if I don't make these lubberly Swedes pay for it!

No sooner had Peter Stuyvesant arrived before Fort Christina than he proceeded without delay to intrench himself, and immediately on running his first parallel, despatched Antony Van Corlear to summon the fortress to surrender. Van Corlear was received with all due formality, hoodwinked at the portal, and conducted through a pestiferous smell of salt fish and onions to the citadel, a substantial hut built of pine logs. His eyes were here uncovered, and he found himself in the august presence of Governor Risingh. This chieftain, as I have before noted, was a very giantly man; and was clad in a coarse blue coat, strapped round the waist with a leathern belt which caused the enormous skirts and pockets to set off with a very warlike sweep. His ponderous legs were cased in a pair of foxy-colored jackboots, and he was straddling in the attitude of the Colossus of Rhodes before a bit of broken looking glass, shaving himself with a villainously dull razor. This afflicting operation caused him to make a series of horrible grimaces that heightened exceedingly the grisly terrors of his visage. On Antony Van Corlear's being announced, the grim commander paused for a moment in the midst of one of his most hard-favored contortions, and after eyeing him askance over the shoulder, with a kind of snarling grin on his countenance, resumed his labors at the glass.

This iron harvest being reaped, he turned once more to the trumpeter and demanded the purport of his errand. Antony Van Corlear delivered in a few words, being a kind of short-hand speaker, a long message from his excellency recounting the whole history of the province, with a recapitulation of grievances and enumeration of claims, and concluding with a peremptory demand of instant surrender; which done, he turned aside, took his nose between his thumb and finger, and blew a tremendous blast not unlike the flourish of a trumpet of defiance—which it had doubtless learned from a long and intimate neighborhood with that melodious instrument.

Governor Risingh heard him through, trumpet and all, but with infinite impatience; leaning at times, as was his usual custom, on the pommel of his sword, and at times twirling a huge steel watch chain or snapping his fingers. Van Corlear having finished, he bluntly replied that Peter Stuyvesant and his summons might go to the D———l, whither he hoped to send him and his crew of ragamuffins before supper time. Then unsheathing his brass-hilted sword and throwing away the scabbard—" 'Fore gad," quod he, "but I will not sheathe thee again until I make a scabbard of the smoke-dried leathern hide of this runagate Dutchman." Then having flung a fierce defiance in the teeth of his adversary by the lips of his messenger, the latter was reconducted to the portal with all the ceremonious civility due to the trumpeter, squire and ambassador of so great a commander; and being again unblinded, was courteously dismissed with a tweak of the nose to assist him in recollecting his message.

No sooner did the gallant Peter receive this insolent reply than he let fly a tremendous volley of red hot execrations that would infallibly have battered down the fortifications and blown up the powder magazine about the ears of the fiery Swede, had not the ramparts been remarkably strong and the magazine bombproof. Perceiving that the works withstood this terrific blast and that it was utterly impossible (as it really was in those unphilosophic days) to carry on a war with words, he ordered his merry men all to prepare for an immediate assault. But here a strange murmur broke out among his troops, beginning with the tribe of the Van Bummels, those valiant trenchermen of the Bronx, and spreading from man to man, accompanied with certain mutinous looks and discontented murmurs. For once in his life, and only for once, did the great Peter turn pale, for he verily thought his warriors were going to falter in this hour of perilous trial and thus tarnish for ever the fame of the province of New Nederlands.

But soon did he discover, to his great joy, that in this suspicion he deeply wronged this most undaunted army; for the cause of this agitation and uneasiness simply was that the hour of dinner was at hand and it would have almost broken the hearts of these regular Dutch warriors to have broken in upon the invariable routine of their habits. Beside, it was an established rule among our valiant ancestors always to fight upon a full stomach, and to this may be doubtless attributed the circumstance that they came to be so renowned in arms.

And now are the hearty men of the Manhattoes and their no less hearty comrades all lustily engaged under the trees, buffeting stoutly with the contents of their wallets and taking such affectionate embraces of their canteens and pottles as though they verily believed they were to be the last. And as I foresee we shall have hot work in a page or two, I advise my readers to do the same, for which purpose I will bring this chapter to a close; giving them my word of honor that no advantage shall be taken of this armistice to surprise or in any wise molest the honest Nederlanders while at their vigorous repast.

Containing the most horrible battle ever recorded in poetry or prose; with the admirable exploits of Peter the Headstrong.

"Now had the Dutchmen snatched a huge repast," and finding themselves wonderfully encouraged and animated thereby, prepared to take the field. Expectation, says the writer of the Stuyvesant manuscript—Expectation now stood on stilts. The world forgot to turn round, or rather stood still, that it might witness the affray; like a fat round-bellied alderman watching the combat of two chivalric flies upon his jerkin. The eyes of all mankind, as usual in such cases, were turned upon Fort Christina. The sun, like a little man in a crowd at a puppet show, scampered about the heavens, popping his head here and there and endeavoring to get a peep between the unmannerly clouds that obtruded themselves in his way. The historians filled their inkhorns—the poets went without their dinners, either that they might buy paper and goose quills or because they could not get anything to eat—antiquity scowled sulkily out of its grave to see itself outdone—while even posterity stood mute, gazing in gaping ecstasy of retrospection on the eventful field.

The immortal deities, who whilom had seen service at the "affair" of Troy—now mounted their feather bed clouds and sailed over the plain, or mingled among the combatants in different disguises, all itching to have a finger in the pie. Jupiter sent off his thunderbolt to a noted coppersmith to have it furbished up for the direful occasion. Venus swore by her chastity she'd patronize the Swedes, and in semblance of a bleareyed trull paraded the battlements of Fort Christina, accompanied by Diana as a sergeant's widow of cracked reputation.— The noted bully, Mars, stuck two horse pistols into his belt, shouldered a rusty firelock and gallantly swaggered at their elbow as a drunken corporal—while Apollo trudged in their rear as a bandy-legged fifer playing most villainously out of tune.

281

On the other side, the ox-eyed Juno, who had gained a pair
of black eyes over night in one of her curtain lectures with old
Jupiter, displayed her haughty beauties on a baggage waggon.
—Minerva, as a brawny gin suttler, tucked up her skirts, brandished her fists and swore most heroically in exceeding bad
Dutch (having but lately studied the language) by way of keeping up the spirits of the soldiers—while Vulcan halted as a club-
footed blacksmith lately promoted to be a captain of militia.
All was silent horror or bustling preparation; war reared his
horrid front, gnashed loud his iron fangs and shook his direful
crest of bristling bayonets.

And now the mighty chieftains marshaled out their hosts.
Here stood stout Risingh, firm as a thousand rocks—incrusted
with stockades and intrenched to the chin in mud batteries—
his artillery consisting of two swivels and a carronade, loaded
to the muzzle, the touch holes primed and a whiskered bom-
bardier stationed at each with a lighted match in hand waiting
the word. His valiant infantry lined the breastwork in grim
array, each having his mustachios fiercely greased and his hair
pomatumed back and queued so stiffly that he grinned above
the ramparts like a grisly death's head.

There came on the intrepid Hard-koppig Piet—a second Bay-
ard, without fear or reproach—his brows knit, his teeth clenched,
his breath held hard, rushing on like ten thousand bellowing
bulls of Bashan. His faithful squire Van Corlear trudged valiantly at his heels, with his trumpet gorgeously bedecked with
red and yellow ribbons, the remembrances of his fair mistresses
at the Manhattoes. Then came waddling on his sturdy comrades, swarming like the myrmidons of Achilles. There were
the Van Wycks and the Van Dycks and the Ten Eycks—the
Van Nesses, the Van Tassels, the Van Grolls; the Van Hœsens,
the Van Giesons and the Van Blarcoms—the Van Warts, the
Van Winkles, the Van Dams; the Van Pelts, the Van Rippers
and the Van Brunts.—There were the Van Hornes, the Van
Hooks, the Van Bunschotens; the Van Gelders, the Van Ars-
dales and the Van Bummels—the Vander Belts, the Vander
Hoofs, the Vander Voorts, the Vander Lyns, the Vander Pools
and the Vander Spiegels.—There came the Hoffmans, the Hoogh-
lands, the Hoppers, the Cloppers, the Ryckmans, the Dyckmans,
the Hogebooms, the Rosebooms, the Oothouts, the Quacken-
bosses, the Roerbacks, the Garrebrantzs, the Bensons, the Brouw-

ers, the Waldrons, the Onderdonks, the Varra Vangers, the Schermerhorns, the Stoutenburghs, the Brinkerhoffs, the Bontecous, the Knickerbockers, the Hockstrassers, the Ten Breecheses and the Tough Breecheses, with a host more of valiant worthies whose names are too crabbed to be written, or if they could be written, it would be impossible for man to utter—all fortified with a mighty dinner, and to use the words of a great Dutch poet,

—"Brimful of wrath and cabbage!"

For an instant the mighty Peter paused in the midst of his career, and mounting on a stump, addressed his troops in eloquent Low Dutch, exhorting them to fight like *duyvels,* and assuring them that if they conquered, they should get plenty of booty—if they fell, they should be allowed the unparalleled satisfaction, while dying, of reflecting that it was in the service of their country—and after they were dead, of seeing their names inscribed in the temple of renown and handed down, in company with all the other great men of the year, for the admiration of posterity.—Finally he swore to them, on the word of a governor (and they knew him too well to doubt it for a moment), that if he caught any mother's son of them looking pale or playing craven, he'd curry his hide till he made him run out of it like a snake in spring time.—Then lugging out his trusty sabre, he brandished it three times over his head, ordered Van Corlear to sound a tremendous charge, and shouting the word "St. Nicholas and the Manhattoes!" courageously dashed forwards. His warlike followers, who had employed the interval in lighting their pipes, instantly stuck them in their mouths, gave a furious puff, and charged gallantly under cover of the smoke.

The Swedish garrison, ordered by the cunning Risingh not to fire until they could distinguish the whites of their assailants' eyes, stood in horrid silence on the covert-way until the eager Dutchmen had ascended the glacis. Then did they pour into them such a tremendous volley that the very hills quaked around and were terrified even unto an incontinence of water, insomuch that certain springs burst forth from their sides, which continue to run unto the present day. Not a Dutchman but would have bitten the dust beneath that dreadful fire, had not the protecting Minerva kindly taken care that the Swedes should one and all observe their usual custom of shutting their eyes and turning away their heads at the moment of discharge.

The Swedes followed up their fire by leaping the counter-scarp and falling tooth and nail upon the foe with furious outcries. And now might be seen prodigies of valor, of which neither history nor song have ever recorded a parallel. Here was beheld the sturdy Stoffel Brinkerhoff brandishing his lusty quarterstaff, like the terrible giant Blanderon his oak tree (for he scorned to carry any other weapon), and drumming a hor-rific tune upon the heads of whole squadrons of Swedes. There were the crafty Van Kortlandts, posted at a distance, like the Locrian archers of yore, and plying it most potently with the long bow, for which they were so justly renowned. At another place were collected on a rising knoll the valiant men of Sing-Sing, who assisted marvellously in the fight by chanting forth the great song of St. Nicholas; but as to the Gardeniers of Hudson, they were absent from the battle, having been sent out on a marauding party to lay waste the neighboring water-melon patches. In a different part of the field might be seen the Van Grolls of Anthony's Nose; but they were horribly per-plexed in a defile between two little hills, by reason of the length of their noses. There were the Van Bunschotens of Nyack and Kakiat, so renowned for kicking with the left foot; but their skill availed them little at present, being short of wind in consequence of the hearty dinner they had eaten, and they would irretrievably have been put to rout had they not been reinforced by a gallant corps of *Voltigeurs* composed of the Hoppers, who advanced to their assistance nimbly on one foot. Nor must I omit to mention the incomparable achievements of Antony Van Corlear, who for a good quarter of an hour waged stubborn fight with a little pursy Swedish drummer whose hide he drummed most magnificently; and had he not come into the battle with no other weapon but his trumpet, would infallibly have put him to an untimely end.

But now the combat thickened—on came the mighty Jacobus Varra Vanger and the fighting men of the Wallabout; after them thundered the Van Pelts of Esopus, together with the Van Rippers and the Van Brunts, bearing down all before them—then the Suy Dams and the Van Dams pressing forward with many a blustering oath at the head of the warriors of Hell Gate, clad in their thunder and lightning gabardines;

and lastly, the standardbearers and bodyguards of Peter Stuyvesant, bearing the great beaver of the Manhattoes.

And now commenced the horrid din, the desperate struggle, the maddening ferocity, the frantic desperation, the confusion and self-abandonment of war. Dutchman and Swede commingled, tugged, panted and blowed. The heavens were darkened with a tempest of missives. Bang! went the guns—whack! struck the broadswords—thump! went the cudgels—crash! went the musket stocks—blows—kicks—cuffs—scratches—black eyes and bloody noses swelling the horrors of the scene! Thick-thwack, cut and hack, helter-skelter, higgledy-piggledy, hurly-burly, head over heels, rough and tumble!—Dunder and blixum! swore the Dutchmen—Splitter and splutter! cried the Swedes—Storm the works! shouted Hard-koppig Peter—Fire the mine; roared stout Risingh —Tantara-ra-ra! twanged the trumpet of Antony Van Corlear— until all voice and sound became unintelligible—grunts of pain, yells of fury, and shouts of triumph commingling in one hideous clamor. The earth shook as if struck with a paralytic stroke— Trees shrunk aghast and withered at the sight—Rocks burrowed in the ground like rabbits,—and even Christina Creek turned from its course and ran up a mountain in breathless terror!

Long hung the conquest doubtful; for though a heavy shower of rain, sent by the "cloud-compelling Jove," in some measure cooled their ardor, as doth a bucket of water thrown on a group of fighting mastiffs, yet did they but pause for a moment, to return with tenfold fury to the charge, belaboring each other with black and bloody bruises. Just at this juncture was seen a vast and dense column of smoke, slowly rolling towards the scene of battle, which for a while made even the furious combatants to stay their arms in mute astonishment—but the wind for a moment dispersing the murky cloud, from the midst thereof emerged the flaunting banner of the immortal Michael Paw. This noble chieftain came fearlessly on, leading a solid phalanx of oyster-fed Pavonians, who had remained behind, partly as a *corps de reserve* and partly to digest the enormous dinner they had eaten. These sturdy yeomen, nothing daunted, did trudge manfully forward, smoking their pipes with outrageous vigor, so as to raise the awful cloud that has been mentioned; but marching exceedingly slow, being short of leg and of great rotundity in the belt.

And now the protecting deities of the army of New Amsterdam having unthinkingly left the field and stepped into a neighboring tavern to refresh themselves with a pot of beer, a direful catastrophe had well nigh chanced to befall the Nederlanders. Scarcely had the myrmidons of the puissant Paw attained the front of battle, before the Swedes, instructed by the cunning Risingh, levelled a shower of blows full at their tobacco pipes. Astounded at this unexpected assault, and totally discomfited at seeing their pipes broken, the valiant Dutchmen fall in vast confusion—already they began to fly—like a frightened drove of unwieldy elephants they throw their own army in an uproar, bearing down a whole legion of little Hoppers —the sacred banner, on which is blazoned the gigantic oyster of Communipaw, is trampled in the dirt.—The Swedes pluck up new spirits, and pressing on their rear, apply their feet *a parte poste* with a vigor that prodigiously accelerates their motions —nor doth the renowned Paw himself fail to receive divers grievous and dishonorable visitations of shoe leather!

But what, Oh muse! was the rage of the gallant Peter, when from afar he saw his army yield? With a voice of thunder did he roar after his recreant warriors, putting up such a war whoop as did the stern Achilles when the Trojan troops were on the point of burning all his galleys. The men of the Manhattoes plucked up new courage when they heard their leader—or rather they dreaded his fierce displeasure, of which they stood in more awe than of all the Swedes in Christendom—but the daring Peter, not waiting for their aid, plunged, sword in hand, into the thickest of the foe. Then did he display some such incredible achievements as have never been known since the miraculous days of the giants. Wherever he went the enemy shrunk before him—with fierce impetuosity he pushed forward, driving the Swedes like dogs into their own ditch—but as he fearlessly advanced, the foe, like rushing waves which close upon the scudding bark, thronged in his rear and hung upon his flank with fearful peril. One crafty Swede, advancing warily on one side, drove his dastard sword full at the hero's heart; but the protecting power that watches over the safety of all great and good men turned aside the hostile blade and directed it to a side pocket where reposed an enormous iron tobacco box, endowed like the shield of Achilles with supernatural powers—no doubt in consequence of its being piously decorated with a portrait of the blessed St. Nicholas. Thus was the dreadful blow repelled, but not without occasioning to the great Peter a fearful loss of wind.

Like as a furious bear, when gored by worrying curs, turns fiercely round, gnashes his teeth and springs upon the foe, so did our hero turn upon the treacherous Swede. The miserable varlet sought in flight for safety—but the active Peter, seizing him by an immeasurable queue that dangled from his head—"Ah, Whoreson Caterpillar!" roared he, "here is what shall make dog's meat of thee!" So saying, he whirled his trusty sword and made a blow that would have decapitated him, had he, like Briareus, half a hundred heads, but that the pitying steel struck short and shaved the queue forever from his crown. At this very moment a cunning arquebusier, perched on the summit of a neighboring mound, levelled his deadly instrument and would have sent the gallant Stuyvesant a wailing ghost to haunt the Stygian shore—had not the watchful Minerva, who had just stopped to tie up her garter, saw the great peril of her favorite chief, and despatched old Boreas with his bellows, who, in the very nick of time, just as the direful match descended to the pan, gave such a lucky blast as blew all the priming from the touchhole!

Thus waged the horrid fight—when the stout Risingh, surveying the battle from the top of a little ravelin, perceived his faithful troops banged, beaten and kicked by the invincible Peter. Language cannot describe the choler with which he was seized at the sight—he only stopped for a moment to disburthen himself of five thousand anathemas; and then drawing his immeasurable falchion, straddled down to the field of combat with some such thundering strides as Jupiter is said by Hesiod to have taken when he strode down the spheres to hurl his thunderbolts at the Titans.

No sooner did these two rival heroes come face to face than they each made a prodigious start, such as is made by your most experienced stage champions. Then did they regard each other for a moment with bitter aspect, like two furious ram cats on the very point of a clapper-clawing. Then did they throw themselves in one attitude, then in another, striking their swords on the ground, first on the right side, then on the left—at last at it they went like five hundred houses on fire! Words cannot tell the prodigies of strength and valor displayed on this direful encounter—an encounter, compared to which the far-famed battles of Ajax with Hector, of Eneas with Turnus, Orlando with Rodomont, Guy of Warwick with Colbrand the Dane, or of that renowned Welsh Knight, Sir Owen of the

Mountains, with the giant Guylon, were all gentle sports and
holiday recreations. At length the valiant Peter, watching his
opportunity, aimed a fearful blow, with the full intention of
cleaving his adversary to the very chine; but Risingh, nimbly
raising his sword, warded it off so narrowly that glancing on
one side, it shaved away a huge canteen that he always carried
swung on one side; thence pursuing its trenchant course, it
severed off a deep coat pocket stored with bread and cheese—
all which dainties rolling among the armies, occasioned a fearful scrambling between the Swedes and Dutchmen, and made
the general battle to wax ten times more furious than ever.

Enraged to see his military stores thus woefully laid waste,
the stout Risingh, collecting all his forces, aimed a mighty
blow full at the hero's crest. In vain did his fierce little cocked
hat oppose its course; the biting steel clove through the stubborn ram beaver and would infallibly have cracked his crown,
but that the skull was of such adamantine hardness that the
brittle weapon shivered into pieces, shedding a thousand sparks
like beams of glory round his grisly visage.

Stunned with the blow, the valiant Peter reeled, turned up
his eyes and beheld fifty thousand suns, besides moons and
stars, dancing about the firmament—at length, missing his footing by reason of his wooden leg, down he came on his seat of
honor with a crash that shook the surrounding hills and would
infallibly have wracked his anatomical system had he not been
received into a cushion softer than velvet, which Providence or
Minerva or St. Nicholas or some kindly cow had benevolently
prepared for his reception.

The furious Risingh, in despite of that noble maxim cherished by all true knights that "fair play is a jewel," hastened
to take advantage of the hero's fall; but just as he was stooping
to give the fatal blow, the ever vigilant Peter bestowed him a
sturdy thwack over the sconce with his wooden leg, that sat
some dozen chimes of bells ringing triple bob-majors in his
cerebellum. The bewildered Swede staggered with the blow,
and in the meantime the wary Peter espying a pocket pistol
lying hard by (which had dropped from the wallet of his faithful squire and trumpeter Van Corlear during his furious encounter with the drummer), discharged it full at the head of
the reeling Risingh.—Let not my reader mistake—it was not a
murderous weapon loaded with powder and ball, but a little
sturdy stone pottle, charged to the muzzle with a double dram

of true Dutch courage, which the knowing Van Corlear always carried about him by way of replenishing his valor. The hideous missive sung through the air, and true to its course as was the mighty fragment of a rock discharged at Hector by bully Ajax, encountered the huge head of the gigantic Swede with matchless violence.

This heaven-directed blow decided the eventful battle. The ponderous pericranium of General Jan Risingh sunk upon his breast; his knees tottered under him; a deathlike torpor seized upon his Titan frame, and he tumbled to the earth with such tremendous violence that old Pluto started with affright lest he should have broken through the roof of his infernal palace.

His fall was the signal of defeat and victory—The Swedes gave way—the Dutch pressed forward; the former took to their heels, the latter hotly pursued—Some entered with them, pell-mell, through the sally port—others stormed the bastion, and others scrambled over the curtain. Thus in a little while the impregnable fortress of Fort Christina, which like another Troy had stood a siege of full ten hours, was finally carried by assault, without the loss of a single man on either side. Victory in the likeness of a gigantic oxfly sat perched upon the cocked hat of the gallant Stuyvesant, and it was universally declared by all the writers whom he hired to write the history of his expedition that on this memorable day he gained a sufficient quantity of glory to immortalize a dozen of the greatest heroes in Christendom!

CHAPTER VIII

In which the author and the reader, while reposing after the battle, fall into a very grave discourse—after which is recorded the conduct of Peter Stuyvesant after his victory.

Thanks to St. Nicholas, we have safely finished this tremendous battle: let us sit down, my worthy reader, and cool ourselves, for I am in a prodigious sweat and agitation—Truly this fighting of battles is hot work! and if your great commanders did but know what trouble they give their historians, they would not have the conscience to achieve so many horrible victories. But methinks I hear my reader complain that throughout this boasted battle there is not the least slaughter, nor a single individual maimed, if we except the unhappy Swede who was shorn of his queue by the trenchant blade of Peter Stuyvesant; all which, he observes, is a great outrage on probability and highly injurious to the interest of the narration.

This is certainly an objection of no little moment, but it arises entirely from the obscurity that envelops the remote periods of time about which I have undertaken to write. Thus, though doubtless, from the importance of the object and the prowess of the parties concerned, there must have been terrible carnage and prodigies of valor displayed before the walls of Christina, yet, notwithstanding that I have consulted every history, manuscript and tradition touching this memorable though long-forgotten battle, I cannot find mention made of a single man killed or wounded in the whole affair.

This is, without doubt, owing to the extreme modesty of our forefathers, who, like their descendants, were never prone to vaunt of their achievements; but it is a virtue that places their historian in a most embarrassing predicament; for, having promised my readers a hideous and unparalleled battle, and having worked them up into a warlike and bloodthirsty state of mind, to put them off without any havoc and slaughter was as bitter a disappointment as to summons a multitude of good people to attend an execution and then cruelly balk them by a reprieve.

Had the inexorable fates only allowed me some half a score dead men, I had been content; for I would have made them such heroes as abounded in the olden time, but whose race is now unfortunately extinct.—Any one of whom, if we may believe those authentic writers, the poets, could drive great armies like sheep before him and conquer and desolate whole cities by his single arm.

But seeing that I had not a single life at my disposal, all that was left me was to make the most I could of my battle by means of kicks and cuffs and bruises and such like ignoble wounds. And here I cannot but compare my dilemma, in some sort, to that of the divine Milton, who, having arrayed with sublime preparation his immortal hosts against each other, is sadly put to it how to manage them and how he shall make the end of his battle answer to the beginning; inasmuch as, being mere spirits, he cannot deal a mortal blow nor even give a flesh wound to any of his combatants. For my part, the greatest difficulty I found was, when I had once put my warriors in a passion and let them loose into the midst of the enemy, to keep them from doing mischief. Many a time had I to restrain the sturdy Peter from cleaving a gigantic Swede to the very waistband or spitting half a dozen little fellows on his sword like so many sparrows.—And when I had set some hundred of missives flying in the air, I did not dare to suffer one of them to reach the ground, lest it should have put an end to some unlucky Dutchman.

The reader cannot conceive how mortifying it is to a writer thus in a manner to have his hands tied, and how many tempting opportunities I had to wink at, where I might have made as fine a deathblow as any recorded in history or song.

From my own experience I begin to doubt most potently of the authenticity of many of Homer's stories. I verily believe that when he had once launched one of his favorite heroes among a crowd of the enemy, he cut down many an honest fellow without any authority for so doing excepting that he presented a fair mark—and that often a poor devil was sent to grim Pluto's domains merely because he had a name that would give a sounding turn to a period. But I disclaim all such unprincipled liberties—let me but have truth and the law on my side, and no man would fight harder than myself—but since the various records I consulted did not warrant it, I had too much conscience to kill a single soldier.—By St. Nicholas, but it would have been a pretty piece of business! My enemies, the critics, who I foresee will be ready enough to lay any crime they can discover at my door, might have charged me with murder outright—and I should have esteemed myself lucky to escape with no harsher verdict than manslaughter!

And now, gentle reader, that we are tranquilly sitting down here, smoking our pipes, permit me to indulge in a melancholy reflection which at this moment passes across my mind.—How vain, how fleeting, how uncertain are all those gaudy bubbles after which we are panting and toiling in this world of fair delusions. The wealth which the miser has amassed with so many weary days, so many sleepless nights, a spendthrift heir may squander away in joyless prodigality—The noblest monu-

ments which pride has ever reared to perpetuate a name, the
hand of time will shortly tumble into ruins—and even the
brightest laurels gained by feats of arms may wither and be
forever blighted by the chilling neglect of mankind.—"How
many illustrious heroes," says the good Boëtius, "who were once
the pride and glory of the age, hath the silence of historians
buried in eternal oblivion!" And this it was that induced the
Spartans, when they went to battle, solemnly to sacrifice to the
Muses, supplicating that their achievements should be worthily
recorded. Had not Homer tuned his lofty lyre, observes the
elegant Cicero, the valor of Achilles had remained unsung.—
And such too, after all the toils and perils he had braved, after
all the gallant actions he had achieved, such too had nearly
been the fate of the chivalric Peter Stuyvesant, but that I fortunately stepped in and engraved his name on the indelible
tablet of history, just as the caitiff Time was silently brushing
it away for ever!

The more I reflect, the more am I astonished at the important
character of the historian. He is the sovereign censor, to decide
upon the renown or infamy of his fellow men.—He is the patron
of kings and conquerors, on whom it depends whether they
shall live in after ages or be forgotten as were their ancestors
before them. The tyrant may oppress while the object of his
tyranny exists, but the historian possesses superior might, for
his power extends even beyond the grave. The shades of departed and long-forgotten heroes anxiously bend down from
above while he writes, watching each movement of his pen,
whether it shall pass by their names with neglect or inscribe
them on the deathless pages of renown. Even the drop of ink
that hangs trembling on his pen, which he may either dash
upon the floor or waste in idle scrawlings—that very drop, which
to him is not worth the twentieth part of a farthing, may be of
incalculable value to some departed worthy—may elevate half
a score in one moment to immortality, who would have given
worlds, had they possessed them, to ensure the glorious meed.

Let not my readers imagine, however, that I am indulging in
vainglorious boastings or am anxious to blazon forth the importance of my tribe. On the contrary, I shrink when I reflect
on the awful responsibility we historians assume—I shudder to
think what direful commotions and calamities we occasion in
the world—I swear to thee, honest reader, as I am a man, I

weep at the very idea! Why, let me ask, are so many illustrious men daily tearing themselves away from the embraces of their families—slighting the smiles of beauty—despising the allurements of fortune, and exposing themselves to the miseries of war?—Why are kings desolating empires and depopulating whole countries? In short, what induces all great men, of all ages and countries, to commit so many victories and misdeeds and inflict so many miseries upon mankind and on themselves, but the mere hope that some historian will kindly take them into notice and admit them into a corner of his volume. For, in short, the mighty object of all their toils, their hardships and privations, is nothing but *immortal fame*—and what is immortal fame? ——why, half a page of dirty paper!——alas! alas! how humiliating the idea—that the renown of so great a man as Peter Stuyvesant should depend upon the pen of so little a man as Diedrich Knickerbocker!

And now, having refreshed ourselves after the fatigues and perils of the field, it behooves us to return once more to the scene of conflict and inquire what were the results of this renowned conquest. The fortress of Christina being the fair metropolis, and in a manner the key to New Sweden, its capture was speedily followed by the entire subjugation of the province. This was not a little promoted by the gallant and courteous deportment of the chivalric Peter. Though a man terrible in battle, yet in the hour of victory was he endued with a spirit generous, merciful, and humane.—He vaunted not over his enemies, nor did he make defeat more galling by unmanly insults; for like that mirror of knightly virtue, the renowned Paladin Orlando, he was more anxious to do great actions than to talk of them after they were done. He put no man to death; ordered no houses to be burnt down; permitted no ravages to be perpetrated on the property of the vanquished, and even gave one of his bravest officers a severe admonishment with his walking staff for having been detected in the act of sacking a hen roost.

He moreover issued a proclamation inviting the inhabitants to submit to the authority of their High Mightinesses; but declaring, with unexampled clemency, that whoever refused should be lodged at the public expense in a goodly castle provided for the purpose, and have an armed retinue to wait on them in the bargain. In consequence of these beneficent terms, about thirty Swedes stepped manfully forward and took the oath of allegiance; in reward for which they were graciously permitted to remain on the banks of the Delaware, where their descendants reside at this very day. But I am told by divers observant travelers that they have never been able to get over the chapfallen looks of their ancestors, and do still unaccountably transmit from father to son manifest marks of the sound drubbing given them by the sturdy Amsterdammers.

The whole country of New Sweden, having thus yielded to the arms of the triumphant Peter, was reduced to a colony called South River, and placed under the superintendence of a lieutenant governor; subject to the control of the supreme government at New Amsterdam. This great dignitary was called Mynher William Beekman, or rather *Beck*-man, who derived his surname, as did Ovidius Naso of yore, from the lordly dimensions of his nose, which projected from the center of his countenance like the beak of a parrot. He was the great progenitor of the tribe of the Beekmans, one of the most ancient and honorable families of the province, the members of which do gratefully commemorate the origin of their dignity, not as your noble families in England would do, by having a glowing proboscis emblazoned in their escutcheon, but by one and all wearing a right goodly nose stuck in the very middle of their faces.

Thus was this perilous enterprise gloriously terminated, with the loss of only two men: Wolfert Van Horne, a tall spare man who was knocked overboard by the boom of a sloop in a flaw of wind; and fat Brom Van Bummel, who was suddenly carried off by an indigestion; both, however, were immortalized as having bravely fallen in the service of their country. True it is, Peter Stuyvesant had one of his limbs terribly fractured, being shattered to pieces in the act of storming the fortress; but as it was fortunately his wooden leg, the wound was promptly and effectually healed.

And now nothing remains to this branch of my history but to mention that this immaculate hero and his victorious army returned joyously to the Manhattoes, marching under the shade of their laurels, as did the followers of young Malcolm under the moving forest of Dunsinane. Thus did they make a solemn and triumphant entry into New Amsterdam, bearing with them the conquered Risingh and the remnant of his battered crew who had refused allegiance. For it appears that the gigantic Swede had only fallen into a swound at the end of the battle, from whence he was speedily restored by a wholesome tweak of the nose.

These captive heroes were lodged, according to the promise of the governor, at the public expense, in a fair and spacious castle; being the prison of state, of which Stoffel Brinkerhoff, the immortal conqueror of Oyster Bay, was appointed governor; and which has ever since remained in the possession of his descendants.*

It was a pleasant and goodly sight to witness the joy of the people of New Amsterdam at beholding their warriors once more return from this war in the wilderness. The old women thronged round Antony Van Corlear, who gave the whole history of the campaign with matchless accuracy; saving that he took the credit of fighting the whole battle himself, and especially of vanquishing the stout Risingh, which he considered himself as clearly entitled to, seeing that it was effected by his own stone pottle.

The schoolmasters throughout the town gave holiday to their little urchins, who followed in droves after the drums, with paper caps on their heads and sticks in their breeches, thus taking the first lesson in the art of war. As to the sturdy rabble, they thronged at the heels of Peter Stuyvesant wherever he went, waving their greasy hats in the air and shouting "Hard-koppig Piet forever!"

It was indeed a day of roaring rout and jubilee. A huge dinner was prepared at the Stadthouse in honor of the conquerors, where were assembled in one glorious constellation the great and the little luminaries of New Amsterdam. There were the lordly Schout and his obsequious deputy—the Burgomasters with their officious Schepens at their elbows—the subaltern officers at the elbows of the Schepens, and so on, to the lowest grade of illustrious hangers-on of police; every Tag having his Rag at his side to finish his pipe, drink off his heeltaps, and laugh at his flights of immortal dullness. In short—for a city feast is a city feast all the world over, and has been a city feast ever since the creation—the dinner went off much the same as do our great corporation junketings and fourth of July banquets. Loads of fish, flesh, and fowl were devoured, oceans of liquor drank, thousands

* This castle, though very much altered and modernized, is still in being, and stands at the corner of Pearl Street, facing Coentie's slip.

of pipes smoked, and many a dull joke honored with much obstreperous fat-sided laughter.

I must not omit to mention that to this far-famed victory Peter Stuyvesant was indebted for another of his many titles— for so hugely delighted were the honest burghers with his achievements that they unanimously honored him with the name of *Pieter de Groodt,* that is to say, Peter the Great, or as it was translated by the people of New Amsterdam, *Piet de Pig* —an appellation which he maintained even unto the day of his death.

BOOK VII

Containing the third part of the reign
of Peter the Headstrong—
his troubles with the British nation, and
the decline and fall of the Dutch dynasty.

CHAPTER I

*How Peter Stuyvesant relieved the sovereign
people from the burthen of taking care of
the nation—with sundry particulars of his
conduct in time of peace.*

The history of the reign of Peter Stuyvesant furnishes a melancholy picture of the incessant cares and vexations inseparable
from government, and may serve as a solemn warning to all
who are ambitious of attaining the seat of power. Though
crowned with victory, enriched by conquest, and returning in
triumph to his metropolis, his exultation was checked by beholding the sad abuses that had taken place during the short
interval of his absence.

The populace, unfortunately for their own comfort, had taken
a deep draught of the intoxicating cup of power during the
reign of William the Testy; and though, upon the accession of
Peter Stuyvesant, they felt, with a certain instinctive perception,
which mobs as well as cattle possess, that the reins of government had passed into stronger hands, yet could they not help
fretting and chafing and champing upon the bit in restive
silence.

It seems, by some strange and inscrutable fatality, to be the
destiny of most countries (and more especially of your enlightened republics) always to be governed by the most incompetent
man in the nation; so that you will scarcely find an individual
throughout the whole community but who will detect to you
innumerable errors in administration, and convince you in the
end that had he been at the head of affairs, matters would have
gone on a thousand times more prosperously. Strange! that
government, which seems to be so generally understood, should

invariably be so erroneously administered—strange, that the talent of legislation, so prodigally bestowed, should be denied to the only man in the nation to whose station it is requisite!

Thus it was in the present instance; not a man of all the herd of pseudo-politicians in New Amsterdam but was an oracle on topics of state and could have directed public affairs incomparably better than Peter Stuyvesant. But so severe was the old governor in his disposition that he would never suffer one of the multitude of able counselors by whom he was surrounded to intrude his advice and save the country from destruction.

Scarcely, therefore, had he departed on his expedition against the Swedes, than the old factions of William Kieft's reign began to thrust their heads above water and to gather together in political meetings to discuss "the state of the nation." At these assemblages the busy burgomasters and their officious schepens made a very considerable figure. These worthy dignitaries were no longer the fat, well-fed, tranquil magistrates that presided in the peaceful days of Wouter Van Twiller—On the contrary, being elected by the people, they formed in a manner a sturdy bulwark between the mob and the administration. They were great candidates for popularity and strenuous advocates for the rights of the rabble; resembling in disinterested zeal the wide-mouthed tribunes of ancient Rome, or those virtuous patriots of modern days emphatically denominated "the friends of the people."

Under the tuition of these profound politicians, it is astonishing how suddenly enlightened the swinish multitude became in matters above their comprehensions. Cobblers, tinkers and tailors, all at once felt themselves inspired, like those religious idiots in the glorious times of monkish illumination; and without any previous study or experience became instantly capable of directing all the movements of government. Nor must I neglect to mention a number of superannuated, wrong-headed old burghers who had come over when boys in the crew of the *Goede Vrouw* and were held up as infallible oracles by the enlightened mob. To suppose that a man who had helped to discover a country did not know how it ought to be governed was preposterous in the extreme.—It would have been deemed as much a heresy as at the present day to question the political talents and universal infallibility of our old "heroes of '76"— and to doubt that he who had fought for a government, however stupid he might naturally be, was not competent to fill any station under it.

But as Peter Stuyvesant had a singular inclination to govern his province without the assistance of his subjects, he felt highly incensed on his return to find the factious appearance they had assumed during his absence. His first measure, therefore, was to restore perfect order by prostrating the dignity of the sovereign people.

He accordingly watched his opportunity, and one evening when the enlightened mob was gathered together listening to a patriotic speech from an inspired cobbler, the intrepid Peter, like his great namèsake of all the Russias, all at once appeared among them with a countenance sufficient to petrify a millstone. The whole meeting was thrown into consternation—the orator seemed to have received a paralytic stroke in the very middle of a sublime sentence, and stood aghast with open mouth and trembling knees while the words horror! tyranny! liberty! rights! taxes! death! destruction! and a deluge of other patriotic phrases came roaring from his throat before he had power to close his lips. The shrewd Peter took no notice of the skulking throng around him, but advancing to the brawling bully-ruffian, and drawing out a huge silver watch which might have served in times of yore as a town clock, and which is still retained by his descendants as a family curiosity, requested the orator to mend it and set it going. The orator humbly confessed it was utterly out of his power, as he was unacquainted with the nature of its construction. "Nay, but," said Peter, "try your ingenuity, man; you see all the springs and wheels, and how easily the clumsiest hand may stop it and pull it to pieces; and why should it not be equally easy to regulate as to stop it?" The orator declared that his trade was wholly different; he was a poor cobbler and had never meddled with a watch in his life—that there were men skilled in the art, whose business it was to attend to those matters, but for his part, he should only mar the workmanship and put the whole in confusion—"Why harkee, master of mine," cried Peter, turning suddenly upon him, with a countenance that almost petrified the patcher of shoes into a perfect lapstone—"dost thou pretend to meddle with the movements of government—to regulate and correct and patch and cobble a complicated machine, the principles of which are above thy comprehension, and its simplest operations too subtle for thy understanding, when thou canst not correct a trifling error in a common piece of mechanism, the whole mystery of which is open to thy inspection?— Hence with thee to the leather and stone, which are emblems of thy head; cobble thy shoes, and confine thyself to the vocation for which heaven has fitted thee—But," elevating his voice until it made the welkin ring, "if ever I catch thee, or any of thy tribe, meddling again with affairs of government, by St. Nicholas but I'll have every mother's bastard of ye flea'd alive and your hides stretched for drum heads, that ye may thenceforth make a noise to some purpose!"

This threat, and the tremendous voice in which it was uttered, caused the whole multitude to quake with fear. The hair of the orator arose on his head like his own swine's bristles, and not a knight of the thimble present but his heart died within him and he felt as though he could have verily escaped through the eye of a needle.

But though this measure produced the desired effect in reducing the community to order, yet it tended to injure the popularity of the great Peter among the enlightened vulgar. Many accused him of entertaining highly aristocratic sentiments and of leaning too much in favor of the patricians. Indeed there appeared to be some ground for such an accusation, as he always carried himself with a very lofty, soldier-like port, and was somewhat particular in his dress; dressing himself, when not in uniform, in simple but rich apparel, and was especially noted for having his sound leg (which was a very comely one) always arrayed in a red stocking, and high-heeled shoe. Though a man of great simplicity of manners, yet there was something about him that repelled rude familiarity, while it encouraged frank and even social intercourse.

He likewise observed some appearance of court ceremony and etiquette. He received the common class of visitors on the *stoop** before his door, according to the custom of our Dutch ancestors. But when visitors were formally received in his parlor, it was expected they would appear in clean linen, by no means to be bare footed, and always to take their hats off. On public occasions he appeared with great pomp of equipage (for, in truth,

---

* Properly spelled *stoeb:* the porch commonly built in front of Dutch houses, with benches on each side.

his station required a little show and dignity), and always rode to church in a yellow waggon with flaming red wheels.

These symptoms of state and ceremony occasioned considerable discontent among the vulgar. They had been accustomed to find easy access to their former governors, and in particular had lived on terms of extreme familiarity with William the Testy. They therefore were very impatient of these dignified precautions which discouraged intrusion. But Peter Stuyvesant had his own way of thinking in these matters, and was a staunch upholder of the dignity of office.

He always maintained that government to be the least popular which is most open to popular access and control; and that the very brawlers against court ceremony, and the reserve of men in power, would soon despise rulers among whom they found even themselves to be of consequence. Such, at least, had been the case with the administration of William the Testy; who, bent on making himself popular, had listened to every man's advice, suffered everybody to have admittance to his person at all hours; and, in a word, treated everyone as his thorough equal. By this means every scrub politician and public busybody was enabled to measure wits with him, and to find out the true dimensions, not only of his person, but his mind—And what great man can stand such scrutiny?

It is the mystery that envelops great men that gives them half their greatness. We are always inclined to think highly of those who hold themselves aloof from our examination. There is likewise a kind of superstitious reverence for office which leads us to exaggerate the merits and abilities of men in power and to suppose that they must be constituted different from other men. And, indeed, faith is as necessary in politics as in religion. It certainly is of the first importance that a country should be governed by wise men; but then it is almost equally important that the people should believe them to be wise, for this belief alone can produce willing subordination.

To keep up, therefore, this desirable confidence in rulers, the people should be allowed to see as little of them as possible. He who gains access to cabinets soon finds out by what foolishness the world is governed. He discovers that there is quackery in legislation as well as in everything else; that many a measure which is supposed by the million to be the result of great wisdom and deep deliberation is the effect of mere chance, or perhaps of harebrained experiment—That rulers have their whims and errors as well as other men, and after all are not so wonderfully superior to their fellow creatures as he at first imagined; since he finds that even his own opinions have had some weight with them. Thus awe subsides into confidence, confidence inspires familiarity, and familiarity produces contempt. Peter Stuyvesant, on the contrary, by conducting himself with dignity and loftiness, was looked up to with great reverence. As he never gave his reasons for anything he did, the public always gave him credit for very profound ones—Every movement, however intrinsically unimportant, was a matter of speculation, and his very red stocking excited some respect, as being different from the stockings of other men.

To these times may we refer the rise of family pride and aristocratic distinctions;* and indeed I cannot but look back with reverence to the early planting of those mighty Dutch families which have taken such vigorous root and branched out so luxuriantly in our state. The blood which has flowed down uncontaminated through a succession of steady, virtuous generations since the times of the patriarchs of Communipaw must certainly be pure and worthy. And if so, then are the Van Rensellaers, the Van Zandts, the Van Hornes, the Rutgers, the Bensons, the Brinkerhoffs, the Schermerhorns, and all the true descendants of the ancient Pavonians, the only legitimate nobility and real lords of the soil.

I have been led to mention thus particularly the well authenticated claims of our genuine Dutch families, because I have noticed with great sorrow and vexation that they have been somewhat elbowed aside in latter days by foreign intruders. It is really astonishing to behold how many great families have sprung up of late years who pride themselves excessively on the score of ancestry. Thus he who can look up to his father without humiliation assumes not a little importance—he who can safely talk of his grandfather is still more vainglorious—but he who can look back to his great-grandfather without blushing is

---

* In a work published many years after the time here treated of (in 1701, by C. W. A. M.) it is mentioned that Frederick Philipse was counted the richest Mynher in New York and was said to have *whole hogsheads of Indian money or wampum;* and had a son and daughter who, according to the Dutch custom, should divide it equally.

absolutely intolerable in his pretensions to family.—Bless us! what a piece of work is here, between these mushrooms of an hour and these mushrooms of a day!

But from what I have recounted in the former part of this chapter, I would not have my reader imagine that the great Peter was a tyrannical governor, ruling his subjects with a rod of iron—on the contrary, where the dignity of authority was not implicated, he abounded with generosity and courteous condescension. In fact he really believed, though I fear my more enlightened republican readers will consider it a proof of his ignorance and illiberality, that in preventing the cup of social life from being dashed with the intoxicating ingredient of politics, he promoted the tranquillity and happiness of the people—and by detaching their minds from subjects which they could not understand, and which only tended to inflame their passions, he enabled them to attend more faithfully and industriously to their proper callings; becoming more useful citizens and more attentive to their families and fortunes.

So far from having any unreasonable austerity, he delighted to see the poor and the laboring man rejoice, and for this purpose was a great promoter of holidays and public amusements. Under his reign was first introduced the custom of cracking eggs at Paas or Easter. New Year's Day was also observed with extravagant festivity—and ushered in by the ringing of bells and firing of guns. Every house was a temple to the jolly god —Oceans of cherry brandy, true Hollands and mulled cyder were set afloat on the occasion; and not a poor man in town but made it a point to get drunk, out of a principle of pure economy— taking in liquor enough to serve him for half a year afterwards.

It would have done one's heart good also to have seen the valiant Peter seated among the old burghers and their wives of a Saturday afternoon under the great trees that spread their shade over the Battery, watching the young men and women as they danced on the green. Here he would smoke his pipe, crack his joke, and forget the rugged toils of war in the sweet oblivious festivities of peace. He would occasionally give a nod of approbation to those of the young men who shuffled and kicked most vigorously, and now and then give a hearty smack, in all honesty of soul, to the buxom lass that held out longest and tired down all her competitors, which he considered as infallible proofs of her being the best dancer. Once, it is true, the harmony of the meeting was rather interrupted. A young vrouw of great figure in the gay world and who, having lately come from Holland, of course led the fashions in the city, made her appearance in not more than half a dozen petticoats, and these too of most alarming shortness.—An universal whisper ran through the assembly; the old ladies all felt shocked in the extreme; the young ladies blushed and felt excessively for the "poor thing," and even the governor himself was observed to be a little troubled in mind. To complete the atonishment of the good folks, she undertook, in the course of a jig, to describe some astonishing figures in algebra which she had learned from a dancingmaster at Rotterdam.—Whether she was too animated in flourishing her feet, or whether some vagabond zephyr took the liberty of obtruding his services, certain it is that in the course of a grand evolution, which would not have disgraced a modern ball room, she made a most unexpected display—whereat the whole assembly was thrown into great admiration, several grave country members were not a little moved, and the good Peter himself, who was a man of unparalleled modesty, felt himself grievously scandalized.

The shortness of the female dresses, which had continued in fashion ever since the days of William Kieft, had long offended his eye; and though extremely averse to meddling with the petticoats of the ladies, yet he immediately recommended that every one should be furnished with a flounce to the bottom. He likewise ordered that the ladies, and indeed the gentlemen, should use no other step in dancing than "shuffle and turn" and "double trouble"; and forbade, under pain of his high displeasure, any young lady thenceforth to attempt what was termed "exhibiting the graces."

These were the only restrictions he ever imposed upon the sex, and these were considered by them as tyrannical oppressions and resisted with that becoming spirit always manifested by the gentle sex whenever their privileges are invaded.—In fact, Peter Stuyvesant plainly perceived that if he attempted to push the matter any further, there was danger of their leaving off petticoats altogether; so like a wise man experienced in the ways of women, he held his peace and suffered them ever after to wear their petticoats and cut their capers as high as they pleased.

How Peter Stuyvesant was much molested by the mosstroopers of the East and the giants of Merryland—and how a dark and horrid conspiracy was carried on in the British cabinet against the prosperity of the Manhattoes.

We are now approaching towards the crisis of our work, and if I be not mistaken in my forebodings, we shall have a world of business to despatch in the ensuing chapters.

It is with some communities as it is with certain meddlesome individuals, they have a wonderful facility at getting into scrapes; and I have always remarked that those are most liable to get in who have the least talent at getting out again. This is, doubtless, owing to the excessive valor of those states; for I have likewise noticed that this rampant and ungovernable quality is always most unruly where most confined; which accounts for its vaporing so amazingly in little states, little men, and ugly little women more especially.

Thus, when one reflects that the province of the Manhattoes, though of prodigious importance in the eyes of its inhabitants and its historian, was really of no very great consequence in the eyes of the rest of the world; that it had but little wealth or other spoils to reward the trouble of assailing it; and that it had nothing to expect from running wantonly into war, save an exceeding good beating—On pondering these things, I say, one would utterly despair of finding in its history either battles or bloodshed, or any other of those calamities which give importance to a nation and entertainment to the reader. But, on the contrary, we find, so valiant is this province that it has already drawn upon itself a host of enemies; has had as many buffetings as would gratify the ambition of the most warlike nation; and is, in sober sadness, a very forlorn, distressed, and woe-begone little province!—all which was, no doubt, kindly ordered by providence to give interest and sublimity to this pathetic history.

But I forbear to enter into a detail of the pitiful maraudings and harassments that for a long while after the victory on the Delaware continued to insult the dignity and disturb the repose of the Nederlanders. Suffice it in brevity to say that the implacable hostility of the people of the east, which had so miraculously been prevented from breaking out, as my readers must remember, by the sudden prevalence of witchcraft and the dissensions in the council of Amphyctions, now again displayed itself in a thousand grievous and bitter scourings upon the borders.

Scarcely a month passed but what the Dutch settlements on the frontiers were alarmed by the sudden appearance of an invading army from Connecticut. This would advance resolutely through the country, like a puissant caravan of the deserts, the women and children mounted in carts loaded with pots and kettles, as though they meant to boil the honest Dutchmen alive and devour them like so many lobsters. At the tail of these carts would stalk a crew of long-limbed, lank-sided varlets with axes on their shoulders and packs on their backs, resolutely bent upon *improving* the country in despite of its proprietors. These settling themselves down would in a short time completely dislodge the unfortunate Nederlanders; elbowing them out of those rich bottoms and fertile valleys in which our Dutch yeomanry are so famous for nestling themselves—For it is notorious that wherever these shrewd men of the east get a footing, the honest Dutchmen do gradually disappear, retiring slowly, like the Indians before the whites; being totally discomfited by the talking, chaffering, swapping, bargaining disposition of their new neighbors.

All these audacious infringements on the territories of their High Mightinesses were accompanied, as has before been hinted, by a world of rascally brawls, ribroastings and bundlings, which would doubtless have incensed the valiant Peter to wreak immediate chastisement, had he not at the very same time been perplexed by distressing accounts from Mynher Beckman, who commanded the territories at South River.

The restless Swedes, who had so graciously been suffered to remain about the Delaware, already began to show signs of mutiny and disaffection. But what was worse, a peremptory claim was laid to the whole territory, as the rightful property of Lord Baltimore, by Fendal, a chieftain who ruled over the colony of Maryland, or Merryland as it was anciently called, because that the inhabitants, not having the fear of the Lord before their eyes, were notoriously prone to get fuddled and make merry with mint julep and apple toddy. Nay, so hostile was this bully Fendal that he threatened, unless his claim were instantly complied with, to march incontinently at the head of a potent force of the roaring boys of Merryland, together with a great and mighty train of giants who infested the banks of the Susquehanna*—and to lay waste and depopulate the whole country of South River.

By this it is manifest that this boasted colony, like all great acquisitions of territory, soon became a greater evil to the conqueror than the loss of it was to the conquered; and caused greater uneasiness and trouble than all the territory of the New Netherlands besides. Thus Providence wisely orders that one evil shall balance another. The conqueror who wrests the property of his neighbor, who wrongs a nation and desolates a country, though he may acquire increase of empire and immortal fame, yet ensures his own inevitable punishment. He takes to himself a cause of endless anxiety—he incorporates with his late sound domain a loose part—a rotten disaffected member; which is an exhaustless source of internal treason and disunion, and external altercation and hostility—Happy is that nation which, compact, united, loyal in all its parts, and concentrated in its strength, seeks no idle acquisition of unprofitable and ungovernable territory—which, content to be prosperous and happy, has no ambition to be great. It is like a man well organized in all his system, sound in health and full of vigor; unencumbered by useless trappings, and fixed in an unshaken attitude. But the nation insatiable of territory, whose domains are scattered, feebly united and weakly organized, is like a senseless miser

---

* We find very curious and wonderful accounts of these strange people (who were doubtless the ancestors of the present Marylanders) made by Master Hariot in his interesting history. "The Susquesahanocks"—observes he—"are a giantly people, strange in proportion, behaviour, and attire—their voice sounding from them as if out a cave. Their tobacco pipes were three-quarters of a yard long, carved at the great end with a bird, beare, or other device sufficient to beat out the braines of a horse (and how many asses braines are beaten out, or rather men's braines smoked out and asses braines haled in, by our lesser pipes at home). The calfe of one of their legges was measured three-quarters of a yard about, the rest of his limbs proportionable."

Master Hariot's Journ. Purch. Pil.

sprawling among golden stores, open to every attack and unable to defend the riches he vainly endeavors to overshadow.

At the time of receiving the alarming despatches from South River, the great Peter was busily employed in quelling certain Indian troubles that had broken out about Esopus, and was moreover meditating how to relieve his eastern borders on the Connecticut. He, however, sent word to Mynher Beckman to be of good heart, to maintain incessant vigilance, and to let him know if matters wore a more threatening appearance; in which case he would incontinently repair with his warriors of the Hudson to spoil the merriment of these Merrylanders; for he coveted exceedingly to have a bout, hand to hand, with some half a score of these giants—having never encountered a giant in his whole life, unless we may so call the stout Risingh, and he was but a little one.

Nothing further, however, occurred to molest the tranquillity of Mynher Beckman and his colony. Fendal and his myrmidons remained at home, carousing it soundly upon hoe cakes, bacon, and mint julep, and running horses and fighting cocks, for which they were greatly renowned. At hearing of this Peter Stuyvesant was very well pleased, for notwithstanding his inclination to measure weapons with these monstrous men of the Susquehanna, yet he had already as much employment nearer home as he could turn his hands to. Little did he think, worthy soul, that this southern calm was but the deceitful prelude to a most terrible and fatal storm, then brewing, which was soon to burst forth and overwhelm the unsuspecting city of New Amsterdam!

Now so it was that while this excellent governor was giving his little senate laws, and not only giving them but enforcing them too—while he was incessantly traveling the rounds of his beloved province—posting from place to place to redress grievances, and while busy at one corner of his dominions, all the rest getting into an uproar—At this very time, I say, a dark and direful plot was hatching against him in that nursery of monstrous projects, the British cabinet. The news of his achievements on the Delaware, according to a sage old historian of New Amsterdam, had occasioned not a little talk and marvel in the courts of Europe. And the same profound writer assures us that the cabinet of England began to entertain great jealousy and uneasiness at the increasing power of the Manhattoes and the valor of its sturdy yeomanry

Agents, the same historian observes, were sent by the Amphyctionic council of the east to entreat the assistance of the British cabinet in subjugating this mighty province. Lord Sterling also asserted his right to Long Island, and at the same time Lord Baltimore, whose agent, as has before been mentioned, had so alarmed Mynher Beckman, laid his claim before the cabinet to the lands of South River, which he complained were unjustly and forcibly detained from him by these daring usurpers of the Nieuw Nederlandts.

Thus did the unlucky empire of the Manhattoes stand in imminent danger of experiencing the fate of Poland and being torn limb from limb to be shared among its savage neighbors. But while these rapacious powers were whetting their fangs and waiting for the signal to fall tooth and nail upon this delicious little fat Dutch empire, the lordly lion, who sat as umpire, all at once laid his mighty paw upon the spoil and settled the claims of all parties by granting none of them. For we are told that his majesty, Charles the Second, not to be perplexed by adjusting these several pretensions, made a present of a large tract of North America, including the province of New Netherlands, to his brother, the Duke of York—a donation truly royal, since none but great monarchs have a right to give away what does not belong to them.

That this munificent gift might not be merely nominal, his majesty, on the 12th of March, 1664, ordered that an armament should be forthwith prepared to invade the city of New Amsterdam by land and water and put his brother in complete possession of the premises.

Thus critically are situated the affairs of the New Netherlanders. The honest burghers, so far from thinking of the jeopardy in which their interests are placed, are soberly smoking their pipes and thinking of nothing at all—the privy counselors of the province are at this moment snoring in full quorum, like the drones of five hundred bagpipes, while the active Peter, who takes all the labor of thinking and acting upon himself, is busily devising some method of bringing the grand council of Amphyctions to terms. In the meanwhile an angry cloud is darkly scowling on the horizon—soon shall it rattle about the ears of these dozing Nederlanders and put the mettle of their stout-hearted governor completely to the trial.

But come what may, I here pledge my veracity that in all warlike conflicts and subtle perplexities he shall still acquit himself with the gallant bearing and spotless honor of a noble-minded, obstinate old cavalier—Forward then to the charge!—shine out, propitious stars, on the renowned city of the Manhattoes; and may the blessing of St. Nicholas go with thee—honest Peter Stuyvesant!

CHAPTER III

Of Peter Stuyvesant's expedition into the East Country, showing that, though an old bird, he did not understand trap.

Great nations resemble great men in this particular, that their greatness is seldom known until they get in trouble; adversity, therefore, has been wisely denominated the ordeal of true greatness, which, like gold, can never receive its real estimation until it has passed through the furnace. In proportion therefore as a nation, a community or an individual (possessing the inherent quality of greatness) is involved in perils and misfortunes, in proportion does it rise in grandeur—and even when sinking under calamity, makes, like a house on fire, a more glorious display than ever it did in the fairest period of its prosperity.

The vast empire of China, though teeming with population and imbibing and concentrating the wealth of nations, has vegetated through a succession of drowsy ages; and were it not for its internal revolution and the subversion of its ancient government by the Tartars, might have presented nothing but an uninteresting detail of dull, monotonous prosperity. Pompeia and Herculaneum might have passed into oblivion with a herd of their contemporaries had they not been fortunately overwhelmed by a volcano. The renowned city of Troy has acquired celebrity only from its ten years distress and final conflagration. Paris rises in importance by the plots and massacres which have ended in the exaltation of the illustrious Napoleon—and even the mighty London itself has skulked through the records of time, celebrated for nothing of moment excepting the plague, the great fire, and Guy Faux's gunpowder plot! Thus cities and empires seem to creep along, enlarging in silent obscurity under the pen of the historian, until at length they burst forth in some tremendous calamity—and snatch, as it were, immortality from the explosion!

The above principle being admitted, my reader will plainly perceive that the city of New Amsterdam and its dependent province are on the high road to greatness. Dangers and hostilities threaten from every side, and it is really a matter of astonishment to me how so small a state has been able in so short a time to entangle itself in so many difficulties. Ever since the province was first taken by the nose, at the Fort of Good Hope in the tranquil days of Wouter Van Twiller, has it been gradually increasing in historic importance; and never could it have had a more appropriate chieftain to conduct it to the pinnacle of grandeur than Peter Stuyvesant.

In the fiery heart of this iron-headed old warrior sat enthroned all those five kinds of courage described by Aristotle; and had the philosopher mentioned five hundred more to the back of them, I verily believe he would have been found master of them all—The only misfortune was that he was deficient in the better part of valor called discretion, a cold-blooded virtue which could not exist in the tropical climate of his mighty soul. Hence it was he was continually hurrying into those unheard-of enterprises that give an air of chivalric romance to all his history, and hence it was that he now conceived a project worthy of the hero of La Mancha himself.

This was no other than to repair in person to the great council of the Amphyctions, bearing the sword in one hand and the olive branch in the other—to require immediate reparation for the innumerable violations of that treaty which in an evil hour he had formed—to put a stop to those repeated maraudings on the eastern borders—or else to throw his gauntlet and appeal to arms for satisfaction.

On declaring this resolution in his privy council, the venerable members were seized with vast astonishment: for once in their lives they ventured to remonstrate, setting forth the rashness of exposing his sacred person in the midst of a strange and barbarous people, with sundry other weighty remonstrances—all which had about as much influence upon the determination of the headstrong Peter as though you were to endeavor to turn a rusty weathercock with a broken-winded bellows.

Summoning therefore to his presence his trusty follower

Antony Van Corlear, he commanded him to hold himself in readiness to accompany him the following morning on this his hazardous enterprise. Now Antony the trumpeter was a little stricken in years, yet by dint of keeping up a good heart, and having never known care or sorrow (having never been married), he was still a hearty, jocund, rubicund, gamesome wag, and of great capacity in the doublet. This last was ascribed to his living a jolly life on those domains at the Hook which Peter Stuyvesant had granted to him for his gallantry at Fort Casimir.

Be this as it may, there was nothing that more delighted Antony than this command of the great Peter, for he could have followed the stout-hearted old governor to the world's end with love and loyalty—and he moreover still remembered the frolicking and dancing and bundling and other disports of the east country, and entertained dainty recollection of numerous kind and buxom lasses whom he longed exceedingly again to encounter.

Thus then did this mirror of hardihood set forth, with no other attendant but his trumpeter, upon one of the most perilous enterprises ever recorded in the annals of knight-errantry.—For a single warrior to venture openly among a whole nation of foes—but above all, for a plain downright Dutchman to think of negotiating with the whole council of New England—never was there known a more desperate undertaking!—Ever since I have entered upon the chronicles of this peerless but hitherto uncelebrated chieftain, has he kept me in a state of incessant action and anxiety with the toils and dangers he is constantly encountering—Oh! for a chapter of the tranquil reign of Wouter Van Twiller, that I might repose on it as on a feather bed!

Is it not enough, Peter Stuyvesant, that I have once already rescued thee from the machinations of these terrible Amphyctions, by bringing the whole powers of witchcraft to thine aid? —Is it not enough that I have followed thee undaunted, like a guardian spirit, into the midst of the horrid battle of Fort Christina?—That I have been put incessantly to my trumps to keep thee safe and sound—now warding off with my single pen the shower of dastard blows that fell upon thy rear—now narrowly shielding thee from a deadly thrust by a mere tobacco box—now casing thy dauntless skull with adamant, when even thy stubborn ram beaver failed to resist the sword of the stout

Risingh—and now, not merely bringing thee off alive, but triumphant, from the clutches of the gigantic Swede by the desperate means of a paltry stone pottle?—Is not all this enough, but must thou still be plunging into new difficulties and jeopardizing in headlong enterprises thyself, thy trumpeter, and thy historian?

And now the ruddy-faced Aurora like a buxom chambermaid draws aside the sable curtains of the night, and out bounces from his bed the jolly red-haired Phoebus, startled at being caught so late in the embraces of Dame Thetis. With many a stable oath he harnesses his brazen-footed steeds and whips and lashes and splashes up the firmament, like a loitering postboy half an hour behind his time. And now behold that imp of fame and prowess, the headstrong Peter, bestriding a rawboned, switch-tailed charger, gallantly arrayed in full regimentals, and bracing on his thigh that trusty brass-hilted sword which had wrought such fearful deeds on the banks of the Delaware.

Behold hard after him his doughty trumpeter, Van Corlear, mounted on a broken-winded, wall-eyed, calico mare; his stone pottle, which had laid low the mighty Risingh, slung under his arm, and his trumpet displayed vauntingly in his right hand, decorated with a gorgeous banner on which is emblazoned the great beaver of the Manhattoes. See them proudly issuing out of the city gate like an iron-clad hero of yore with his faithful squire at his heels, the populace following them with their eyes and shouting many a parting wish and hearty cheering—Farewell, Hard-koppig Piet! Farewell, honest Antony!—Pleasant be your wayfaring—prosperous your return!—the stoutest hero that ever drew a sword, and the worthiest trumpeter that ever trod shoe leather.

Legends are lamentably silent about the events that befell our adventurers in this their adventurous travel, excepting the Stuyvesant Manuscript, which gives the substance of a pleasant little heroic poem written on the occasion by Domini AEgidius Luyck,* who appears to have been the poet-laureate of New Amsterdam. This inestimable manuscript assures us that it was a rare spectacle to behold the great Peter and his loyal follower hailing the morning sun and rejoicing in the clear countenance

---

* This Luyck was moreover rector of the Latin school in Nieuw Nederlandt, 1663. There are two pieces of AEgidius Luyck in D. Selyn's MSS. of poesies, upon his marriage with Judith Isendoorn. Old. MS.

of nature as they pranced it through the pastoral scenes of
Bloemen Dael;* which in those days was a sweet and rural
valley beautified with many a bright wild flower, refreshed
by many a pure streamlet, and enlivened here and there by a
delectable little Dutch cottage sheltered under some sloping
hill and almost buried in embowering trees.

Now did they enter upon the confines of Connecticut, where
they encountered many grievous difficulties and perils. At one
place they were assailed by a troop of country squires and
militia colonels, who, mounted on goodly steeds, hung upon
their rear for several miles, harassing them exceedingly with
guesses and questions, more especially the worthy Peter, whose
silver chased leg excited not a little marvel. At another place,
hard by the renowned town of Stamford, they were set upon
by a great and mighty legion of church deacons who imperiously
demanded of them five shillings for traveling on Sunday and
threatened to carry them captive to a neighboring church whose
steeple peered above the trees; but these the valiant Peter put
to rout with little difficulty, insomuch that they bestrode their
canes and gallopped off in horrible confusion, leaving their
cocked hats behind in the hurry of their flight. But not so
easily did he escape from the hands of a crafty man of Pyquag;
who with undaunted perseverance and repeated onsets fairly
bargained him out of his goodly switch-tailed charger, leaving
in place thereof a villainous, spavined foundered Naraganset
pacer.

But maugre all these hardships, they pursued their journey
cheerily along the course of the soft-flowing Connecticut, whose
gentle waves, says the song, roll through many a fertile vale
and sunny plain; now reflecting the lofty spires of the bustling
city, and now the rural beauties of the humble hamlet, now
echoing with the busy hum of commerce, and now with the
cheerful song of the peasant.

At every town would Peter Stuyvesant, who was noted for
warlike punctilio, order the sturdy Antony to sound a courteous
salutation; though the manuscript observes that the inhabitants
were thrown into great dismay when they heard of his approach.
For the fame of his incomparable achievements on the Delaware
had spread throughout the east country, and they dreaded lest

---

* Now called Blooming Dale, about four miles from New York.

he had come to take vengeance on their manifold transgressions.

But the good Peter rode through these towns with a smiling aspect; waving his hand with inexpressible majesty and condescension; for he verily believed that the old clothes which these ingenious people had thrust into their broken windows, and the festoons of dried apples and peaches which ornamented the fronts of their houses, were so many decorations in honor of his approach; as it was the custom in the days of chivalry to compliment renowned heroes by sumptuous displays of tapestry and gorgeous furniture. The women crowded to the doors to gaze upon him as he passed, so much does prowess in arms delight the gentle sex. The little children, too, ran after him in troops, staring with wonder at his regimentals, his brimstone breeches, and the silver garniture of his wooden leg. Nor must I omit to mention the joy which many strapping wenches betrayed at beholding the jovial Van Corlear who had whilom delighted them so much with his trumpet when he bore the great Peter's challenge to the Amphyctions. The kind-hearted Antony alighted from his calico mare and kissed them all with infinite loving-kindness—and was right pleased to see a crew of little trumpeters crowding around him for his blessing; each of whom he patted on the head, bade him be a good boy, and gave him a penny to buy molasses candy.

The Stuyvesant manuscript makes but little further mention of the governor's adventures upon this expedition, excepting that he was received with extravagant courtesy and respect by the great council of the Amphyctions, who almost talked him to death with complimentary and congratulatory harangues. I will not detain my readers by dwelling on his negotiations with the grand council. Suffice it to mention, it was like all other negotiations—a great deal was said, and very little done; one conversation led to another—one conference begat misunderstandings which it took a dozen conferences to explain; at the end of which the parties found themselves just where they were at first; excepting that they had entangled themselves in a host of questions of etiquette, and conceived a cordial distrust of each other that rendered their future negotiations ten times more difficult than ever.*

---

* For certain of the particulars of this ancient negotiation see Haz. Col. State Pap. It is singular that Smith is entirely silent with respect to this memorable expedition of Peter Stuyvesant.

In the midst of all these perplexities which bewildered the brain and incensed the ire of the sturdy Peter, who was perhaps of all men in the world least fitted for diplomatic wiles, he privately received the first intimation of the dark conspiracy which had been matured in the cabinet of England. To this was added the astounding intelligence that a hostile squadron had already sailed from England, destined to reduce the province of New Netherlands, and that the grand council of Amphyctions had engaged to cooperate by sending a great army to invade New Amsterdam by land.

Unfortunate Peter! did I not enter with sad forebodings upon this ill-starred expedition? did I not tremble when I saw thee, with no other counselor but thine own head, with no other armor but an honest tongue, a spotless conscience, and a rusty sword? with no other protector but St. Nicholas—and no other attendant but a trumpeter—did I not tremble when I beheld thee thus sally forth to contend with all the knowing powers of New England?

Oh, how did the sturdy old warrior rage and roar when he found himself thus entrapped, like a lion in the hunter's toil! Now did he determine to draw his trusty sword and manfully to fight his way through all the countries of the east. Now did he resolve to break in upon the council of the Amphyctions and put every mother's son of them to death.—At length, as his direful wrath subsided, he resorted to safer though less glorious expedients.

Concealing from the council his knowledge of their machinations, he privately despatched a trusty messenger with missives to his counselors at New Amsterdam, apprising them of the impending danger, commanding them immediately to put the city in a posture of defence, while in the meantime he would endeavor to elude his enemies and come to their assistance. This done, he felt himself marvelously relieved, rose slowly, shook himself like a rhinoceros, and issued forth from his den, in much the same manner as Giant Despair is described to have issued from Doubting Castle, in the chivalric history of the Pilgrim's Progress.

And now much does it grieve me that I must leave the gallant Peter in this imminent jeopardy: but it behooves us to hurry back and see what is going on at New Amsterdam, for greatly do I fear that city is already in a turmoil. Such was ever the fate of Peter Stuyvesant; while doing one thing with heart and

soul, he was too apt to leave every thing else at sixes and sevens.
While, like a potentate of yore, he was absent attending to
those things in person which in modern days are trusted to
generals and ambassadors, his little territory at home was sure
to get in an uproar—All which was owing to that uncommon
strength of intellect which induced him to trust to nobody
but himself, and which had acquired him the renowned appellation of Peter the Headstrong.

CHAPTER IV

*How the people of New Amsterdam were
thrown into a great panic by the news of a
threatened invasion, and the manner in
which they fortified themselves.*

There is no sight more truly interesting to a philosopher than
to contemplate a community where every individual has a voice
in public affairs, where every individual thinks himself the
Atlas of the nation, and where every individual thinks it his
duty to bestir himself for the good of his country—I say, there
is nothing more interesting to a philosopher than to see such
a community in a sudden bustle of war. Such a clamor of
tongues—such a bawling of patriotism—such running hither and
thither—everybody in a hurry—everybody up to the ears in
trouble—everybody in the way, and everybody interrupting his
industrious neighbor—who is busily employed in doing nothing!
It is like witnessing a great fire, where every man is at work
like a hero—some dragging about empty engines—others scampering with full buckets, and spilling the contents into the boots
of their neighbors—and others ringing the church bells all
night by way of putting out the fire. Little firemen—like sturdy
little knights storming a breach, clambering up and down
scaling ladders and bawling through tin trumpets by way of
directing the attack—here one busy fellow, in his great zeal
to save the property of the unfortunate, catches up an anonymous chamber utensil and gallants it off with an air of as much

self-importance as if he had rescued a pot of money—another throws looking glasses and china out of the window to save them from the flames—while those who can do nothing else to assist the great calamity run up and down the streets with open throats, keeping up an incessant cry of *Fire! Fire! Fire!*

"When the news arrived at Sinope," says the grave and profound Lucian—though I own the story is rather trite, "that Philip was about to attack them, the inhabitants were thrown into violent alarm. Some ran to furbish up their arms; others rolled stones to build up the walls—everybody, in short, was employed, and everybody was in the way of his neighbor. Diogenes alone was the only man who could find nothing to do—whereupon, determining not to be idle when the welfare of his country was at stake, he tucked up his robe and fell to rolling his tub with might and main up and down the Gymnasium." In like manner did every mother's son in the patriotic community of New Amsterdam, on receiving the missives of Peter Stuyvesant, busy himself most mightily in putting things in confusion and assisting the general uproar. "Every man"— saith the Stuyvesant Manuscript—"flew to arms!"—by which is meant that not one of our honest Dutch citizens would venture to church or to market without an old-fashioned spit of a sword dangling at his side and a long Dutch fowling piece on his shoulder—nor would he go out of a night without a lantern; nor turn a corner without first peeping cautiously round, lest he should come unawares upon a British army—And we are informed that Stoffel Brinkerhoff, who was considered by the old women almost as brave a man as the governor himself, actually had two one-pound swivels mounted in his entry, one pointing out at the front door and the other at the back.

But the most strenuous measure resorted to on this awful occasion, and one which has since been found of wonderful efficacy, was to assemble popular meetings. These brawling convocations, I have already shown, were extremely offensive to Peter Stuyvesant; but as this was a moment of unusual agitation, and as the old governor was not present to repress them, they broke out with intolerable violence. Hither, there- fore, the orators and politicians repaired, and there seemed to be a competition among them who should bawl the loudest and exceed the others in hyperbolical bursts of patriotism and in resolutions to uphold and defend the government. In these sage and all-powerful meetings it was determined *nem. con.* that they were the most enlightened, the most dignified, the most formidable, and the most ancient community upon the face of the earth.—Finding that this resolution was so universally and readily carried, another was immediately proposed—whether it were not possible and politic to exterminate Great Britain? upon which sixty-nine members spoke most eloquently in the affirmative and only one arose to suggest some doubts—who, as a punishment for his treasonable presumption, was immediately seized by the mob and tarred and feathered—which punishment being equivalent to the Tarpeian Rock, he was afterwards considered as an outcast from society and his opinion went for nothing. The question, therefore, being unanimously carried in the affirmative, it was recommended to the grand council to pass it into a law; which was accordingly done.—By this measure the hearts of the people at large were wonderfully encouraged, and they waxed exceedingly choleric and valorous. Indeed, the first paroxysm of alarm having in some measure subsided—the old women having buried all the money they could lay their hands on, and their husbands daily getting fuddled with what was left—the community began even to stand on the offensive. Songs were manufactured in Low Dutch and sung about the streets, wherein the English were most woefully beaten and shown no quarter; and popular addresses were made, wherein it was proved to a certainty that the fate of Old England depended upon the will of the New Amsterdammers.

Finally, to strike a violent blow at the very vitals of Great Britain, a multitude of the wiser inhabitants assembled, and having purchased all the Brtish manufactures they could find, they made thereof a huge bonfire; and, in the patriotic glow of the moment, every man present who had a hat or breeches of English workmanship pulled it off and threw it most undauntedly into the flames—to the irreparable detriment, loss and ruin of the English manufacturers. In commemoration of this great exploit, they erected a pole on the spot, with a device on the top intended to represent the province of Nieuw Nederlandts destroying Great Britain, under the similitude of an eagle picking the little island of Old England out of the globe; but either through the unskilfulness of the sculptor or his ill-timed waggery, it bore a striking resemblance to a goose vainly striving to get hold of a dumpling.

Showing how the Grand Council of the New Netherlands came to be miraculously gifted with long tongues.—Together with a great triumph of Economy.

It will need but very little penetration in anyone acquainted with the character and habits of that most potent and blustering monarch, the sovereign people,—to discover that notwithstanding all the bustle and talk of war that stunned him in the last chapter, the renowned city of New Amsterdam is, in sad reality, not a whit better prepared for defense than before. Now, though the people, having gotten over the first alarm and finding no enemy immediately at hand, had, with that valor of tongue for which your illustrious rabble is so famous, run into the opposite extreme, and by dint of gallant vaporing and rodomontado had actually talked themselves into the opinion that they were the bravest and most powerful people under the sun, yet were the privy counselors of Peter Stuyvesant somewhat dubious on that point. They dreaded, morover, lest that stern hero should return and find that instead of obeying his peremptory orders they had wasted their time in listening to the hectorings of the mob, than which, they well knew, there was nothing he held in more exalted contempt.

To make up, therefore, as speedily as possible for lost time, a grand divan of the counselors and burgomasters was convened to talk over the critical state of the province and devise measures for its safety. Two things were unanimously agreed upon in this venerable assembly: first, that the city required to be put in a state of defence; and secondly, that, as the danger was imminent, there should be no time lost—which points being settled, they immediately fell to making long speeches and belaboring one another in endless and intemperate disputes. For about this time was this unhappy city first visited by that talking endemic so universally prevalent in this country and which so invariably evinces itself wherever a number of wise men assemble together; breaking out in long, windy speeches caused, as physicians suppose, by the foul air which is ever generated in a crowd. Now it was, moreover, that they first introduced the ingenious method of measuring the merits of an harangue by the hour glass; he being considered the ablest orator who spoke longest on a question—For which excellent invention, it is recorded, we are indebted to the same profound Dutch critic who judged of books by their size.

This sudden passion for endless harangues, so little consonant with the customary gravity and taciturnity of our sage forefathers, was supposed by certain learned philosophers to have been imbibed, together with divers other barbarous propensities, from their savage neighbors; who were peculiarly noted for their *long talks* and *council fires;* who would never undertake any affair of the least importance, without previous debates and harangues among their chiefs and *old men.* But the real cause was that the people in electing their representatives to the grand council were particular in choosing them for their talents at talking, without inquiring whether they possessed the more rare, difficult, and ofttimes important talent of holding their tongues. The consequence was that this deliberative body was composed of the most loquacious men in the community. As they considered themselves placed there to talk, every man concluded that his duty to his constituents, and, what is more, his popularity with them, required that he should harangue. on every subject, whether he understood it or not. There was an ancient mode of burying a chieftain, by every soldier throwing his shield full of earth on the corpse until a mighty mound was formed; so whenever a question was brought forward in this assembly, every member pressing forward to throw on his quantum of wisdom, the subject was quickly buried under a huge mass of words.

We are told in the Attic Nights of Aulus Gellius that when disciples were admitted into the school of Pythagoras they were for two years enjoined silence and were neither permitted to ask questions nor make remarks. After they had thus acquired the inestimable art of holding their tongues, they were gradually permitted to make inquiries, and finally to communicate their own opinions.

What a pity is it that while superstitiously hoarding up the rubbish and rags of antiquity we should suffer these precious gems to lie unnoticed! What a beneficial effect would this wise regulation of Pythagoras have if introduced in legislative bodies —and how wonderfully would it have tended to expedite business in the grand council of the Manhattoes!

Thus, however, did dame Wisdom (whom the wags of antiquity have humorously personified as a woman) seem to take mischievous pleasure in jilting the venerable counselors of New Amsterdam. The old factions of Long Pipes and Short Pipes, which had been almost strangled by the Herculean grasp of Peter Stuyvesant, now sprung up with tenfold violence. Not that the original cause of difference still existed, but it has ever been the fate of party names and party rancor to remain long after the principles that gave rise to them have been forgotten. To complete the public confusion and bewilderment, the fatal word *Economy,* which one would have thought was dead and buried with William the Testy, was once more set afloat, like the apple of discord, in the grand council of Nieuw Nederlandts—according to which sound principle of policy it was deemed more expedient to throw away twenty thousand guilders upon an inefficient plan of defense than thirty thousand on a good and substantial one—the province thus making a clear saving of ten thousand guilders.

But when they came to discuss the mode of defense, then began a war of words that baffles all description. The members being, as I observed, enlisted in opposite parties, were enabled to proceed with amazing system and regularity in the discussion of the questions before them. Whatever was proposed by a Long Pipe was opposed by the whole tribe of Short Pipes, who, like true politicians, considered it their first duty to effect the downfall of the Long Pipes—their second, to elevate themselves— and their third, to consult the welfare of the country. This at least was the creed of the most upright among the party, for as to the great mass, they left the third consideration out of the question altogether.

In this great collision of hard heads, it is astonishing the number of projects for defense that were struck out, not one of which had ever been heard of before, nor has been heard of since, unless it be in very modern days—projects that threw the windmill system of the ingenious Kieft completely in the background. Still, however, nothing could be decided on; for so soon as a formidable host of air castles were reared by one party, they were demolished by the other—the simple populace stood gazing in anxious expectation of the mighty egg that was to be hatched with all this cackling, but they gazed in vain, for it appeared that the grand council was determined to protect the province as did the noble and gigantic Pantagruel his army —by covering it with his tongue.

Indeed there was a portion of the members consisting of fat, self-important old burghers who smoked their pipes and said nothing excepting to negative every plan of defense that was offered. These were of that class of wealthy old citizens who, having amassed a fortune, button up their pockets, shut their mouths, look rich, and are good for nothing all the rest of their lives—like some phlegmatic oyster, which, having swallowed a pearl, closes its shell, settles down in the mud, and parts with its life sooner than its treasure. Every plan of defense seemed to these worthy old gentlemen pregnant with ruin. An armed force was a legion of locusts preying upon the public property—to fit out a naval armament was to throw their money into the sea—to build fortifications was to bury it in the dirt. In short, they settled it as a sovereign maxim, so long as their pockets were full, no matter how much they were drubbed—a kick left no scar—a broken head cured itself—but an empty purse was of all maladies the slowest to heal, and one in which nature did nothing for the patient.

Thus did this venerable assembly of *sages* lavish away that time, which the urgency of affairs rendered invaluable, in empty brawls and long-winded speeches, without ever agreeing, except on the point with which they started, namely, that there was no time to be lost and delay was ruinous. At length St. Nicholas, taking compassion on their distracted situation and anxious to preserve them from anarchy, so ordered that in the midst of one of their most noisy debates on the subject of fortification and defense, when they had nearly fallen to loggerheads in consequence of not being able to convince each other, the question was happily settled by a messenger who bounced into the chamber and informed them that the hostile fleet had arrived and was actually advancing up the bay!

Thus was all further necessity of either fortifying or disputing completely obviated, and thus was the grand council saved a world of words and the province a world of expense—a most absolute and glorious triumph of economy!

CHAPTER VI

*In which the troubles of New Amsterdam
appear to thicken—Showing the bravery, in
time of peril, of a people who defend themselves by resolutions.*

Like as an assemblage of politic cats engaged in clamorous
gibberings and caterwaulings, eyeing one another with hideous
grimaces, spitting in each other's faces, and on the point of
breaking forth into a general clapper-clawing, are suddenly put
to scampering rout and confusion by the startling appearance
of a house dog—so was the no less vociferous council of New
Amsterdam amazed, astounded, and totally dispersed by the
sudden arrival of the enemy. Every member made the best of
his way home, waddling along as fast as his short legs could
fag under their heavy burthen, and wheezing as he went with
corpulency and terror. When he arrived at his castle, he barricadoed the street door and buried himself in the cider cellar,
without daring to peep out lest he should have his head carried
off by a cannon ball.

The sovereign people all crowded into the market place,
herding together with the instinct of sheep who seek for safety
in each other's company when the shepherd and his dog are
absent and the wolf is prowling round the fold. Far from finding
relief, however, they only increased each other's terrors. Each
man looked ruefully in his neighbor's face in search of en-
couragement, but only found in its woebegone lineaments a
confirmation of his own dismay. Not a word now was to be
heard of conquering Great Britain, not a whisper about the
sovereign virtues of economy—while the old women heightened
the general gloom by clamorously bewailing their fate and
incessantly calling for protection on St. Nicholas and Peter
Stuyvesant.

Oh, how did they bewail the absence of the lion-hearted
Peter!—and how did they long for the comforting presence of

Antony Van Corlear! Indeed, a gloomy uncertainty hung over the fate of these adventurous heroes. Day after day had elapsed since the alarming message from the governor, without bringing any further tidings of his safety. Many a fearful conjecture was hazarded as to what had befallen him and his loyal squire. Had they not been devoured alive by the cannibals of Marblehead and Cape Cod?—were they not put to the question by the great council of Amphyctions?—were they not smothered in onions by the terrible men of Pyquag?—In the midst of this consternation and perplexity, when horror like a mighty nightmare sat brooding upon the little, fat, plethoric city of New Amsterdam, the ears of the multitude were suddenly startled by a strange and distant sound—it approached—it grew louder and louder—and now it resounded at the city gate. The public could not be mistaken in the well-known sound—A shout of joy burst from their lips as the gallant Peter, covered with dust and followed by his faithful trumpeter, came galloping into the market place.

The first transports of the populace having subsided, they gathered round the honest Antony as he dismounted from his horse, overwhelming him with greetings and congratulations. In breathless accents he related to them the marvelous adventures through which the old governor and himself had gone in making their escape from the clutches of the terrible Amphyctions. But though the Stuyvesant Manuscript, with its customary minuteness where anything touching the great Peter is concerned, is very particular as to the incidents of this masterly retreat, yet the particular state of the public affairs will not allow me to indulge in a full recital thereof. Let it suffice to say that while Peter Stuyvesant was anxiously revolving in his mind how he could make good his escape with honor and dignity, certain of the ships sent out for the conquest of the Manhattoes touched at the eastern ports to obtain needful supplies and to call on the grand council of the league for its promised cooperation. Upon hearing of this, the vigilant Peter, perceiving that a moment's delay were fatal, made a secret and precipitate decampment, though much did it grieve his lofty soul to be obliged to turn his back even upon a nation of foes. Many hairbreadth scapes and divers perilous mishaps did they sustain as they scoured, without sound of trumpet, through the fair regions of the east. Already was the country in an uproar with hostile preparation, and they were obliged to take a large circuit in their flight, lurking along through the woody mountains of the Devil's Backbone; from whence the valiant Peter sallied forth one day like a lion and put to rout a whole legion of squatters, consisting of three generations of a prolific family who were already on their way to take possession of some corner of the New Netherlands. Nay, the faithful Antony had great difficulty at sundry times to prevent him, in the excess of his wrath, from descending down from the mountains and falling, sword in hand, upon certain of the border towns who were marshalling forth their draggletailed militia.

The first movements of the governor, on reaching his dwelling, was to mount the roof, from whence he contemplated with rueful aspect the hostile squadron. This had already come to anchor in the bay, and consisted of two stout frigates, having on board, as John Josselyn, gent. informs us, "three hundred valiant red coats." Having taken this survey, he sat himself down and wrote an epistle to the commander demanding the reason of his anchoring in the harbor without obtaining previous permission so to do. This letter was couched in the most dignified and courteous terms, though I have it from undoubted authority that his teeth were clinched and he had a bitter sardonic grin upon his visage all the while he wrote. Having despatched his letter, the grim Peter stumped to and fro about the town with a most war-betokening countenance, his hands thrust into his breeches pockets, and whistling a Low Dutch psalm tune which bore no small resemblance to the music of a northeast wind when a storm is brewing.—The very dogs as they eyed him skulked away in dismay—while all the old and ugly women of New Amsterdam ran howling at his heels, imploring him to save them from murder, robbery, and pitiless ravishment!

The reply of Colonel Nichols, who commanded the invaders, was couched in terms of equal courtesy with the letter of the governor—declaring the right and title of his British Majesty to the province; where he affirmed the Dutch to be mere interlopers; and demanding that the town, forts &c. should be forthwith rendered into his majesty's obedience and protection—promising, at the same time, life, liberty, estate, and free trade to every Dutch denizen who should readily submit to his Majesty's government.

Peter Stuyvesant read over this friendly epistle with some such harmony of aspect as we may suppose a crusty farmer, who has long been fattening upon his neighbor's soil, reads the loving letter of John Stiles that warns him of an action of ejectment. The old governor, however, was not to be taken by surprise, but, thrusting the summons into his breeches pocket, he stalked three times across the room, took a pinch of snuff with great vehemence, and then, loftily waving his hand, promised to send an answer the next morning. In the meantime he called a general council of war of his privy counselors and burgomasters, not for the purpose of asking their advice, for that, as has been already shown, he valued not a rush, but to make known unto them his sovereign determination and require their prompt adherence.

Before, however, he convened his council, he resolved upon three important points: *first,* never to give up the city without a little hard fighting, for he deemed it highly derogatory to the dignity of so renowned a city to suffer itself to be captured and stripped without receiving a few kicks into the bargain. *Secondly,* that the majority of his grand council was composed of arrant poltroons, utterly destitute of true bottom—and, *thirdly*—that he would not therefore suffer them to see the summons of Colonel Nichols, lest the easy terms it held out might induce them to clamor for a surrender.

His orders being duly promulgated, it was a piteous sight to behold the late valiant burgomasters, who had demolished the whole British empire in their harangues, peeping ruefully out of their hiding places and then crawling cautiously forth, dodging through narrow lanes and alleys—starting at every little dog that barked, as though it had been a discharge of artillery—mistaking lamposts for British grenadiers, and in the excess of their panic metamorphosing pumps into formidable soldiers leveling blunderbusses at their bosoms! Having, however, in despite of numerous perils and difficulties of the kind, arrived safe, without the loss of a single man, at the hall of assembly, they took their seats and awaited in fearful silence the arrival of the governor. In a few moments the wooden leg of the intrepid Peter was heard in regular and stout-hearted thumps upon the staircase—He entered the chamber, arrayed in full suit of regimentals and carrying his trusty toledo, not girded on his thigh but tucked under his arm. As the governor never equipped himself in this portentous manner unless something of martial nature were working within his fearless pericranium, his council regarded him ruefully, as a very Janus bearing fire and sword in his iron countenance, and forgot to light their pipes in breathless suspense.

The great Peter was as eloquent as he was valorous—indeed, these two rare qualities seemed to go hand in hand in his composition; and unlike most great statesmen, whose victories are only confined to the bloodless field of argument, he was always ready to enforce his hardy words by no less hardy deeds. His speeches were generally marked by a simplicity approaching to bluntness and by truly categorical decision. Addressing the grand council, he touched briefly upon the perils and hardships he had sustained in escaping from his crafty foes. He next reproached the council for wasting in idle debate and party feuds that time which should have been devoted to their country. He was particularly indignant at those brawlers who, conscious of individual security, had disgraced the councils of the province by impotent hectorings and scurrilous invectives against a noble and a powerful enemy—those cowardly curs who were incessant in their barkings and yelpings at the lion, while distant or asleep, but the moment he approached, were the first to skulk away. He now called on those who had been so valiant in their threats against Great Britain to stand forth and support their vauntings by their actions—for it was *deeds*, not *words*, that bespoke the spirit of a nation. He proceeded to recall the golden days of former prosperity, which were only to be gained by manfully withstanding their enemies; for the peace, he observed, which is effected by force of arms is always more sure and durable than that which is patched up by temporary accommodations. He endeavored, moreover, to arouse their martial fire by reminding them of the time when, before the frowning walls of Fort Christina, he had led them on to victory.—He strove likewise to awaken their confidence by assuring them of the protection of St. Nicholas, who had hitherto maintained them in safety amid all the savages of the wilderness, the witches and squatters of the east, and the giants of Merry-land. Finally, he informed them of the insolent summons he had received to surrender, but concluded by swearing to defend the province as long as heaven was on his side and he had a wooden leg to stand upon. Which noble sentence he emphasized by a tremendous thwack with the broad side of his sword upon the table, that totally electrified his auditors.

The privy counselors, who had long been accustomed to the governor's way, and in fact had been brought into as perfect discipline as were ever the soldiers of the great Frederick, saw that there was no use in saying a word—so lighted their pipes and smoked away in silence like fat and discreet counselors. But the burgomasters being less under the governor's control, considering themselves as representatives of the sovereign people, and being moreover inflated with considerable importance and self-sufficiency, which they had acquired at those notable schools of wisdom and morality, the popular meetings, were not so easily satisfied. Mustering up fresh spirit, when they found there was some chance of escaping from their present jeopardy without the disagreeable alternative of fighting, they requested a copy of the summons to surrender, that they might show it to a general meeting of the people.

So insolent and mutinous a request would have been enough to have roused the gorge of the tranquil Van Twiller himself— what then must have been its effect upon the great Stuyvesant, who was not only a Dutchman, a governor, and a valiant wooden-legged soldier to boot, but withal a man of the most stomachful and gunpowder disposition. He burst forth into a blaze of noble indignation, to which the famous rage of Achilles was a mere pouting fit—swore not a mother's son of them should see a syllable of it—that they deserved, every one of them, to be hanged, drawn, and quartered for traitorously daring to question the infallibility of government—that as to their advice or concurrence, he did not care a whiff of tobacco for either—that he had long been harassed and thwarted by their cowardly counsels; but that they might thenceforth go home and go to bed like old women; for he was determined to defend the colony himself, without the assistance of them or their adherents! So saying, he tucked his sword under his arm, cocked his hat upon his head, and girding up his loins, stumped indignantly out of the council chamber—everybody making room for him as he passed.

No sooner had he gone than the busy burgomasters called a public meeting in front of the Stadthouse, where they appointed as chairman one Dofue Roerback, a mighty gingerbread-baker in the land, and formerly of the cabinet of William the Testy. He was looked up to with great reverence by the populace, who considered him a man of dark knowledge, seeing he was the first that imprinted New Year cakes with the mysterious hieroglyphics of the Cock and Breeches and such like magical devices.

This great burgomaster, who still chewed the cud of ill will against the valiant Stuyvesant, in consequence of having been ignominiously kicked out of his cabinet at the time of his taking the reins of government—addressed the greasy multitude in what is called a patriotic speech, in which he informed them of the courteous summons to surrender—of the governor's refusal to comply therewith—of his denying the public a sight of the summons, which he had no doubt contained conditions highly to the honor and advantage of the province.

He then proceeded to speak of his excellency in high-sounding terms suitable to the dignity and grandeur of his station, comparing him to Nero, Caligula, and those other great men of yore who are generally quoted by popular orators on similar occasions. Assuring the people that the history of the world did not contain a despotic outrage to equal the present for atrocity, cruelty, tyranny, and bloodthirstiness!—that it would be recorded in letters of fire on the bloodstained tablet of history! —that ages would roll back with sudden horror when they came to view it!—that the womb of time (by the way, your orators and writers take strange liberties with the womb of time, though some would fain have us believe that time is an old gentleman) —that the womb of time, pregnant as it was with direful horrors, would never produce a parallel enormity!— with a variety of other heart-rending, soul-stirring tropes and figures which I cannot enumerate—Neither indeed need I, for they were exactly the same that are used in all popular harangues and patriotic orations at the present day, and may be classed in rhetoric under the general title of RIGMAROLE.

The speech of this inspired burgomaster being finished, the meeting fell into a kind of popular fermentation, which produced not only a string of right wise resolutions, but likewise a most resolute memorial addressed to the governor, remonstrating at his conduct—which was no sooner handed to him than he handed it into the fire; and thus deprived posterity of an invaluable document that might have served as a precedent to the enlightened cobblers and tailors of the present day in their sage intermeddlings with politics.

Containing a doleful disaster of Antony the Trumpeter—And how Peter Stuyvesant, like a second Cromwell, suddenly dissolved a rump Parliament.

Now did the high-minded Pieter de Groodt shower down a pannier load of benedictions upon his burgomasters for a set of self-willed, obstinate, headstrong varlets who would neither be convinced nor persuaded; and determined thenceforth to have nothing more to do with them, but to consult merely the opinion of his privy counselors, which he knew from experience to be the best in the world—inasmuch as it never differed from his own. Nor did he omit, now that his hand was in, to bestow some thousand left-handed compliments upon the sovereign people, whom he railed at for a herd of poltroons who had no relish for the glorious hardships and illustrious misadventures of battle—but would rather stay at home and eat and sleep in ignoble ease than gain immortality and a broken head by valiantly fighting in a ditch.

Resolutely bent, however, upon defending his beloved city in despite even of itself, he called unto him his trusty Van Corlear, who was his right-hand man in all times of emergency. Him did he adjure to take his war-denouncing trumpet and, mounting his horse, to beat up the country night and day—sounding the alarm along the pastoral borders of the Bronx—startling the wild solitudes of Croton—arousing the rugged yeomanry of Weehawk and Hoboeken—the mighty men of battle of Tappan Bay*—and the brave boys of Tarrytown and Sleepy Hollow—together with all the other warriors of the country round about; charging them one and all to sling their powder horns, shoulder their fowling pieces, and march merrily down to the Manhattoes.

* A corruption of Top-paun; so called from a tribe of Indians which boasted 150 fighting men. See Ogilvie's History.

Now there was nothing in all the world, the divine sex excepted, that Antony Van Corlear loved better than errands of this kind. So just stopping to take a lusty dinner, and bracing to his side his junk bottle, well charged with heart-inspiring Hollands, he issued jollily from the city gate that looked out upon what is at present called Broadway; sounding as usual a farewell strain that rung in sprightly echoes through the winding streets of New Amsterdam—Alas! never more were they to be gladdened by the melody of their favorite trumpeter!

It was a dark and stormy night when the good Antony arrived at the famous creek (sagely denominated Haerlem *River*) which separates the island of Manna-hata from the main land. The wind was high, the elements were in an uproar, and no Charon could be found to ferry the adventurous sounder of brass across the water. For a short time he vapored like an impatient ghost upon the brink, and then bethinking himself of the urgency of his errand, took a hearty embrace of his stone bottle, swore most valorously that he would swim across *en spijt den Duyvel* (in spite of the devil!), and daringly plunged into the stream.—Luckless Antony! scarce had he buffeted halfway over when he was observed to struggle violently, as if battling with the spirit of the waters—instinctively he put his trumpet to his mouth, and giving a vehement blast—sunk forever to the bottom!

The potent clangor of his trumpet, like the ivory horn of the renowned Paladin Orlando when expiring in the glorious field of Roncesvalles, rung far and wide through the country, alarming the neighbors round, who hurried in amazement to the spot—Here an old Dutch burgher, famed for his veracity, and who had been a witness of the fact, related to them the melancholy affair; with the fearful addition (to which I am slow of giving belief) that he saw the duyvel, in the shape of a huge mossbunker, seize the sturdy Antony by the leg and drag him beneath the waves. Certain it is, the place, with the adjoining promontory which projects into the Hudson, has been called *Spijt den duyvel,* or *Spiking Devil,* ever since—the restless ghost of the unfortunate Antony still haunts the surrounding solitudes, and his trumpet has often been heard by the neighbors, of a stormy night, mingling with the howling of the blast. Nobody ever attempts to swim over the creek after dark; on the contrary, a bridge has been built to guard against such melancholy accidents in future—and as to mossbunkers, they are held in such abhorrence that no true Dutchman will admit them to his table who loves good fish and hates the devil.

Such was the end of Antony Van Corlear—a man deserving of a better fate. He lived roundly and soundly, like a true and jolly bachelor, until the day of his death; but though he was never married, yet did he leave behind some two or three dozen children in different parts of the country—fine chubby, brawling, flatulent little urchins, from whom, if legends speak true (and they are not apt to lie), did descend the innumerable race of editors who people and defend this country and who are bountifully paid by the people for keeping up a constant alarm—and making them miserable. Would that they inherited the worth, as they do the wind, of their renowned progenitor!

The tidings of this lamentable catastrophe imparted a severer pang to the bosom of Peter Stuyvesant than did even the invasion of his beloved Amsterdam. It came ruthlessly home to those sweet affections that grow close around the heart and are nourished by its warmest current. As some lorn pilgrim, wandering in trackless wastes while the tempest whistles through his locks and dreary night is gathering around, sees stretched cold and lifeless his faithful dog—the sole companion of his journeying, who had shared his solitary meal and so often licked his hand in humble gratitude—so did the generous-hearted hero of the Manhattoes contemplate the untimely end of his faithful Antony. He had been the humble attendant of his footsteps—he had cheered him in many a heavy hour by his honest gaity, and had followed him in loyalty and affection through many a scene of direful peril and mishap—he was gone for ever—and that, too, at a moment when every mongrel cur seemed skulking from his side. —This—Peter Stuyvestant—this was the moment to try thy fortitude; and this was the moment when thou didst indeed shine forth—Peter *the Headstrong!*

The glare of day had long dispelled the horrors of the last stormy night; still all was dull and gloomy. The late jovial Apollo hid his face behind lugubrious clouds, peeping out now and then for an instant, as if anxious yet fearful to see what was going on in his favorite city. This was the eventful morning when the great Peter was to give his reply to the summons of the invaders. Already was he closeted with his privy council, sitting in grim state, brooding over the fate of his favorite trumpeter, and anon boiling with indignation as the insolence

of his recreant burgomasters flashed upon his mind. While in
this state of irritation, a courier arrived in all haste from Winthrop, the subtle governor of Connecticut, counseling him in
the most affectionate and disinterested manner to surrender the
province, and magnifying the dangers and calamities to which
a refusal would subject him.—What a moment was this to intrude
officious advice upon a man who never took advice in his whole
life!—The fiery old governor strode up and down the chamber
with a vehemence that made the bosoms of his counselors to
quake with awe—railing at his unlucky fate that thus made him
the constant butt of factious subjects and jesuitical advisers.

Just at this ill-chosen juncture, the officious burgomasters, who
were now completely on the watch and had heard of the arrival
of mysterious despatches, came marching in a resolute body into
the room, with a legion of schepens and toadeaters at their heels,
and abruptly demanded a perusal of the letter. Thus to be
broken in upon by what he esteemed a "rascal rabble," and that
too at the very moment he was grinding under an irritation from
abroad, was too much for the spleen of the choleric Peter. He
tore the letter in a thousand pieces*—threw it in the face of the
nearest burgomaster—broke his pipe over the head of the next
—hurled his spitting box at an unlucky schepen who was just
making a masterly retreat out at the door, and finally prorogued
the whole meeting *sine die* by kicking them down stairs with
his wooden leg.

As soon as the burgomasters could recover from the confusion
into which their sudden exit had thrown them, and had taken
a little time to breathe, they protested against the conduct of
the governor, which they did not hesitate to pronounce tyrannical, unconstitutional, highly indecent, and somewhat disre-
spectful. They then called a public meeting, where they read
the protest, and addressing the assembly in a set speech, related
at full length, and with appropriate coloring and exaggeration,
the despotic and vindictive deportment of the governor; declaring that for their own parts they did not value a straw the
being kicked, cuffed, and mauled by the timber toe of his excellency, but they felt for the dignity of the sovereign people, thus
rudely insulted by the outrage committed on the seats of honor
of their representatives. The latter part of the harangue had a

---

* Smith's History of N. Y.

violent effect upon the sensibility of the people, as it came home at once to that delicacy of feeling and jealous pride of character vested in all true mobs: who, though they may bear injuries without a murmur, yet are marvelously jealous of their sovereign dignity—and there is no knowing to what act of resentment they might have been provoked against the redoubtable Peter—had not the greasy rogues been somewhat more afraid of their sturdy old governor than they were of St. Nicholas, the English—or the D—l himself.

CHAPTER VIII

How Peter Stuyvesant defended the city of New Amsterdam for several days, by dint of the strength of his head.

There is something exceedingly sublime and melancholy in the spectacle which the present crisis of our history presents. An illustrious and venerable little city—the metropolis of an immense extent of uninhabited country—garrisoned by a doughty host of orators, chairmen, committeemen, burgomasters, schepens, and old women—governed by a determined and strong-headed warrior—and fortified by mud batteries, pallisadoes, and resolutions—blockaded by sea, beleaguered by land, and threatened with direful desolation from without; while its very vitals are torn with internal faction and commotion! Never did historic pen record a page of more complicated distress, unless it be the strife that distracted the Israelites during the siege of Jerusalem—where discordant parties were cutting each other's throats at the moment when the victorious legions of Titus had toppled down their bulwarks and were carrying fire and sword into the very sanctum sanctorum of the temple.

Governor Stuyvesant having triumphantly, as has been recorded, put his grand council to the rout and thus delivered himself from a multitude of impertinent advisers, dispatched a categorical reply to the commanders of the invading squadron;

wherein he asserted the right and title of their High Mightinesses the Lords States General to the province of New Netherlands, and trusting in the righteousness of his cause, set the
whole British nation at defiance! My anxiety to extricate my
readers and myself from these disastrous scenes prevents me
from giving the whole of this gallant letter, which concluded in
these manly and affectionate terms:

"As touching the threats in your conclusion, we have nothing
to answer, only that we fear nothing but what God (who is as
just as merciful) shall lay upon us; all things being in his gracious disposal, and we may as well be preserved by him with
small forces as by a great army; which makes us to wish you all
happiness and prosperity, and recommend you to his protection.
—My lords, your thrice humble and affectionate servant and
friend

P. STUYVESANT."

Thus having resolutely thrown his gauntlet, the brave Peter
stuck a pair of horse pistols in his belt, girded an immense
powder horn on his side—thrust his sound leg into a Hessian
boot, and clapping his fierce little war hat on the top of his
head—paraded up and down in front of his house, determined to
defend his beloved city to the last.

While all these woeful struggles and dissensions were pre-
vailing in the unhappy city of New Amsterdam, and while its
worthy but ill-starred governor was framing the above quoted
letter, the English commanders did not remain idle. They had
agents secretly employed to foment the fears and clamors of
the populace; and moreover circulated far and wide through
the adjacent country a proclamation repeating the terms they
had already held out in their summons to surrender, and be-
guiling the simple Nederlanders with the most crafty and con-
ciliating professions. They promised that every man who vol-
untarily submitted to the authority of his British majesty should
retain peaceable possession of his house, his vrouw, and his
cabbage garden.—That he should be suffered to smoke his pipe,
speak Dutch, wear as many breeches as he pleased, and import
bricks, tiles, and stone jugs from Holland instead of manufacturing them on the spot.—That he should on no account be compelled to learn the English language, or keep accounts in any
other way than by casting them up on his fingers and chalking

them down upon the crown of his hat; as is still observed among the Dutch yeomanry at the present day.—That every man should be allowed quietly to inherit his father's hat, coat, shoe buckles, pipe, and every other personal appendage; and that no man should be obliged to conform to any improvements, inventions, or any other modern innovations; but on the contrary should be permitted to build his house, follow his trade, manage his farm, rear his hogs, and educate his children precisely as his ancestors did before him since time immemorial.—Finally, that he should have all the benefits of free trade, and should not be required to acknowledge any other saint in the calendar than St. Nicholas, who should thenceforward, as before, be considered the tutelar saint of the city.

These terms, as may be supposed, appeared very satisfactory to the people, who had a great disposition to enjoy their property unmolested and a most singular aversion to engage in a contest where they could gain little more than honor and broken heads—the first of which they held in philosophic indifference, the latter in utter detestation. By these insidious means, therefore, did the English succeed in alienating the confidence and affections of the populace from their gallant old governor, whom they considered as obstinately bent upon running them into hideous misadventures; and did not hesitate to speak their minds freely and abuse him most heartily—behind his back.

Like as a mighty grampus, who, though assailed and buffeted by roaring waves and brawling surges, still keeps on an undeviating course; and though overwhelmed by boisterous billows, still emerges from the troubled deep, spouting and blowing with tenfold violence—so did the inflexible Peter pursue, unwavering, his determined career, and rise, contemptuous, above the clamors of the rabble.

But when the British warriors found, by the tenor of his reply, that he set their power at defiance, they forthwith despatched recruiting officers to Jamaica and Jericho and Nineveh and Quag and Patchog and all those towns on Long Island which had been subdued of yore by the immortal Stoffel Brinkerhoff; stirring up the valiant progeny of Preserved Fish and Determined Cock and those other illustrious squatters to assail the city of New Amsterdam by land. In the meanwhile the hostile ships made awful preparation to commence an assault by water.

The streets of New Amsterdam now presented a scene of wild dismay and consternation. In vain did the gallant Stuyvesant order the citizens to arm and assemble in the public square or market place. The whole party of Short Pipes in the course of a single night had changed into arrant old women—a metamorphosis only to be paralleled by the prodigies recorded by Livy as having happened to Rome at the approach of Hannibal, when statues sweated in pure affright, goats were converted into sheep, and cocks turning into hens ran cackling about the streets.

The harassed Peter, thus menaced from without and tormented from within—baited by the burgomasters and hooted at by the rabble—chafed and growled and raged like a furious bear tied to a stake and worried by a legion of scoundrel curs. Finding, however, that all further attempts to defend the city were in vain, and hearing that an irruption of borderers and mosstroopers was ready to deluge him from the east, he was at length compelled, in spite of his proud heart, which swelled in his throat until it had nearly choked him, to consent to a treaty of surrender.

Words cannot express the transports of the people on receiving this agreeable intelligence; had they obtained a conquest over their enemies, they could not have indulged greater delight—The streets resounded with their congratulations—they extolled their governor as the father and deliverer of his country —they crowded to his house to testify their gratitude, and were ten times more noisy in their plaudits than when he returned, with victory perched upon his beaver, from the glorious capture of Fort Christina.—But the indignant Peter shut his doors and windows, and took refuge in the innermost recesses of his mansion, that he might not hear the ignoble rejoicings of the rabble.

In consequence of this consent of the governor, a parley was demanded of the besieging forces to treat of the terms of surrender. Accordingly a deputation of six commissioners was appointed on both sides, and on the 27th August, 1664, a capitulation highly favorable to the province and honorable to Peter Stuyvesant was agreed to by the enemy, who had conceived a high opinion of the valor of the men of the Manhattoes and the magnanimity and unbounded discretion of their governor.

One thing alone remained, which was that the articles of surrender should be ratified and signed by the governor. When the commissioners respectfully waited upon him for this purpose, they were received by the hardy old warrior with the most grim and bitter courtesy. His warlike accoutrements were laid aside—an old India nightgown was wrapped about his rugged limbs, a red nightcap overshadowed his frowning brow, and an iron-gray beard of three days' growth gave additional grimness to his visage. Thrice did he seize a little worn-out stump of a pen and essay to sign the loathsome paper—thrice did he clinch his teeth and make a most horrible countenance, as though a pestiferous dose of rhubarb, senna, and ipecacuanha had been offered to his lips; at length, dashing it from him, he seized his brass-hilted sword, and jerking it from the scabbard, swore by St. Nicholas he'd sooner die than yield to any power under heaven.

In vain was every attempt to shake this sturdy resolution— menaces, remonstrances, revilings were exhausted to no purpose—for two whole days was the house of the valiant Peter besieged by the clamorous rabble, and for two whole days did he partake himself to his arms and persist in a magnanimous refusal to ratify the capitulation—thus, like another Horatius Cocles, bearing the whole brunt of war and defending this modern Rome with the prowess of his single arm!

At length the populace, finding that boisterous measures did but incense more determined opposition, bethought themselves of an humble expedient by which, happily, the governor's lofty ire might be soothed and his resolution undermined. And now a solemn and mournful procession, headed by the burgomasters and schepens, and followed by the populace, moves slowly to the governor's dwelling, bearing the capitulation. Here they found the stout old hero drawn up like a giant into his castle, the doors strongly barricadoed, and himself in full regimentals with his cocked hat on his head, firmly posted with a blunder- buss at the garret window.

There was something in this formidable position that struck even the ignoble vulgar with awe and admiration. The brawling multitude could not but reflect with self-abasement upon their own pusillanimous conduct when they beheld their hardy but deserted old governor thus faithful to his post, like a forlorn hope, and fully prepared to defend his ungrateful city to the last. These compunctions, however, were soon overwhelmed by the recurring tide of public apprehension. The populace ar- ranged themselves before the house, taking off their hats with most respectful humility—Burgomaster Roerback, who was of that popular class of orators described by old Sallust as being "talkative rather than eloquent," stepped forth and addressed the governor in a speech of three hours length, detailing in the most pathetic terms the calamitous situation of the province, and urging him in a constant repetition of the same arguments and words to sign the capitulation.

The mighty Peter eyed him from his little garret window in grim silence—now and then his eye would glance over the surrounding rabble, and an indignant grin, like that of an angry mastiff, would mark his iron visage.—But though he was a man of most undaunted mettle—though he had a heart as big as an ox, and a head that would have set adamant to scorn—yet after all he was a mere mortal:—wearied out by these repeated oppositions and this eternal haranguing; and perceiving that unless he complied, the inhabitants would follow their inclinations, or rather their fears, without waiting for his consent, he testily ordered them to hand him up the paper. It was accordingly hoisted to him on the end of a pole, and having scrawled his name at the bottom of it, he anathematized them all for a set of cowardly, mutinous, degenerate poltroons—threw the capitulation at their heads, slammed down the window, and was heard stumping down stairs with the most vehement indignation. The rabble incontinently took to their heels; even the burgomasters were not slow in evacuating the premises, fearing lest the sturdy Peter might issue from his den and greet them with some unwelcome testimonial of his displeasure.

Within three hours after the surrender, a legion of British beef-fed warriors poured into New Amsterdam, taking possession of the fort and batteries. And now might be heard from all quarters the sound of hammers made by the old Dutch burghers who were busily employed nailing up their doors and windows to protect their vrouws from these fierce barbarians, whom they contemplated in silent sullenness from the garret windows as they paraded through the streets.

Thus did Col. Richard Nichols, the commander of the British forces, enter into quiet possession of the conquered realm as *locum tenens* for the Duke of York. The victory was attended with no other outrage than that of changing the name of the province and its metropolis, which thenceforth were denominated NEW YORK, and so have continued to be called unto the present day. The inhabitants, according to treaty, were allowed to maintain quiet possession of their property; but so inveterately did they retain their abhorrence to the British nation, that in a private meeting of the leading citizens it was unanimously determined never to ask any of their conquerors to dinner.

CHAPTER IX

Containing the dignified retirement and mortal surrender of Peter the Headstrong.

Thus then have I concluded this great historical enterprise; but before I lay aside my weary pen, there yet remains to be performed one pious duty. If among the variety of readers that may peruse this book there should haply be found any of those souls of true nobility which glow with celestial fire at the history of the generous and the brave, they will doubtless be anxious to know the fate of the gallant Peter Stuyvesant. To gratify one such sterling heart of gold I would go more lengths than to instruct the cold-blooded curiosity of a whole fraternity of philosophers.

No sooner had that high-mettled cavalier signed the articles of capitulation than, determined not to witness the humiliation of his favorite city, he turned his back on its walls and made a growling retreat to his *Bouwery,* or country seat, which was situated about two miles off; where he passed the remainder of his days in patriarchal retirement. There he enjoyed that tranquillity of mind which he had never known amid the distracting cares of government; and tasted the sweets of absolute and uncontrolled authority, which his factious subjects had so often dashed with the bitterness of opposition.

No persuasions could ever induce him to revisit the city—on the contrary he would always have his great armchair placed with its back to the windows which looked in that direction; until a thick grove of trees planted by his own hand grew up and formed a screen that effectually excluded it from the prospect. He railed continually at the degenerate innovations and improvements introduced by the conquerors—forbade a word of their detested language to be spoken in his family; a prohibition readily obeyed, since none of the household could speak anything but Dutch—and even ordered a fine avenue to be cut down in front of his house because it consisted of English cherry trees.

The same incessant vigilance that blazed forth when he had a vast province under his care now showed itself with equal vigor, though in narrower limits. He patrolled with unceasing watchfulness around the boundaries of his little territory; repelled every encroachment with intrepid promptness; punished every vagrant depredation upon his orchard or his farmyard with inflexible severity—and conducted every stray hog or cow in triumph to the pound. But to the indigent neighbor, the friendless stranger or the weary wanderer, his spacious doors were ever open and his capacious fireplace, that emblem of his own warm and generous heart, had always a corner to receive and cherish them. There was an exception to this, I must confess, in case the ill-starred applicant was an Englishman or a Yankee, to whom, though he might extend the hand of assistance, he could never be brought to yield the rites of hospitality. Nay, if peradventure some straggling merchant of the east should stop at his door with his cartload of tinware or wooden bowls, the fiery Peter would issue forth like a giant from his castle and make such a furious clattering among his pots and kettles that the vender of *"notions"* was fain to betake himself to instant flight.

His ancient suit of regimentals, worn threadbare by the brush, were carefully hung up in the state bedchamber and regularly aired the first fair day of every month—and his cocked hat and trusty sword were suspended in grim repose over the parlor mantlepiece, forming supporters to a full length portrait of the renowned admiral Von Tromp. In his domestic empire he maintained strict discipline and a well organized, despotic government; but though his own will was the supreme law, yet the good of his subjects was his constant object. He watched over not merely their immediate comforts but their morals and their ultimate welfare; for he gave them abundance of excellent admonition, nor could any of them complain that when occasion required he was by any means niggardly in bestowing wholesome correction.

The good old Dutch festivals, those periodical demonstrations of an overflowing heart and a thankful spirit, which are falling into sad disuse among my fellow citizens, were faithfully observed in the mansion of Governor Stuyvesant. New Year was truly a day of open-handed liberality, of jocund revelry and warm-hearted congratulation—when the bosom seemed to swell with genial good-fellowship—and the plenteous table was attended with an unceremonious freedom and honest broadmouthed merriment, unknown in these days of degeneracy and refinement. Paas and Pinxter were scrupulously observed throughout his dominions; nor was the day of St. Nicholas suffered to pass by without making presents, hanging the stocking in the chimney, and complying with all its other ceremonies.

Once a year, on the first day of April, he used to array himself in full regimentals, being the anniversary of his triumphal entry into New Amsterdam after the conquest of New Sweden. This was always a kind of saturnalia among the domestics, when they considered themselves at liberty in some measure to say and do what they pleased; for on this day their master was always observed to unbend and become exceeding pleasant and jocose, sending the old gray-headed negroes on April fool's errands for pigeon's milk; not one of whom but allowed himself to be taken in, and humored his old master's jokes as became a faithful and well-disciplined dependent. Thus did he reign happily and peacefully on his own land—injuring no man—envying no man—molested by no outward strifes; perplexed by no internal commotions—and the mighty monarchs of the earth, who were vainly seeking to maintain peace and promote the welfare of mankind by war and desolation, would have done well to have made a voyage to the little island of Manna-hata and learned a lesson in government from the domestic economy of Peter Stuyvesant.

In process of time, however, the old governor, like all other children of mortality, began to exhibit evident tokens of decay. Like an aged oak, which, though it long has braved the fury of the elements and still retains its gigantic proportions, yet begins to shake and groan with every blast—so the gallant Peter, though he still bore the port and semblance of what he was in the days of his hardihood and chivalry, yet did age and infirmity begin to sap the vigor of his frame—but his heart, that most unconquerable citadel, still triumphed unsubdued. With match-

less avidity would he listen to every article of intelligence concerning the battles between the English and Dutch—Still would
his pulse beat high whenever he heard of the victories of De
Ruyter—and his countenance lower and his eyebrows knit when
fortune turned in favor of the English. At length, as on a certain day he had just smoked his fifth pipe and was napping
after dinner in his armchair, conquering the whole British
nation in his dreams, he was suddenly aroused by a fearful
ringing of bells, rattling of drums, and roaring of cannon that
put all his blood in a ferment. But when he learnt that these
rejoicings were in honor of a great victory obtained by the combined English and French fleets over the brave De Ruyter and
the younger Von Tromp, it went so much to his heart that he
took to his bed and in less than three days was brought to
death's door by a violent cholera morbus! But even in this
extremity he still displayed the unconquerable spirit of Peter
the Headstrong; holding out to the last gasp, with the most inflexible obstinacy, against a whole army of old women who were
bent upon driving the enemy out of his bowels, after a true
Dutch mode of defense, by inundating the seat of war with
catnip and pennyroyal.

While he thus lay lingering on the verge of dissolution, news
was brought him that the brave De Ruyter had suffered but
little loss—had made good his retreat—and meant once more to
meet the enemy in battle. The closing eye of the old warrior
kindled at the words—he partly raised himself in bed—a flash of
martial fire beamed across his visage—he clenched his withered
hand as if he felt within his gripe that sword which waved in
triumph before the walls of Fort Christina—and giving a grim
smile of exultation, sunk back upon his pillow and expired.

Thus died Peter Stuyvesant: a valiant soldier—a loyal subject
—an upright governor—and an honest Dutchman—who wanted
only a few empires to desolate to have been immortalized as
a hero!

His funeral obsequies were celebrated with the utmost grandeur and solemnity. The town was perfectly emptied of its
inhabitants, who crowded in throngs to pay the last sad honors
to their good old governor. All his sterling qualities rushed in
full tide upon their recollections, while the memory of his
foibles and his faults had expired with him. The ancient
burghers contended who should have the privilege of bearing

the pall; the populace strove who should walk nearest to the bier—and the melancholy procession was closed by a number of grey-headed negroes who had wintered and summered in the household of their departed master for the greater part of a century.

With sad and gloomy countenances, the multitude gathered round the grave. They dwelt with mournful hearts on the sturdy virtues, the signal services, and the gallant exploits of the brave old worthy. They recalled with secret upbraidings their own factious oppositions to his government—and many an ancient burgher, whose phlegmatic features had never been known to relax nor his eyes to moisten, was now observed to puff a pensive pipe, and the big drop to steal down his cheek— while he muttered with affectionate accent and melancholy shake of the head—"Well den!—Hard-koppig Peter ben gone at last!"

His remains were deposited in the family vault, under a chapel which he had piously erected on his estate and dedicated to St. Nicholas—and which stood on the identical spot at present occupied by St. Mark's church, where his tombstone is still to be seen. His estate, or *Bouwery* as it was called, has ever continued in the possession of his descendants, who, by the uniform integrity of their conduct and their strict adherence to the customs and manners that prevailed in the *"good old times,"* have proved themselves worthy of their illustrious ancestor. Many a time and oft has the farm been haunted at night by enterprising money-diggers in quest of pots of gold, said to have been buried by the old governor—though I cannot learn that any of them have ever been enriched by their researches—and who is there among my native-born fellow citizens that does not remember when in the mischievous days of his boyhood he conceived it a great exploit to rob "Stuyvesant's orchard" on a holiday afternoon.

At this stronghold of the family may still be seen certain memorials of the immortal Peter. His full length portrait frowns in martial terrors from the parlor wall—his cocked hat and sword still hang up in the best bedroom—his brimstone-colored breeches were for a long while suspended in the hall, until some years since they occasioned a dispute between a new-married couple—and his silver-mounted wooden leg is still treasured up in the storeroom as an invaluable relic.

CHAPTER X

The author's reflections upon what has been said.

Among the numerous events which are each in their turn the most direful and melancholy of all possible occurences in your interesting and authentic history, there is none that occasions such deep and heart-rending grief as the decline and fall of your renowned and mighty empires. Where is the reader who can contemplate without emotion the disastrous events by which the great dynasties of the world have been extinguished? While wandering in imagination among the gigantic ruins of states and empires, and marking the tremendous convulsions that wrought their overthrow, the bosom of the melancholy inquirer swells with sympathy commensurate to the surrounding desolation. Kingdoms, principalities, and powers have each had their rise, their progress, and their downfall—each in its turn has swayed a potent scepter—each has returned to its primeval nothingness. And thus did it fare with the empire of their High Mightinesses at the Manhattoes under the peaceful reign of Walter the Doubter—the fretful reign of William the Testy— and the chivalric reign of Peter the Headstrong.

Its history is fruitful of instruction and worthy of being pondered over attentively; for it is by thus raking among the ashes of departed greatness that the sparks of true knowledge are found and the lamp of wisdom illumined. Let then the reign of Walter the Doubter warn against yielding to that sleek, contented security, that overweening fondness for comfort and repose, that are produced by a state of prosperity and peace. These tend to unnerve a nation, to destroy its pride of character; to render it patient of insult, deaf to the calls of honor and of justice, and cause it to cling to peace like the sluggard to his pillow, at the expense of every valuable duty and consideration. Such supineness ensures the very evil from which it shrinks. One right yielded up produces the usurpation of a second; one encroachment passively suffered makes way for another; and the nation that thus, through a doting love of peace, has sacrificed honor and interest will at length have to fight for existence.

Let the disastrous reign of William the Testy serve as a salutary warning against that fitful, feverish mode of legislation that acts without system; depends on shifts and projects, and trusts to lucky contingencies. That hesitates and wavers and at length decides with the rashness of ignorance and imbecility. That stoops for popularity by courting the prejudices and flattering the arrogance, rather than commanding the respect of the rabble. That seeks safety in a multitude of counselors, and distracts itself by a variety of contradictory schemes and opinions. That mistakes procrastination for deliberate wariness—hurry for decision—starveling parsimony for wholesome economy—bustle for business, and vaporing for valor. That is violent in council—sanguine in expectation—precipitate in action, and feeble in execution. That undertakes enterprises without forethought—enters upon them without preparation—conducts them without energy, and ends them in confusion and defeat.

Let the reign of the good Stuyvesant show the effects of vigor and decision, even when destitute of cool judgment and surrounded by perplexities. Let it show how frankness, probity, and high-souled courage will command respect and secure honor, even where success is unattainable. But at the same time, let it caution against a too ready reliance on the good faith of others and a too honest confidence in the loving professions of powerful neighbors, who are most friendly when they most mean to betray. Let it teach a judicious attention to the opinions and wishes of the many, who in times of peril must be soothed and led, or apprehension will overpower the deference to authority.

Let the empty wordiness of his factious subjects, their intemperate harangues, their violent "resolutions," their hectorings against an absent enemy and their pusillanimity on his approach, teach us to distrust and despise those clamorous patriots whose courage dwells but in the tongue. Let them serve as a lesson to repress that insolence of speech, destitute of real force, which too often breaks forth in popular bodies and bespeaks the vanity rather than the spirit of a nation. Let them caution us against vaunting too much of our own power and prowess, and reviling a noble enemy. True gallantry of soul would always lead us to treat a foe with courtesy and proud punctilio; a contrary conduct but takes from the merit of victory and renders defeat doubly disgraceful.

But I cease to dwell on the stores of excellent example to be drawn from the ancient chronicles of the Manhattoes. He who reads attentively will discover the threads of gold which run throughout the web of history and are invisible to the dull eye of ignorance. But before I conclude, let me point out a solemn warning furnished in the subtle chain of events by which the capture of Fort Casimir has produced the present convulsions of our globe.

Attend then, gentle reader, to this plain deduction, which, if thou art a king, an emperor, or other powerful potentate, I advise thee to treasure up in thy heart—though little expectation have I that my work will fall into such hands, for well I know the care of crafty ministers to keep all grave and edifying books of the kind out of the way of unhappy monarchs—lest peradventure they should read them and learn wisdom.

By the treacherous surprisal of Fort Casimir, then, did the crafty Swedes enjoy a transient triumph; but drew upon their heads the vengeance of Peter Stuyvesant, who wrested all New Sweden from their hands—By the conquest of New Sweden, Peter Stuyvesant aroused the claims of Lord Baltimore, who appealed to the Cabinet of Great Britain, who subdued the whole province of New Netherlands—By this great achievement the whole extent of North America from Nova Scotia to the Floridas was rendered one entire dependency upon the British crown—But mark the consequence: the hitherto scattered colonies being thus consolidated, and having no rival colonies to check or keep them in awe, waxed great and powerful, and finally becoming too strong for the mother country, were enabled to shake off its bonds, and by a glorious revolution became an independent empire.—But the chain of effects stopped not here; the successful revolution in America produced the sanguinary revolution in France, which produced the puissant Buonaparte, who produced the French despotism, which has thrown the whole world in confusion!—Thus have these great powers been successively punished for their ill-starred conquests —and thus, as I asserted, have all the present convulsions, revolutions, and disasters that overwhelm mankind originated in the capture of the little Fort Casimir, as recorded in this eventful history.

And now, worthy reader, ere I take a sad farewell—which, alas! must be for ever—willingly would I part in cordial fellow-ship, and bespeak thy kindhearted remembrance. That I have not written a better history of the days of the patriarchs is not my fault—had any other person written one as good, I should not have attempted it at all.—That many will hereafter spring up and surpass me in excellence, I have very little doubt, and still less care; well knowing that when the great Christovallo Colon (who is vulgarly called Columbus) had once stood his egg upon its end, everyone at table could stand his up a thousand times more dexterously.—Should any reader find matter of of-fence in this history, I should heartily grieve, though I would on no account question his penetration by telling him he is mistaken—his good nature by telling him he is captious—or his pure conscience by telling him he is startled at a shadow.—Surely if he is so ingenious in finding offence where none is intended, it were a thousand pities he should not be suffered to enjoy the benefit of his discovery.

I have too high an opinion of the understanding of my fellow citizens to think of yielding them any instruction, and I covet too much their good will to forfeit it by giving them good advice. I am none of those cynics who despise the world because it despises them—on the contrary, though but low in its regard, I look up to it with the most perfect good nature, and my only sorrow is that it does not prove itself more worthy of the un-bounded love I bear it.

If however in this my historic production—the scanty fruit of a long and laborious life—I have failed to gratify the dainty palate of the age, I can only lament my misfortune—for it is too late in the season for me even to hope to repair it. Already has withering age showered his sterile snows upon my brow; in a little while, and this genial warmth which still lingers around my heart and throbs—worthy reader—throbs kindly towards thy-self, will be chilled for ever. Haply this frail compound of dust, which while alive may have given birth to naught but unprofit-able weeds, may form a humble sod of the valley, from whence may spring many a sweet wild flower to adorn my beloved island of Manna-hata!

The following preface
first appeared in the
revised edition of 1848.

THE AUTHOR'S APOLOGY.

The following work, in which at the outset nothing more was contemplated than a temporary jeu d'esprit, was commenced in company with my brother, the late Peter Irving, Esq. Our idea was to parody a small handbook which had recently appeared, entitled "A Picture of New York." Like that, our work was to begin with an historical sketch; to be followed by notices of the customs, manners, and institutions of the city; written in a serio-comic vein, and treating local errors, follies, and abuses with good-humored satire.

To burlesque the pedantic lore displayed in certain American works, our historical sketch was to commence with the creation of the world; and we laid all kinds of works under contribution for trite citations, relevant or irrelevant, to give it the proper air of learned research. Before this crude mass of mock erudition could be digested into form, my brother departed for Europe, and I was left to prosecute the enterprise alone.

I now altered the plan of the work. Discarding all idea of a parody on the "Picture of New York," I determined that what had been originally intended as an introductory sketch should comprise the whole work, and form a comic history of the city. I accordingly moulded the mass of citations and disquisitions into introductory chapters forming the first book; but it soon became evident to me that, like Robinson Crusoe with his boat, I had begun on too large a scale, and that to launch my history successfully I must reduce its proportions. I accordingly resolved to confine it to the period of the Dutch domination, which in its rise, progress, and decline presented that unity of subject required by classic rule. It was a period, also, at that time almost a terra incognita in history. In fact, I was surprised to find how few of my fellow-citizens were aware that New York had ever been called New Amsterdam, or had heard of the names of its early Dutch governors, or cared a straw about their ancient Dutch progenitors.

This, then, broke upon me as the poetic age of our city; poetic from its very obscurity; and open, like the early and obscure days of ancient Rome, to all the embellishments of heroic fiction. I hailed my native city as fortunate above all other American cities in having an antiquity thus extending back into the regions of doubt and fable; neither did I conceive I was committing any grievous historical sin in helping out the few facts I could collect in this remote and forgotten region with figments of my own brain, or in giving characteristic attributes to the few names connected with it which I might dig up from oblivion.

In this, doubtless, I reasoned like a young and inexperienced writer besotted with his own fancies; and my presumptuous trespasses into this sacred, though neglected, region of history have met with deserved rebuke from men of soberer minds. It is too late, however, to recall the shaft thus rashly launched. To any one whose sense of fitness it may wound, I can only say with Hamlet,

> Let my disclaiming from a purposed evil
> Free me so far in your most generous thoughts,
> That I have shot my arrow o'er the house,
> And hurt my brother.

I will say this in further apology for my work: that if it has taken an unwarrantable liberty with our early provincial history, it has at least turned attention to that history and provoked research. It is only since this work appeared that the forgotten archives of the province have been rummaged, and the facts and personages of the olden time rescued from the dust of oblivion and elevated into whatever importance they may actually possess.

The main object of my work, in fact, had a bearing wide from the sober aim of history, but one which I trust will meet with some indulgence from poetic minds. It was to embody the traditions of our city in an amusing form; to illustrate its local humors, customs, and peculiarities; to clothe home scenes and places and familiar names with those imaginative and whimsical associations so seldom met with in our new country, but which live like charms and spells about the cities of the old world, binding the heart of the native inhabitant to his home.

In this I have reason to believe I have in some measure succeeded. Before the appearance of my work the popular traditions of our city were unrecorded; the peculiar and racy customs and usages derived from our Dutch progenitors were unnoticed or regarded with indifference or adverted to with a sneer. Now they form a convivial currency and are brought forward on all occasions; they link our whole community together in good humor and good fellowship; they are the rallying points of home feeling; the seasoning of our civic festivities; the staple of local tales and local pleasantries; and are so harped upon by our writers of popular fiction that I find myself almost crowded off the legendary ground which I was the first to explore, by the host who have followed in my footsteps.

I dwell on this head because, at the first appearance of my work, its aim and drift were misapprehended by some of the descendants of the Dutch worthies; and because I understand that now and then one may still be found to regard it with a captious eye. The far greater part, however, I have reason to flatter myself, receive my good humored picturings in the same temper with which they were executed; and when I find, after a lapse of nearly forty years, this hap-hazard production of my youth still cherished among them; when I find its very name become a "household word," and used to give the home stamp to everything recommended for popular acceptation, such as Knickerbocker societies, Knickerbocker insurance companies, Knickerbocker steamboats, Knickerbocker omnibuses, Knicker-bocker bread, and Knickerbocker ice; and when I find New Yorkers of Dutch descent priding themselves upon being "genu-ine Knickerbockers," I please myself with the persuasion that I have struck the right chord; that my dealings with the good old Dutch times, and the customs and usages derived from them, are in harmony with the feelings and humors of my townsmen; that I have opened a vein of pleasant associations and quaint charac-teristics peculiar to my native place, and which its inhabitants will not willingly suffer to pass away; and that, though other his-tories of New York may appear of higher claims to learned acceptation, and may take their dignified and appropriate rank in the family library, Knickerbocker's history will still be received with good-humored indulgence and be thumbed and chuckled over by the family fireside.

W. I.

Sunnyside, 1848.

133.8   Wolf, Stacey.
Wolf
         Stacey Wolf's psychic
         living.

$19.95

DATE			
	14 DAY LOAN		

NOV   1998

BAKER & TAYLOR